CONTESTED
BONES

Christopher Rupe *and*
Dr. John Sanford

Franzie Smith
Technical Editor

CONTESTED BONES

First Edition

Second printing

ISBN # 9780981631677

Copyright © 2017, 2019

Christopher Rupe and Dr. John Sanford

Published by
FMS Publications
A Division of FMS Foundation

— Dedication & Thanks —

From Chris Rupe:

First and foremost, I dedicate this book to my Heavenly Father.

I would also like to dedicate this book to my parents, Randy and Janice Rupe. You have been my greatest source of support and encouragement, a true gift from God that I will never take for granted.

And to John—thank you for believing in me.

From John Sanford:

Helen—I dedicate this book to you. My faithful and loving wife, my partner in life and in ministry, my best friend for 43 years. I thank the Lord for you every day.

From both of us:

We thank Dr. Franzie Smith for her great patience, and countless hours of editing, formatting, and correcting this book. We thank Dr. Peter Line for technical improvements. We also thank Dr. Andrew Snelling for reviewing chapter 12. Finally, we thank Dr. Rob Carter for improvements.

Contents

Personal Prologue

By John Sanford

Why did Chris and I write this book? As a Cornell University research scientist and geneticist, I was a committed evolutionist for most of my adult life. For most of that time I was fully persuaded that ape-to-man evolution was a simple and obvious fact of science. But I did not hold that view based upon careful examination of the evidence. Since I only had a superficial understanding of the topic, where did my certainty come from? Like any other scientist who is outside of their field of expertise, I was primarily persuaded by the pervasive "group-think," which is especially strong within the academic community. A key component of the academic group-think is that evolution explains everything. For a scientist like myself, this over-arching group-think about evolution was powerfully reinforced by lay-level science articles and powerful visuals promoted through the mass media. Such reinforcement was inherently superficial but made me feel I was scientifically well informed, and so had good reason to feel very certain. But I never took time to actually study the relevant scientific literature (I was already certain). I am sure that many other academics have had the same basic experience. This would explain why so many academics are extremely certain of human evolution, yet have never actually studied it, and have almost no grasp of the subject.

More specifically, my certainty in human evolution was derived from my faith in the experts in the field. I assumed there was no ideological agenda, I assumed the researchers were in agreement regarding the evidence, and I assumed the experts must actually have ways to know for certain what happened in the very distant past.

I was about 50 years old before I first began to seriously question human evolution. My initial skepticism was not based upon the fossil record, but upon my own genetic research. I was learning that there are clear limits to what can realistically be accomplished by the Darwinian process (i.e., random genetic mutations filtered by natural selection). Ever since that time (16 years ago), I have been doing original scientific research addressing this fundamental question: can mutation/selection transform an ape into a human being? This work has resulted in over a dozen scientific papers and three books. My research has confirmed what many population geneticists have recognized for decades—the mutation/selection process has major problems, which profoundly limit what it can realistically accomplish. It turns out that the mutation/selection process cannot even begin to create the large networks of new information that would be required for the genetic transformation of ape to man. Even more surprising, there is evidence that human evolution is going backward, because good mutations are extremely rare while bad mutations are occurring much more quickly than natural selection can select them away. It is true that the mutation/selection process is happening all the time. However, the best it can accomplish is adaptive fine-tuning (microevolution), and purifying selection (removal of the worst deleterious mutations).

There is now strong genetic evidence against ape-to-man evolution. However, people argue that the genetic evidence must be wrong because the fossil record clearly proves ape-to-man evolution. It is for this reason that Chris Rupe and I began to carefully examine the fossil evidence that is said to prove ape-to-man evolution. For the last four years we have been critically examining the evidence reported in several hundred technical papers, which describe the bones of tentative "transitional forms" between ape and man. Chris, a biologist, has done the lion's share of researching the relevant literature. Together we have connected the dots and co-labored in writing this book.

We have been surprised by our findings. The raw data (the bones themselves) do not show what is widely claimed. Furthermore, it is clear that most of the workers in the field sharply disagree about the key discoveries. Nearly all of the important bones are contested—hence our title. We will be extensively quoting the experts in the field (usually quoting directly from their technical papers), to show that the bones really are contested (longer quotes are shown in blue).

Neither Chris nor I have a PhD in paleoanthropology. So why should you bother reading this book? Perhaps it is because of this simple fact: fresh scientific perspectives (paradigm shifts) almost never arise from established members of a given field. Outsiders are very often needed to help break free from the shackles of the "group-think." The field of paleoanthropology consists of a very small group of specialists, who are perhaps sometimes blinded by their shared assumptions and traditions. We do not wish to disrespect this community of scientists, but as earnest scholars seeking truth, we feel justified in examining the evidence for ourselves. If more people outside the field examined the evidence, we feel many would agree that the fossil evidence for human evolution is surprisingly weak. So perhaps Chris and I are playing the role of those little children who were not afraid to ask the question: "Where are the emperor's clothes?"

The serious problems associated with the Darwinian mutation/selection process, combined with the serious problems associated with the fossil record (the discussion of which make up the bulk of this book), are sufficient for any reasonable person to question the ape-to-man story. Given the problems, it seems only reasonable to consider alternative explanations for the origin of man. What reasonable alternative explanations are possible, which might explain the origin of man?

CHAPTER 1

Power of the Paradigm

My reservations concern not so much this book [R. Leakey's "Origins"], *but the whole subject and methodology of paleoanthropology. ... perhaps generations of students of human evolution, including myself, have been flailing about in the dark; that our data base is too sparse, too slippery, for it to be able to mold to our theories. Rather, the theories are more statements about us and ideology than about the past. Paleoanthropology reveals more about how humans view themselves than it does about how humans came about. But that is heresy.*[1]

David Pilbeam, Professor at Harvard University, curator of paleoanthropology at the Peabody Museum of Archaeology and Ethnology and National Academy of Sciences member

The Iconic "Ape Parade"

In 1965, natural history painter Rudolph Zallinger created the most famous icon of evolution—the "March of Progress." The illustration was a foldout in the Time-Life Nature Library book, *Early Man.*[2] It portrays a series of alleged ape-like ancestors that become progressively more human as they march across the page. Interestingly, the figure's caption cautioned readers that the artistic representations were based upon "fragmentary fossil evidence." The book freely confesses: "*Although protoapes and apes were quadrupedal, all are shown here standing for the purpose of comparison.*" At that time there was no compelling fossil evidence to suggest that so-called "protoapes" evolved into man: the transitional forms existed

---

1. *American Scientist* 66(3): 378-379, 1978.
2. Howell F.C., *Early Man*, Time-Life Books, New York, 1965.

primarily in the artist's mind. Unfortunately, most people ignored the fine print, because it was overshadowed by the persuasive image. A life-long researcher of human evolution, describes how the "Ape Parade" icon impacted western culture:

> This parade has been one of the most successful tools ever used to promote human evolution. It is constituted as a powerful visual "proof" for human evolution that even a small child could grasp. ...There were few social studies classrooms and school library bulletin boards where this parade was not prominently displayed. Because of its graphic power, it is still indelibly etched into the minds of billions of people worldwide. ... That visually powerful parade was so successful in advancing human evolution because it received a far greater distribution and viewing than did the *Early Man* book. Worldwide mailings for advertising purposes were made of the particular pages featuring the parade. The posting of these pages in classrooms and libraries meant that far more people saw the parade than possessed the book. Perhaps less than five percent of those who had the book actually read it, but they would have seen the parade. Thus, the visual image of the parade sold the concept of human evolution even though the book revealed that the parade was fictitious.[3]

There is no doubt that this mental image has been used to powerfully influence public thought, and it is now very deeply embedded in the modern mind. To this day, different versions of the iconic "Ape Parade" can be found in textbooks and classrooms across the globe, and throughout the Internet. Since 1965 most people have been convinced primarily by the graphic itself. The power of the graphic has been strongly reinforced by sporadic headlines proclaiming important new fossil evidences, which appear to always validate ape-to-man evolution. Most people have been persuaded (from childhood) that the fossil evidence is so overwhelming that human evolution is virtually undeniable. Very few people are aware that virtually every reputed "ape-man" bone has been contested by experts in the field.

We have written this book to simply make more people aware that the actual fossil evidence is fragmentary and it is typically self-contradicting. Contrary to what is widely believed, the fossil evidence is weak and does not provide compelling evidence for human evolution.

We ask you, the reader, to open your mind just a little and give us a fair hearing as we critically examine the scientific evidence that seriously challenges the popular point of view. We ask you to begin to discern between the hype on this subject and the actual science. We do not ask you to believe us based upon our limited authority; we ask you to believe the actual data and writings (in blue font) from experts in the field. We trust that when you are done reading this book you will at least acknowledge that the bones in question really are *contested*.

---

3. Lubenow M.L., *Bones of Contention*, Baker Books, Grand Rapids, Michigan, pp. 39-40, 2004.

Human Evolution—The Basics

Before we examine the problems associated with the current paradigm, we need to begin by outlining the "popular science" view of human evolution, and by introducing some basic terminology.

Magazines like *National Geographic* and *Popular Science* simplify scientific topics for the sake of their very broad audiences. The same is true of museums and textbooks. They typically give something of a cartoon picture of any challenging subject. Most people only understand a topic such as human evolution, or say the big bang, in the light of popular writings, or other popular media (such as NOVA science programs).

The popularized story regarding human origins can be outlined as follows: over 3 billion years ago, the first bacteria-like cell arose spontaneously from non-living matter. Then, through the Darwinian mutation/selection process those bacteria gradually became fish, which later became apes, which later became man. An unknown ape-ish creature that lived about 6 million years ago was the common ancestor of both man and chimpanzee.[4,5] The common ancestor split into two branches, with the chimp lineage staying largely the same. However, during the same time the human lineage was radically transformed into modern man. It is not thought that we evolved from chimpanzees, but rather humans and chimps diverged from an unknown African ape, which is now extinct and which apparently left no bones. This unknown creature is simply referred to as the "Last Common Ancestor" (LCA) of man and chimp.

The evolutionary branch that would eventually lead to modern man is said to have evolved through a series of "transitional forms," whose bones have been recovered from various sites. The reputed ape-human intermediates (sometimes informally referred to as "ape-men") are more correctly termed "hominin" (i.e., all the intermediate types between the hypothetical LCA and man). The term hominin is different from the broader term hominid, which refers to any human, or any ape, or any possible intermediate. Most of the hominin types that we will be examining in this book involve just two classifications (i.e., taxonomic "genera"). The two genera are named *Australopithecus* (Latin for "southern ape"), and *Homo* (which is Latin for "man"). There are a few other peripheral genera that have been named, which are quite clearly apes and have no clear place in the ape-to-man progression. For example, *Ardipithecus* (nicknamed Ardi), is just one partial skeleton, and is essentially the same as many other *Australopithecus* specimens, and was originally classified as belonging to *Australopithecus* by the discoverers. Later we will describe *Ardipithecus* in detail—but for now we will just say that it does not

---

4. Patterson N. *et al.*, Genetic evidence for complex speciation of humans and chimpanzees, *Nature*, 441:29, 2006. DOI: 10.1038/nature04789

5. Langergraber K.E. *et al.*, Generation times in wild chimpanzees and gorillas suggest earlier divergence times in great ape and human evolution, *Proc Natl Acad Sci*, USA 109(39):15716-15721, 2012.

seem to merit its own genus name, nor does it merit the status of "hominin" (ape/human intermediate).

The study of reputed hominin bones and their artifacts (such as stone tools) is called paleoanthropology. A similar term, paleontology, is applied to the broader study of any ancient fossil remains. Paleoanthropology is a very cumbersome word, and so we will most often simply refer to it as "the field." Because "paleoanthropologists" is a mouthful, we will often just say "paleo-experts" or collectively as the "paleo-community." Various bones that are claimed as hominin transitional forms, have been given long Latin names such as *Australopithecus bahrelghazali*. Scientists and science writers often shorten these names, and we will do the same whenever possible. Like other researchers and writers, we will generally refer to the numerous *Australopithecus* species (which are really all the same basic type) in a more general sense, simply calling them "australopithecines" or more simply—"australopiths." We will typically replace long Latin names with shortened forms. For example, we will use "Afarensis" for *Australopithecus afarensis*, "Ardi" for *Ardipithecus ramidus*, and "Hobbit" for *Homo floresiensis*. Similarly, we will use "Sediba" for *Australopithecus sediba*, "Habilis" for *Homo habilis*, "Naledi" for *Homo naledi*, "Erectus" for *Homo erectus*, and "Neanderthal" for *Homo neanderthalensis*. Certain fossil discoveries have received so much media coverage that specific bones have been given nicknames, which we will also use (e.g., "Lucy").

Paleo-experts will often use the terms "type specimen", "defining specimen", or "holotype". Each of these terms mean the same thing and are used interchangeably. The type specimen refers to a single bone or set of bones that are used to describe and name a new species. Oftentimes, the type specimen is the first or most complete set of bones discovered. The type specimen is important because it is used as a basis for classifying other fossils that may (or may not) belong to the same species. Ideally, the type specimen should be the most complete specimen attributed to a species—yet this is not always the case. For example, the type specimen for Afarensis is an isolated jawbone (LH-4), which is not very helpful if you're trying to identify limb bones, for instance. Not surprisingly, some paleo-experts have argued that the better preserved "Lucy" skeleton is more informative and would serve as a better type specimen for Afarensis. All other bones attributed to a given species are known as the "hypodigm"—the total collection of bones assigned to a species.

The story of human evolution has been under continuous revision ever since the time of Darwin. The traditional "cartoon" version of the human evolution story (which is now rejected) would say that an unknown ape-like creature evolved into Ardi, which evolved into Lucy, which evolved into Habilis, which evolved into Erectus, which evolved into modern man. As we will see, this out-dated and over-simplified picture has been eclipsed by a very different story. The new story says there is no clear "fossil trail" leading to man. Instead there is only a "tangled bush" with no discernible ancestor/descendant lineages. This is the updated version of the story, as it is found in the more up-to-date popular media, museums, and textbooks. Jean-Jacques Hublin, Director of the Department of Human Evolution at the Max Planck Institute for Evolutionary Anthropology in Leipzig (Germany) states in the journal *Nature*: *"The once-popular fresco showing a single file of marching hominids becoming ever more vertical, tall, and hairless now appears to be fiction."*[6] Leading evolutionary paleoanthropologist, Bernard Wood, of George Washington University, writes similarly in *New Scientist*:

> There is a popular image of human evolution that you'll find all over the place ... On the left of the picture there's an ape ... On the right, a man ... Between the two is a succession of figures that become ever more like humans ... Our progress from ape to human looks so smooth, so tidy. It's such a beguiling image that even the experts are loath to let it go. But it is an illusion.[7]

Scientific Method—The Basics

There are two types of scientific inquiry that are very different—operational science and historical science. Unfortunately, many people fail to grasp the difference.

Operational science is the type of science that involves conducting repeatable experiments in the present. This is classical "hard science," which teaches us how nature operates, and has given rise to modern technologies like computers, modern medicine, and modern agriculture. Operational science includes the physical sciences such as chemistry and physics, and the life sciences such as cell biology. This type of science is extremely powerful, but still has limitations. A popular biology textbook provides a good definition:

> Scientific inquiry is a powerful way to know nature, but there are limitations to the kinds of questions it can answer. These limits are set by science's requirements that hypotheses be testable and falsifiable and that observations and experimental results be repeatable.[8]

Notice there are limitations to the kinds of questions that operational science can address. For example, operational science cannot give us definitive answers regarding events that happened long ago. Operational science requires the development of hypotheses that are testable and falsifiable—followed by controlled experiments that are rigorous and can be reproduced by other scientists.

Historical science is the type of science that deals with questions about the past (if about the recent past, it is often called "forensic science"). Historical science is a "soft science," because history cannot be repeated, and is not generally accessible through experiments conducted in the present. Historical data is usually very limited, and fragmentary, and is often modified or corrupted. Observation of such

6. Hublin J.J., An evolutionary odyssey, *Nature* 403:363, 2000.
7. Wood B., "Who are we?", *New Scientist* 2366:44, 2002.
8. Campbell N.A. and Reece J.B., *Biology*, 7th edition, Pearson Education Inc., publishing as Benjamin Cummings, 2005.

data is made in the present, and then inferences (educated guesses) are made about a hypothetical past event. Historical science is inherently uncertain, and inferences are strongly affected by presuppositions and personal prejudice. Historical science routinely goes beyond the defined limits of the scientific method. Ernst Mayr, a renowned evolutionary biologist from Harvard, explained this critical distinction between historical and operational science:

> Evolutionary biology, in contrast with physics and chemistry, is a historical science—the evolutionist attempts to explain events and processes that have already taken place. Laws and experiments are inappropriate techniques for the explication of such events and processes. Instead one constructs a historical narrative, consisting of a tentative reconstruction of the particular scenario that led to the events one is trying to explain.[9]

Mayr understood that when it comes to evolutionary biology (i.e., ape-to-man evolution), scientists construct a story or narrative about what they believe happened in the past. Mayr described this man-made history as a "tentative reconstruction"—meaning it is subject to change whenever the theorist feels it is necessary. This historical narrative is used as a framework to interpret the evidence (hominin bones). The basic concept of the ape-to-man narrative was constructed during the time of Darwin, 150 years ago. It was accepted as a fact long before any significant hominin fossils were found to validate the theory. This evolutionary narrative has consistently influenced how the bones have been interpreted. The bones have always been interpreted in light of the widely accepted ape-to-man story. This is very significant—it means that the science of paleoanthropology is not merely a matter of digging up fossils and describing what they look like. Speculations, assumptions, and inferences about the unverifiable past play a pivotal role in how the hominin bones are interpreted.

Taxonomic Classification—The Basics

Assigning bones to specific species (i.e., making taxonomic distinctions), in our opinion, should be based upon obvious similarities and should be consistent with common sense. However taxonomists have a great deal of "artistic" license, and taxonomic groupings are typically defined based upon who has the most influence in a given biological arena. The criteria for distinguishing taxonomic groupings often involve minutia. Because taxonomic groupings are often very subjective, such groupings are largely based upon arbitrary distinctions. As new people enter the field, taxonomic groupings are continuously being revised. Taxonomy is as much an art as it is a science. It is as much about personal taste as it is about training and qualification.

Taxonomists tend to fall into two competing camps, the "lumpers" and the "splitters." Splitters are naturally inclined to "split hairs"—they sub-divide taxonomic groups

---

9. Mayr E., Darwin's influence on modern thought, *Scientific American* November 24, 2009. https://www.scientificamerican.com/article/darwins-influence-on-modern-thought/

based upon minute differences. If splitters did not know about dogs, and they were to dig up a vast dog graveyard, they would be inclined to think that every breed was a different species. Similarly, splitters would say there are many species of baboons. There are 5 different "species" of baboon, possibly 7 depending on whom you ask. Each species has certain morphological distinctions, yet they are also all very similar in their general anatomy (and can probably interbreed). If the casual observer were to look at those different "species," they would likely make no distinction and call them all "baboons" without hesitation. Other taxonomists (lumpers) would agree, and would say that all the baboon species should be lumped together as a single variable species. If scientists tend to arbitrarily split species that are alive today (where living specimens can be studied in detail), imagine the potential for making this error based upon a handful of bone fragments. The problem of splitting or lumping is addressed by famous paleo-expert Lee Berger, who asked:

> And what if many of these bones are fragmented, distorted, or broken? The scientist is faced with the most taxing jigsaw puzzle. …if experts argue over how to lump or split clear human and clear nonhuman, think of how difficult it is to map out what once lay between us [referring to the remains of "ape-human" intermediates].[10]

When a paleo-expert finds a new bone, there is a strong motivation to become a splitter, to have their discovery be a new and important species (you do not get famous by discovering already-recognized species). Bernard Wood, a leading paleo-expert at George Washington University acknowledges that not everyone in the field agrees with the ever-growing taxonomic distinctions: "*...critics of the bushy family tree have charged that paleoanthropologists have been overzealous in identifying new species from their finds—presumably out of a desire for fame and further research funding.*"[11] Perhaps this explains why so many ancient bones are claimed to be in the human lineage, while only one bone has been attributed to the chimp lineage.[12] As Donald Johanson, discoverer of "Lucy" confesses, "*In everybody who is looking for hominids there is a strong urge to learn more about where the human line started.*"[13] He describes this motivation as very "*seductive*" making it easy to find yourself "*straining your eyes*" to see the bones a certain way. This highlights a fundamental problem in the field of paleoanthropology, summarized best by science writer Jim Shreeve who said; "*Everybody knows fossils are fickle; bones will sing any song you want to hear.*"[14] It is no wonder we are seeing a growing number of scientific papers with titles like "*Early hominids—Diversity*

10. Berger L.R. and Aronson M., *The Skull in the Rock*, National Geographic, Washington D.C., USA, 2012.
11. Wood B., Welcome to the Familiy, *Scientific American*, p.46, September 2016.
12. McBrearty S. and Jablonski N.G., First fossil chimpanzee, *Nature* 437:105-108, 2005. DOI: 10.1038/nature04008
13. Johanson D.C. and Edey M.A., *Lucy—The Beginnings of Humankind*, Simon & Schuster Paperbacks, p.257, 1981.
14. Shreeve J., Argument over a woman, *Discover* 11(8):58, 1990.

or Distortion?"[15] or "Hominin taxic diversity: fact or fiction?"[16] Species designations will always be highly subjective and contested.

We, along with many biologists, are "lumpers." We do not trust the tendency of splitters to define every variant as a new species. We feel lumpers are more realistic. We understand that many populations constitute one large inter-fertile group, even when they display diverse morphologies and are separated geographically. While extreme splitters would sub-divide the dog breeds into many species, lumpers would say that all canines (dogs, wolves, coyotes, dingoes, etc.) are the same species. Biologically this is very reasonable, because all canines are inter-fertile and can produce viable hybrid progeny. This is consistent with the "biological species concept"—the most widely accepted definition of a species.

When we classify the different forms of life, the lowest category is "species." Biologists know that the species distinction is based on relatively superficial differences between the same basic kind of animal. For example, there are about 500 species of mosquito.[17] Likewise, although dogs and wolves are extremely similar and can interbreed, they are considered to be different species. Because the term "species" is based upon such superficial and often arbitrary differences within the same basic kind of life form, taxonomists waste a great deal of time arguing endlessly about where to draw lines in distinguishing different species. In a very real sense the species designation is a matter of taxonomic taste— species designations are largely artificial man–made categories. At the next higher taxonomic level (genus), there can still be much debate, and taxonomists who are lumpers may take a cluster of previously classified genera and argue they are all really just one genus. We feel splitters are lost in the details, calling every variant a new species.

Within the hypothetical "family tree" of modern man, there are really only two meaningful genera. The first genus is *Australopithecus*, Latin for "southern ape." This genus is extinct, and while we find many variations within these bones—all the *Australopithecus* bones seem to reveal an animal type that is very similar to living apes (such as chimpanzee). This is perfectly consistent with the name of the genus. The second genus is *Homo*, Latin for "man" (or "human"). The *Homo* type is consistently seen to be distinctly human, regardless of whether we are talking about living people or the bones of people who lived long ago. Again, this is in perfect keeping with the genus name.

This creates a serious evolutionary problem, because there is no intermediate transitional genus. One genus is clearly ape-like; the other genus is clearly human-like. The large anatomical gap between the two kinds is very striking. For this reason paleo-experts wish to bridge the gap, and are especially eager to find

---

15. White T., Early Hominids—Diversity or Distortion? *Science* 299:1994-1997, 2003.

16. Wood B. and Boyle K.E., Homin taxic diversity: Fact or fantasy? *Am J Phys Anthropol (Yearbook of Physical Anthropology)* 159:S61:37-78, 2016. DOI: 10.1002/ajpa.22902.

17. White T., Early Hominids—Diversity or Distortion? *Science* 299:1994-1997, 2003.

Australopithecus bones that seem more human-like, or *Homo* bones that seem more ape-like. This tension will become apparent as we begin to examine the most recent fossils.

Dating Bones and Artifacts—The Basics

Just as the hominin bones have been contested, the hominin dates have also been contested. Throughout this book we use the currently accepted dates, based upon the published literature. However, in chapter 12 we will describe some of the the dating problems—including conflicting dates, changing dates, dates with extensive margins of error, and the selective use of dates (preferentially choosing the desired date).

CHAPTER 2

A Theory in Crisis

Even with all the fossil evidence and analytical techniques from the past 50 years, a convincing hypothesis for the origin of Homo remains elusive.[1]

Paleoanthropologist Bernard Wood of George Washington University

Darwin's Prediction

Darwin knew that if his theory of evolution was correct, the fossil record should show innumerable intermediate forms—reflecting countless gradual evolutionary transitions, wherein species were continuously morphing into other species. However, no such transitional fossils were seen in his day. Darwin viewed this problem as a potential fatal flaw in his theory, which he openly confessed:

> Why then is not every geological stratum full of such intermediate links? Geology assuredly does not reveal any such finely-graduated organic chain; and this, perhaps, is the most obvious and serious objection which can be urged against the theory.[2]

For Darwin's theory to be true, there would need to be countless transitional forms linking all forms of life into one single "organic chain." Darwin predicted that the fossils of all the countless missing transitional forms would eventually be found. It has been 150 years since Darwin's time, so if he was correct there should now be a great multitude of transitional fossils. However, this has not happened. For example, the late Stephen Jay Gould, evolutionary paleontologist at Harvard, confessed:

> The extreme rarity of transitional forms in the fossil record persists as the trade secret of paleontology. The evolutionary trees that adorn our textbooks have data only at the tips and nodes of their branches; the rest is inference, however reasonable, not the evidence of fossils.[3]

Leading paleoanthropologists Niles Eldredge and Ian Tattersall had a similar

---

1. Wood B., Fifty years after *Homo habilis*, *Nature* 508:31-33, 2014.
2. Darwin C., *The Origin of Species*, Barnes & Noble Books, New York, p. 227, 2004.
3. Gould S.J., Evolution's erratic place, *Natural History* 86:14, 1977.

thought saying:

> ...One hundred and twenty years of paleontological research later, it has become abundantly clear that the fossil record will not confirm this part of Darwin's prediction...[4]

Although transitional links are generally missing, it is still widely claimed that in the instance of ape-to-man evolution, there really is very compelling fossil evidence that proves the transition. But are these claims valid? There is no question that since the time of Darwin there have been many determined people who have searched for missing links between ape and man. Bones have indeed been found, and some of these bones have been held up as ape-human transitional forms. A casual examination of textbooks and mass media seems to suggest that the hominin fossil evidence is now abundant and compelling. In this book we will show that the textbooks and mass media are misrepresenting the situation, and that ape-to-man evolution is actually a theory in crisis, as is acknowledged by experts in the field.

This book will show that the theory of human evolution has the following profound problems:

- The history of the field of paleoanthropology consists of a long series of bone discoveries, each of which initially appeared to suggest a transitional form leading to man. But in each case the claim has either been debunked, or at least has become contested.

- The history of the field has been a long series of just-so stories, each new story invalidating the story before it.

- As more bones have been discovered, the basic story has *not* come into clearer focus; rather, the story keeps getting more convoluted, more confusing, and more contested. The result is an evolutionary tree that experts refer to as a "messy, tangled, indecipherable bush." This speaks of a field in disarray.

- Even the most credible hominin fossils are contested in terms of their place in the human evolutionary tree.

- There are only two meaningful genera: *Australopithecus* ("southern apes"), and *Homo* (humans). There is no clear evidence of a transitional "bridge" genus.

- The ape-like australopith "precursors" did not significantly precede man. They appear to have coexisted with man until the australopiths went extinct. The earliest evidence of *Homo* (man), seems to date back to the same era as do the earliest australopiths.

- The methods used to date most hominin fossils (such as potassium-argon dating), have been shown to be unreliable, and when different dating methods are used to date the same sample, the resulting dates typically do not agree.

---

4. Eldredge N. and Tattersall I., *The Myths of Human Evolution*, Columbia University Press, New York, pp. 45-46, 1982.

Therefore, assigned dates can be misleading and in serious error.

- New discoveries in the field of genetics make ape-to-man evolution virtually impossible. Furthermore, there is strong evidence that the deviant forms within the *Homo* genus appear to manifest various pathologies (such as Erectus and Hobbit). These deviant forms do not necessarily reflect pre-humans, but rather seem to reflect genetic degeneration associated with inbreeding and accelerated mutation accumulation.

Does the Fossil Record Support the Concept of Ape-to-man Evolution?

The traditional view of human evolution has been pictured as a simple family lineage something like the iconic March of Progress illustration, where a series of "ape-like" creatures become progressively more human as they march through time. At the time the image was created, evolution was thought to proceed in a straight line, with each ancestral species being replaced by the next. At that time, the thinking was that *Australopithecus afarensis* simply evolved into *Homo habilis*, which evolved into *Homo erectus*, which evolved into early *Homo sapiens*. Ernst Mayr championed this view in the 1950s and 60s and it became deeply entrenched. However, over the past few decades the picture of human evolution has changed dramatically. New species have replaced the species previously imagined to be the transitional forms, and the idea of a simple linear progression has been completely abandoned. The traditional straight-line view of human evolution is officially dead.

Scientists expected that as more fossils were catalogued, the standard linear view of human evolution would come into clear focus. What has actually happened is just the opposite. After a century and a half of fossil hunting, the picture that has emerged is chaotic. The human fossil record does not in any way reveal a linear evolutionary progression, as the experts in the field freely confess. Paleoanthropologists now universally describe the human fossil record as a messy, tangled bush, and they make no apologies for that description. The picture of human evolution has become more confusing and uncertain with every new discovery. Every twig that is added onto the hominin bush is raising new questions, and is simultaneously calling into question previous claims. Nearly every article that boasts of a new hominin fossil also claims that the new discovery will require a major rewrite of the human evolution story. Most people do not seem to realize that every re-write of the story suggests that the story must have previously been wrong. But if the story is always changing, why should we trust the latest revision? Indeed, paleoanthropologists now widely acknowledge that the hominin bush has become so messy and tangled that it is not even possible to trace our evolutionary lineage through a series of ape-like ancestors.

Most of the major finds that have historically been headlined have later been rejected by leading experts in the field or the paleo-community as a whole. This includes the famous bones referred to as "Neanderthal Man," "Piltdown Man,"

"Zinj," "Lucy," "Habilis," "Ardi," and "Hobbit." Even the very recent finds of "Sediba" and "Naledi" have been quickly ousted from the direct human lineage. This list of debunked human ancestors can be expanded to include more obscure species not widely known to the public, such as *Australopithecus africanus, Orrorin tugenensis, Sahelanthropus tchadensis*, and others. The status of nearly every hominin species and its hypothetical place in the human lineage has been subject to continuous revision. While some have argued that Habilis is a legitimate taxon, others have argued it is a "wastebasket" species and should be "scrapped." While some have argued that Erectus is a separate species, others have insisted that Erectus is essentially a variant of *Homo sapiens*, and that the differences have been exaggerated. While some argue Naledi is a "non-human animal," others argue it is simply a variant of Erectus (and is therefore fully human). While some argue that the "Hobbit" is a new species of *Homo*, others argue it is a diseased modern human. While some argue the australopithecines were bipedal hominins, others argue they are essentially apes and spent most of their lives in the trees. While some believe "Ardi" is the oldest human ancestor, others insist it is nothing more than an extinct ape. While some argue "Lucy" belongs in the direct human lineage, others prefer *Australopithecus africanus, Kenyanthropus platyops, or Australopithecus deyiremeda*.[5] Others reject all of these candidate ancestors and instead confess that the origin of the genus *Homo* remains "elusive," "clouded," and "totally confusing."

What are we to make of these contested bones? Perhaps an on-going debate is a sign of a healthy field of science. However, if a field persists in chaotically changing its claims, and cannot firmly establish its own fundamentals, this is not evidence of scientific progress, but is evidence of confusion. It appears that the paleo-experts can't get their story straight because they really can't make sense of the hominin fossil record. Is it possible that the field is in disarray because their starting assumption (apes morphing into humans) is simply wrong? There appears to be only one firm consensus within the field—the human fossil record does not reveal a clear linear progression from an ape-like australopith to man.

Strong Doubts Expressed by Leading Experts in the Field

Textbooks and the mainstream media mislead the public by presenting the fossil evidence as if there are no serious controversies, suggesting that we know for a fact ape-to-man evolution happened. Standard biology textbooks throughout the world typically show a family tree of our evolution from hominin ancestors over a period of time spanning some 6–10 million years. For example, Figure 1 is from an introductory-level biology textbook currently used in numerous colleges and universities. Notice the advancing stages of evolution from the earliest ape-like creatures—from the australopithecines to modern *Homo sapiens*. The general

---

5. Paleo-expert Yohannes Haile-Selassie states, "*The new species [Au. deyiremeda] is yet another confirmation that Lucy's species, Australopithecus afarensis, was not the only potential human ancestor species that roamed in what is now the Afar region of Ethiopia during the middle Pliocene.*" https://www.cmnh.org/nature2015

pattern shown resembles the famous "Ape Parade" discussed earlier, except this time the marching ape-men are replaced by illustrations of actual fossil remains (mostly skulls). The impression given to students is very clear: human evolution is backed by a wealth of fossil evidences that no real scientist could question. In reality many scientists, especially within the field, question what the fossil evidence shows. Students and the general public are not told that the evidence taken as a whole looks very different from the stylized figures we see in textbooks.

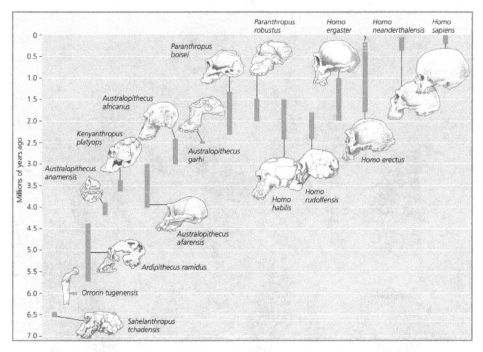

Figure 1. This popular textbook's illustration misleadingly shows a near–seamless gradation from the earliest ape-like creatures to fully modern humans, carefully leaving out any conflicting data. Notice the x-axis is arbitrary, but implies a left-to-right evolutionary progression. Only one (tiny) question mark is shown. It is not intended to cast doubt on human evolution theory as a whole; all that is being suggested here is that evolutionists are unclear about when exactly the reputed *Homo erectus* species went extinct. The figure legend admits, *"some species are controversial, reflecting debates about the interpretation of skeletal details and biogeography."* However, the points actually being debated are not mere "skeletal details"—they call into question the most fundamental claims of human evolution.[6]

Leading experts in the field are the first to acknowledge that there is a serious lack of fossil evidence in support of the ape-to-man story. For instance, famed paleo-experts Richard Leakey and David Pilbeam have confessed:

> Biologists would dearly like to know how modern apes, modern humans and the various ancestral hominids have evolved from a common ancestor. Unfortunately, the fossil record is somewhat incomplete as far as the hominids are concerned, and it is all but blank for the apes. The best we can hope for is that more fossils will be found over the next few years which will fill the present gaps in the evidence.

---

6. Reece J.B. *et al.*, *Campbell Biology* (10th Edition) p. 743, Figure 34.45, Kindle Edition (2013-10-18).

Figure 2. Bernard Wood's latest tree diagram (2014) raises more questions than tree diagrams made over 20 years ago. Wood acknowledges that the hominin fossil record is more convoluted than ever before, and still fails to show any hint of a discernable ape-to-man progression. Colored bars represent actual fossil data.

David Pilbeam comments wryly, "If you brought in a smart scientist from another discipline and showed him the meagre evidence we've got he'd surely say, 'forget it: there isn't enough to go on.'"[7]

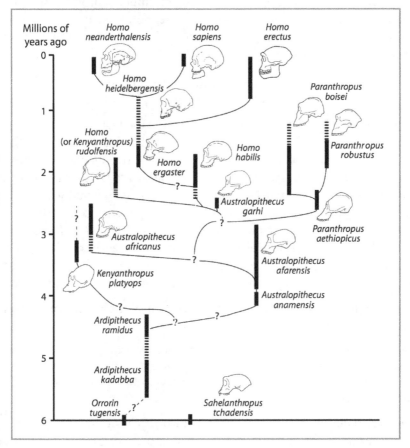

Figure 3. A tree diagram published in *Proc Natl Acad Sci* by paleo-expert Richard Klein. Thick vertical bars show actual fossil evidence. Dashed lines and thin solid lines indicating evolutionary relationships are inferences (not based on actual fossil evidence).

The extreme uncertainty regarding the lineage of man can be seen in a surprisingly transparent article of *National Geographic*, which showcases two charts on human evolution. This article provides a more honest portrayal of the fossil record. The charts are from two world authorities on human evolution, each with a competing view—Phillip Tobias and Bernard Wood. Tobias's chart is covered with nine question marks, at every major evolutionary junction. Wood shows fifteen question marks, starting with the first link to the *Homo* genus and continuing all the way down to the earliest ape-like australopiths. Both experts portray an overview of human evolution where there are no certain ancestors. These charts

7. Leakey R.E., *The Making of Mankind*, E.P. Dutton, New York, p. 43, 1981.

were shown in *National Geographic* over twenty years ago.[8] With many thousands of fossils found since then, the situation has not improved. Wood published an updated tree diagram in 2014 in *Scientific American* (Figure 2).[9] In place of the question marks, Wood now shows an equivalent number of broken, disconnected branches. He admits the picture has only become more obscure, more uncertain, and more convoluted with every new discovery. In a article published in *Nature* (2014), Wood states:

> Even with all the fossil evidence and analytical techniques from the past 50 years, a convincing hypothesis for the origin of *Homo* remains elusive.[10]

With an evergrowing collection of hominin fossils the picture that has emerged is anything but an ape-to-man progression. On the 200th anniversary of Charles Darwin's birth, paleo-expert Richard Klein showed a tree diagram (Figure 3) in *Proceedings of the National Academy of Sciences*.[11] Similar to Wood's latest depiction, there are question marks and dashed lines at every major evolutionary junction. Klein's tree diagram shows that there is no fossil evidence connecting Ardi to Afarensis; no fossil evidence connecting Afarensis to Habilis; no fossil evidence connecting Habilis to Ergaster/Erectus, and no fossil evidence connecting them to *Homo sapiens* through an archaic intermediate form. The solid lines drawn from the early australopithecine apes to the first humans is speculation and inference.

Paleoanthropologist Ian Tattersall, emeritus curator of the American Museum of Natural History now expresses similar doubts:

> Even allowing for the poor record we have of our close extinct kin, *Homo sapiens* appears as distinctive and unprecedented…there is certainly no evidence to support the notion that we gradually became who we inherently are over an extended period, in either the physical or intellectual sense.[12]

These honest remarks expressed by experts in the field, would most often be in private conversations or in obscure books. Numerous expressions of uncertainty are found in the technical journals, but they are generally not reader-friendly or readily accessible to the public. However, no trace of uncertainty is seen in textbooks or popular media. When it comes to the classroom, the mandate seems to be that "the fact of human evolution" must be vigorously championed—even at the expense of academic transparency. The controversial aspects about the hominin bones are largely hidden from public view. One is not allowed to question *if* ape-to-man evolution happened—only *how* it happened.

---

8. Gore R., The first steps: the dawn of humans, *National Geographic* 191(2): 72-97, 1997.

9. Wood B., Welcome to the Family, *Sci Am* 311(3):42-47, 2014. https://www.scientificamerican.com/article/the-origin-of-humans-is-surprisingly-complicated/

10. Wood B., Fifty years after *Homo habilis*, *Nature* 508:31-33, 2014.

11. Klein R.G., Darwin and the recent African origin of modern humans, *Proc Natl Acad Sci*, USA 106(38): 16007–16009, 2009.

12. Tattersall I., *Masters of the Planet: The Search for Our Human Origins*, Palgrave MacMillan, New York, 266 pp., 2012.

Contested Bones

In our investigation of this topic, we have found that every major new claim that has been widely proclaimed to the public has been challenged by other experts in the field. In many, perhaps most, of those cases, one of the competing views offered by paleo-experts happens to line up remarkably well with our own alternative model (see chapter 14).

The competing views are not merely held by rare dissidents or eccentrics. Typically, it is leading authorities in the field who are expressing dissenting views in highly prestigious scientific journals including *Nature, Science, Journal of Human Evolution, American Journal of Physical Anthropology, Proceedings of the National Academy of Sciences, PLOS ONE*, and more.

Why doesn't the public hear about all the controversies within paleoanthropology? Introductory-level textbooks and the media have failed to present the controversy to students and the general public. This has created the false impression that paleo-experts are in general agreement with one another regarding all the major claims. This has given the public a false sense of confidence in the ape-to-man story. People may ask, "How could so many scientists be wrong?" They are unaware that there are competing views within the scientific community regarding the interpretation of each of the reputed hominins and the fundamentals of the field.

In *Contested Bones* we will share with our readers the competing views which are largely unknown to students, the general public, and scientists outside the field of paleoanthropology. Our goal is to help people hear both sides of these controversies, so they can make better-informed decisions regarding the important question of where we came from.

In the next three sections of this book we will examine in detail the bones of the eight primary hominin finds. In section I we will examine the hominin bones of the human type (Neanderthal, Erectus, and Hobbit). In section II we will examine the bones of the ape-type (Ardi and Lucy). In section III we will look at the bones of the supposed "bridge" species (Habilis, Sediba, and Naledi). We conclude with an alternative model (chapter 14).

**Latest Developments

A series of milestone papers were published as this book was going to press. The findings summarized below have profound implications for the ape-to-man story and call into question many major claims that have been made in the field since the 70s. These findings confirm that the ape-to-man story is a theory in deepening crisis, and simultaneously confirm our diverse theses outlined in multiple chapters in this book.

1) Anatomically modern human-looking footprints have been found in Crete

that date to approximately 5.7 million years ago.[13] This finding suggests humans significantly predate our reputed australopithecine "ancestors." Thus Lucy, Ardi, Sediba, Habilis, or any other Pliocene hominin species,[14] cannot reasonably be our ancestor. Greece's island of Crete is well outside of Africa (the assumed pre-Pliocene hominin range), and so directly conflicts with the ape-to-man story. Yet, these findings are remarkably consistent with our alternative model (see chapter 14).

2) *Homo sapiens* fossils from Morocco were assigned a revised age of 315,000 years.[15] The *H. sapiens* collection from Morocco predates what was previously seen as the oldest known occurrence of *H. sapiens* (skullcaps from Omo Kibish), dated about 195,000 years old. This date greatly extends the coexistence of *H. sapiens* with their reputed archaic forbearers/contemporaries including Neanderthals, Denisovans, Erectus, Naledi, and Hobbit (see chapter 11). This greatly confounds any claims of an evolutionary progression within the genus *Homo*.

3) A new paper in *Nature* (2017) announced finding hammerstones and anvils in Southern California associated with processed mastodon remains.[16] These tools were assigned an age of approximately 130,000 years, which presents a serious problem for the Out of Africa theory. This is long before the reputed migration of early *H. sapiens* out of Africa 50,000–100,000 years ago.[17] Previous to these findings, the earliest evidence of humans in the Americas dates from roughly 12,000–14,000 years ago.

All the major paleoanthropological claims from the last 50 years are now in doubt. The modern theory is clearly in a state of disarray and confusion. Paleo-experts can no longer be certain that the genus *Homo* evolved from the australopiths. They can no longer say when and where the first *Homo sapiens* appeared. They can no longer trust the techniques they have used to date hominin bones and artifacts.

13. Gierlinski G.D. *et al.*, Possible hominin footprints from the late Miocene (c. 5.7 Ma) of Crete? *Proceedings of the Geologists' Association* 621:1-14, 2017. DOI: 10.1016/j.pgeola.2017.07.006

14. The time period spanning from 2.58-5.33 million years before present.

15. Hublin J. *et al.*, New fossils from Jebel Iroud, Morocco and the pan-African origin of *Homo sapiens*, *Nature* 546:289-292, 2017. DOI:10.1038/nature22336

16. Holen S.R. *et al.*, A 130,000-year-old archaeological site in southern California, USA, *Nature* 544:479-483, 2017. DOI: 10.1038/nature22065

17. Klein R.G., Darwin and the recent African origin of modern humans, *Proc Natl Acad Sci*, USA 106(38): 16007–16009, 2009.

Section I—Bones of the Human Type
Introduction to Chapters 3–5

In this first Section, we will be examining the hominin bones of the human type. Because many paleo-experts are "splitters," there are many species in the *Homo* genus. Most significantly, paleo-experts recognize the following human species: *Homo sapiens* ("modern man"), *Homo neanderthalensis* ("Neanderthal"), *Homo erectus* ("Erectus") and *Homo floresiensis* ("Hobbit"). Splitters would argue that there are many more *Homo* species. However, most "lumpers," would say that all of these sub-groupings reflect variation within a single species (i.e., they are all *Homo sapiens*). We agree with the lumpers.

As we discussed, the slightest anatomical difference is sufficient basis for splitters to declare the discovery of a new species. Indeed, it is not unheard of for a new hominin species to be declared on the basis of a single broken bone. While a splitter might argue there are over a dozen *Homo* species, a lumper might say there is just one *Homo* species. For instance, one group of paleo-experts, known as multiregionalists, tend to be lumpers and maintain that over the past 2 million years only one hominin species has been in existence—*Homo sapiens*. They are saying that *Homo sapiens* includes many variants—including various people-groups that splitters would call separate species. This would include *Homo ergaster*, *H. erectus*, *H. georgicus*, *H. antecessor*, *H. heidelbergensis*, *H. rhodesiensis*, *H. helmei*, *H. floresiensis*, *H. neanderthalensis*, and *H. denisova*. Distinguished paleo-expert Chris Stringer confirms, "*...multiregionalists often regard Homo sapiens as the only human species on Earth during the last million years, so species like Homo erectus and Homo heidelbergensis have no real meaning for them.*"[1]

There are four strong arguments for lumping these slightly different skeletal forms into a single group:

1. All the extinct *Homo* forms clearly display modern human anatomy from the neck down. Apart from some aberrant skull types (which have very reasonable explanations), all these skeletons have a body shape that is clearly different from all living apes and all australopith-like fossils.

2. This group is distinctly human in having unique body designs that enable highly optimized functions. As we will see, only humans have just the right

---

1. Stringer C., *Lone Survivors: How we came to be the only Humans on Earth*, Times Books, Henry Holt and Company LLC, New York, p.28, 2013.

anatomy to enable graceful upright walking, deft handling of complex tools, inborn competence for speaking complex languages, and inborn ability to think in a truly human way.

3. The human-like bone types are consistently associated with artifacts that disclose the cultural hallmarks of modern man. For example, they used and carefully fashioned tools, utilized fire, made artwork, ceremonially buried their dead, and could sail impressive seafaring vessels against an ocean current.

4. These groups quite clearly interbred with each other and produced hybrid populations. Inter-fertility is the classic proof that anatomically variable groups still belong to the same species.

These four points constitute compelling evidence that all of these hominin bones of the human type were indeed fully human, and so were not ape/human transitional forms.

This section describes *Homo neanderthalensis*—"Neanderthal" (chapter 3), *Homo erectus*—"Erectus" (chapter 4), and *Homo floresiensis*—"Hobbit" (chapter 5). *Homo habilis* (Habilis), and *Homo naledi* (Naledi), will be described separately in Section III (Bones of the "Middle" Type).

CHAPTER 3

Homo neanderthalensis
The First Hominin Bones

The irony is that the scientific community is going to have to come round to the acceptance that the Denisovans and the Neandertals also belonged to the species which we all call Homo sapiens.[1]

Paleoanthropologist Clive Finlayson, Director of Gibraltar Museum

Early History

"Neanderthal" was initially used as a nickname for a non-mineralized skullcap and a few associated bones and bone fragments which were discovered in the Neander Valley of Düsseldorf, Germany in 1856 (Figure 1). This was the first set of bones to be considered a pre-human hominin. These few bones became popularly known as "Neanderthal Man."[2] The quotes we cite below will use both acceptable spellings ("Neanderthal" and "Neandertal" meaning "Neander valley" in German). The second spelling reflects the most common pronunciation.

Figure 1. The original Neanderthal bones discovered in the Neander valley of Düsseldorf, Germany in 1856. Since then nearly 500 Neanderthal skeletons have been found.

---

1. Finlayson C., All change: theories of human ancestry get an overhaul. BBC News, 31 December, 2010. Date accessed Nov. 2016. http://www.bbc.com/news/science-environment-12093345
2. Vogt K.C., *Lectures on Man: His Place in Creation, and in the History of the Earth*, Longman, Green, Longman and Roberts, London, pp. 302, 473, 1864.

Since that first discovery, many skeletons have been found displaying similar characteristics. Those bones are collectively described by the paleo-community as "Neanderthal" and they are typically given the formal designation *Homo neanderthalensis*. However, an increasing number of paleo-experts prefer to classify Neanderthal as *Homo sapiens*. Over the past 150 years there has been considerable debate regarding the status of Neanderthals. Were they a brutish-looking "missing link" between ape and man; were they a separate sub-human species that went extinct (an evolutionary side branch); or were they fully human (*Homo sapiens*)? Generally speaking, the paleoanthropology community has come to regard Neanderthals as an extinct variant of man.

Neanderthals and *Homo sapiens* are said to have evolved from a common African ancestor about 650,000 years ago. This age estimate is based upon the sequencing of the DNA within the Neanderthal bones and the number of different mutations compared to modern humans. This type of "molecular clock dating" will be discussed in an upcoming book. Molecular clock methods require questionable assumptions about mutation rates.[3] The first European Neanderthal fossils are thought to be 400,000 years old, based on uranium-series dating (see chapter 12).[4]

Nearly 500 Neanderthal skeletons have been discovered at 124 sites located in Europe, the Middle East, and western Asia. The primary distinctive feature of Neanderthal skeletons involves the shape of the skull, which is typically elongated front to back. The result is a pushed-back forehead, which exposes strong brow ridges, a pushed-forward lower face, a reduced chin, and a slightly enlarged occipital bun (a slight bulge at the rear of the skull). The braincase of the Neanderthal was large, typically larger than most modern humans.

Neanderthals are not significantly different from modern man from the neck down. They are described as being stout, with robust (rugged) skeletons indicating powerful musculature. They had relatively short arms and legs, and had deep funnel-shaped chests. They stood fully upright and walked and moved like modern humans.

The Neanderthal people were nomadic hunter-gatherers who lived in the harsh middle latitude climate of glacial Europe. Neanderthals lived alongside anatomically modern humans. The contact zone between them is described as "*extensive and long lasting*," providing ample opportunity for interbreeding.[5] Recent genetic analyses have confirmed what many paleo-experts had long suspected—Neanderthals and *Homo sapiens* were inter-fertile and interbred. Neanderthal genes are present in modern populations. The DNA of Europeans and Asians contain approximately 1–4% Neanderthal DNA.

3. https://www.sciencenews.org/article/ancient-dna-reveals-who-spain's-'pit-bones'-cave
4. Bischoff L. *et al.*, High-Resolution U-Series Dates from the Sima de los Huesos Hominids Yields 600+/-66 kyrs: implications for the Evolution of the Early Neanderthal, PAYS-BAS (Elsevier, Amsterdam), vol. 34, 2007.
5. Cartmill M. and Smith F.H., *The Human Lineage*, Wiley-Blackwell, Hoboken, NJ, p. 412, 2009.

Recently, paleo-experts have classified a new form of *Homo*, which lived along side both Neanderthals and modern humans. In 2008, bone fragments were found together with Neanderthal bones in the Denisova Cave, in southern Siberia. The remains were very meager—just the tip of a finger bone and a few teeth (Figure 2).

Figure 2. Replica of a finger bone fragment recovered from Denisova cave, Russia in 2008 (right). Replica of the Denisovan molar that was also recovered from Denisova cave in 2000 (left). Mitochondrial DNA was extracted from each of these fossils and sequenced.

What really distinguished the "Denisovan" bones was the DNA extracted from them—which displayed some distinctive mutations. These "Denisovans" have not yet been given an official species designation. David Reich of Harvard has said, *"Denisovans are a genome in search of a fossil."*[6] Recent DNA analyses suggest Denisovans also were found, along with Neanderthals and modern humans, in a cave in Spain.[7] In our opinion, Denisovans were simply a genetic variant of Neanderthal. Just as Neanderthal DNA has been found within Europeans and Asians, traces of Denisovan DNA appear to be present in people groups living in Southeast Asia (i.e., the New Guinea Papuans, Australian Aborigines, and the Mamanwa people of the Philippines).[8,9] However, when considering ancient DNA evidence, caution is required because ancient DNA is usually highly degraded, and thus is difficult to reconstruct with fidelity. DNA contamination is routinely a problem when studying ancient DNA, even when great care is taken to avoid this type of genetic contamination.[10] Assuming that the Denisovan genomes have been accurately sequenced, this new genetic evidence adds to the cultural and fossil evidence that Neanderthals, Denisovans, and modern humans were all members

6. Marshall M., Mystery Relations, *New Scientist*, 2014. http://web.uvic.ca/~mackie/Mystery_relations_New_Scientist_April_5,_201.pdf
7. Reich D. *et al.*, Genetic history of an archaic hominin group from Denisova cave in Siberia, *Nature* 468 (7327):1053-1060, 2014.
8. Meyer M. *et al.*, A high-coverage genome sequence from an archaic Denisovan individual, *Science* 338, 222-226, 2012.
9. Prüfer K. *et al.*, The complete genome sequence of a Neanderthal from the Altai Mountains, *Nature* 505:43-49, 2014.
10. Green R.E. *et al.*, A draft sequence of the Neandertal genome, *Science* 328(5979):710-722, 2010. *"A special challenge in analyzing DNA sequences from the Neanderthal nuclear genome is that most DNA fragments are expected to be identical to present-day humans. Thus, contamination of the experiments with DNA from present-day humans may be mistaken for endogenous* [Neanderthal] *DNA."*

of a large interbreeding metapopulation,[11] and so were all just variants of *Homo sapiens*.

Over the years it became increasingly evident to the paleo-community that Neanderthals (and Denisovans) were fully human and were very much like us. The Neanderthals are said to have gone extinct roughly 30,000 years ago.[12] However the latest DNA evidence indicates that the Neanderthal population never truly went extinct,[13] but rather, was assimilated into other human populations.[14] Again, this argues that Neanderthal was *Homo sapiens*.

The Dehumanization of Neanderthals

To "dehumanize" means to deprive a person or group of positive human qualities. There is no better example of this in the field of paleoanthropology than "Neanderthal Man." William King (1809–1886), professor of geology at Queen's College in Galway, Ireland, was the first scientist to impose a sub-human interpretation onto the fossils. When examining the skullcap found in Neander Valley cave, King commented, *"I feel myself constrained to believe that the thoughts and desires which once dwelt within it never soared beyond those of a brute."*[15] King focused on the heavy brow ridges and noted its resemblance to those of chimps and gorillas. He decided "Neanderthal Man" could not possibly have been an intelligent human being. At a meeting of the British Association for the Advancement of Science in 1863, King assigned the fossils to a sub-human species of man, *Homo neanderthalensis*. In his view, the Neanderthals were too brutish to be considered human. A few years later, in 1866, German biologist and radical Darwinist Ernst Haeckel proposed the name *Homo stupidus*. Such demeaning interpretations were further reinforced by highly inaccurate reconstructions of Neanderthal skeletons. For instance, in 1886, two nearly complete skeletons were found in association with stone tools and artifacts at a Belgian site in Spy. Max Lohest and Julien Fraipont from the University of Liège misleadingly reconstructed the skeletons with an ape-like, bent-kneed posture. Modern paleo-expert Ian Tattersall writes:

> From the anatomy of the leg bones, Fraipont and Lohest came to the conclusion that these individuals had walked upright, but with bent knees—just as, in fact, apes do when they stand up. Thus started the myth of the bent-kneed Neanderthals, a myth that was to endure more than half a century.[16]

In 1908 another nearly complete Neanderthal skeleton, dubbed the "Old Man,"

11. Roebroeks W. and Soressi M., Neandertals revised, *Proc Natl Acad Sci*, USA 113(23):6372-6379, 2016.

12. Green R.E. *et al.*, A draft sequence of the Neandertal genome, *Science* 328(5979):710-722, 2010.

13. Villa P. and Roebroeks W., Neandertal demise: and archeological analysis of the modern human superiority complex, *PLoS ONE* 9(4): e96424, 2014. *"In that sense* [in light of genetic evidence revealing inbreeding], *Neandertals did not go extinct, even though their distinctive morphology did disappear."*

14. Roebroeks W. and Soressi M., Neandertals revised, *Proc Natl Acad Sci*, USA 113(23):6372-6379, 2016. The first region to be colonized is believed to be the Levant (in the eastern Mediterranean).

15. Zimmer C., Are Neanderthals Human? *Nova scienceNOW* 9 September, 2010. http://www.pbs.org/wgbh/nova/evolution/are-neanderthals-human.html

16. Tattersall I., *The Last Neandertal*, Macmillan (Nevraumont) Publishing Company, New York, p.77, 1995.

was discovered in a cave in La Chapelle-aux-Saints, France. The highly esteemed paleontologist Marcellin Boule of the National Museum of Natural History in Paris, was called in to examine the fossils. Boule was considered a foremost authority on Neanderthals at that time, having written an extensive volume describing their anatomy. Despite his prestige, Marcellin Boule is responsible for what the paleoanthropology community now regards as the most inaccurate reconstruction of a hominin skeleton, second only to the "Piltdown Man" fraud.[17] Like the Spy reconstructions, the "Old Man" from La Chapelle was made to appear very ape-ish with a grasping big toe and a bent-knee/bent-hip posture. Boule's characterization inspired the first artistic depiction of a Neanderthal, as shown in Figure 3.

Figure 3. The first artist's depiction of "Neanderthal Man" shown in the Illustrated London News in 1909. The drawing by Czech artist Frantižek Kupka was heavily influenced by Boule's fraudulent reconstruction of a Neanderthal skeleton from La Chapelle-Aux-Saints in France.

Other influential scientists approved of Boule's reconstruction, such as Elliot Smith (1871–1937), a highly esteemed professor of anatomy at the University of London. These high-profile endorsements helped to promote a grossly inaccurate view of Neanderthals to the world. Smith provided the following description of the so-called *"uncouth and repellent Neanderthal Man"*:

> His short, thick-set, and coarsely built body was carried in a half-stooping slouch upon short, powerful, and half-flexed legs of peculiarly ungraceful form. His thick neck sloped forward from the broad shoulders to support the massive flattened head, which protruded forward, so as to form an unbroken curve of neck and back, in place of the alternation of curves which is one of the graces of the truly erect

17. Price M., Study reveals culprit behind Piltdown Man, one of science's most famous hoaxes, *Science Magazine* 9 August, 2016. http://www.sciencemag.org/news/2016/08/study-reveals-culprit-behind-piltdown-man-one-science-s-most-famous-hoaxes

Homo sapiens. The heavy overhanging eyebrow-ridges and retreating forehead, the great coarse face with its large eye-sockets, broad nose, and receding chin, combined to complete the picture of unattractiveness, which it is more probable than not was still further emphasized by a shaggy covering of hair over most of the body. The arms were relatively short, and the exceptionally large hands lacked the delicacy and nicely balanced co-operation of thumb and fingers which is regarded as one of the most distinctive of human characteristics.[18]

Boule's faulty reconstruction was undoubtedly influenced by his evolutionary preconception that "Neanderthal Man" was a descendant of apes and unrelated to humans. Modern paleo-expert Erik Trinkaus acknowledges this, writing:

Boule, like many of his contemporaries (and many subsequent human paleontologists), let his preconceived evolutionary notions unduly influence his interpretation of functional morphology, so as to provide an overall reconstruction of the Neandertals that fit their perceived evolutionary relationship to modern *Homo sapiens*. He was able to do this and convince the discipline that his reconstruction was accurate …[19]

The Smithsonian National Museum of Natural History website tells of Boule's fraudulent reconstruction stating:

The original reconstruction of the 'Old Man of La Chapelle' by scientist Pierre Marcellin Boule led to the reason why popular culture stereotyped Neanderthals as dim-witted brutes for so many years. In 1911, Boule reconstructed this skeleton with a severely curved spine indicative of a stooped, slouching stance with bent knees, forward flexed hips, and the head jutted forward. He thought the low vaulted cranium and the large brow ridge, somewhat reminiscent of that seen in large apes such as gorillas, indicated a generally primitive early human and a lack of intelligence. However, additional discoveries of Neanderthal skeletons coupled with a re-examination of the Old Man's skeleton in the 1950's showed that many of the features thought to be unique in Neanderthals fall within the range of modern human variation, and that the Old Man suffered from "gross deforming osteoarthritis." Thus, the slouching posture of the original reconstruction may have been based on an unfortunate individual with a deforming disability. But this isn't quite the whole story. A more recent evaluation of the entire skeleton by scientist Erik Trinkaus has shown that, while the Old Man of La Chapelle did suffer from a degenerative joint disease, the deformation caused by this should not have affected Boule's original reconstruction of the individual's posture. It appears that Boule's own preconceptions about early humans, and his rejection of the hypothesis that Neanderthals were the ancestors of modern humans, led him to reconstruct a stooped, brutish creature, effectively placing Neanderthals on a side branch of the human evolutionary tree. (Boule even gave his reconstruction an opposable big toe like the great apes, but there was no bone deformity that

---

18. Smith E.G., *The Evolution of Man*, Oxford University Press, London, 1927.
19. Trinkaus E., Pathology and posture of the La Chapelle-aux-Saints Neandertal, *Am J Phys Anthropol* 67:19-41, 1985. https://www.ncbi.nlm.nih.gov/pubmed/3904471

should or could have led to this interpretation.)[20]

Boule grossly misrepresented Neanderthal more than a century and a half ago. Yet his ape-like caricature of "Neanderthal Man" is still deeply embedded in modern culture. As Tattersall acknowledges, *"The skeleton of the "Old Man" from La Chapelle, now thought to be 50 thousand years old, was misinterpreted by Marcellin Boule in 1908-11 to yield the classic caricature of the Neanderthals as shuffling, bent-kneed brutes."*[21] To this day, illustrations and comic movies commonly portray "Neanderthal Man" as sub-human. It is only very recently that museum displays and artistic renditions of Neanderthals have begun to change (Figure 4). The general public and scientists outside the paleo-community are still largely unaware of what the real "Neanderthal Man" looked like.

Figure 4. Earlier reconstructions portray Neanderthals as a brutish sub-human species (left). Newer museum displays are replacing the outdated representations. In keeping with the latest DNA analyses, Neanderthal replacement displays appear more modern in appearance (right).

In the 1900s, debates continued regarding the status of Neanderthals. On one side were those who advocated an evolutionary interpretation of Neanderthals, as either descendants of apes excluded from the branch leading to man as Boule believed, or a "missing link" between *Pithecanthropus*, aka "Java Man", and modern humans.[22] On the other side were those who took issue with Boule's reconstruction and insisted Neanderthals were fully human. Among those who disagreed with Boule were William Straus and A.J.E. Cave—anatomists who provided a much

---

20. Information on La Chapelle-aux-Saints from Smithsonian National Museum of Natural History, last updated 30 March 2016. http://humanorigins.si.edu/evidence/human-fossils/fossils/la-chapelle-aux-saints
21. Tattersall I. and Schwartz J., *Extinct Humans*, Westview Press, New York, p.86, 2000.
22. Reader J., *Missing Links*, Oxford University Press, New York, pp. 84, 104, 105, 2011. Boule believed Neanderthals had evolved from apes and were not directly related to modern humans, rather than a "missing link" between ape and man as others had claimed. He wrote, *"we are aware of no descendants."* Instead, he accepted "Piltdown Man" as the likely ancestor to man. Others, such as K. Gorgjanovic-Kramberger and Gustav Schwalbe, disagreed and maintained that Neanderthal was the immediate ancestor to man.

more accurate reconstruction of the "Old Man" from La Chapelle.[23] These paleo-experts could not ignore the fact that Neanderthal clearly had an anatomy that was fully human. They wrote in *The Quarterly Review of Biology* (1957), *"If he could be reincarnated and placed in a New York subway—provided that he were bathed, shaved, and dressed in modern clothing—it is doubtful whether he would attract any more attention than some of its other denizens."*[24]

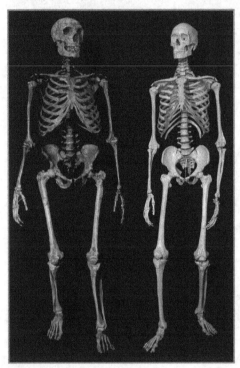

Figure 5. A side-by-side comparison of a composite Neanderthal skeleton (left) and a modern human skeleton (right). Neanderthals were thicker-boned with larger joint surfaces and had differently shaped skulls, yet their overall anatomy is unmistakably human.

This view eventually carried the day within the paleo-community. Neanderthal expert Erik Trinkaus lists in the *American Journal of Physical Anthropology* numerous scientific publications dating from the 50s until recent times that have all confirmed what is now widely accepted in the paleo-community: *"the total morphological pattern of Neandertal axial and appendicular remains* [which comprises the entire skeleton] *was fully compatible with erect posture and bipedality of modern humans."*[25] There is now unanimous agreement within the paleo-community that the real "Neanderthal Man" was anatomically human (Figure 5). The primary distinctives are confined to the skull shape and the overall robustness of the skeleton, yet neither of these two features is outside the range of human variation. Erik Trinkaus, a foremost authority on Neanderthals has concluded:

Detailed comparisons of Neanderthal skeletal remains with those of modern humans have shown that there is nothing in Neanderthal anatomy that conclusively indicates locomotor, manipulative, intellectual or linguistic abilities inferior to those of modern humans.[26]

While the paleo-community has abandoned the ape-ish depictions of Neanderthals,

23. Straus W. L. and Cave A.J.E., Pathology and Posture of Neandertal Man, *Quarterly Review of Biology* 32:348-363, 1957.

24. Straus W. L. and Cave A.J.E., Pathology and Posture of Neandertal Man, *Quarterly Review of Biology* 32:348-363, 1957.

25. Trinkaus E., Pathology and posture of the La Chapelle-aux-Saints Neandertal, *Am J Phys Anthropol* 67:19-41, 1985. https://www.ncbi.nlm.nih.gov/pubmed/3904471

26. Trinkaus E., Hard Times Among the Neandertals, *Natural History* 87(10):58-63, December, 1978.

people outside the field still envision Neanderthal as being less evolved than are modern humans. As Jared Diamond, professor of geology at UCLA writes, Neanderthals were *"humans, and yet not really human."*[27] What is the basis of this assertion, apart from his evolutionary preconception? Diamond's assertion was made in ignorance of what is actually widely accepted within the paleo-community.

While some paleo-experts still maintain that Neanderthal is a separate human species, a growing number argue Neanderthal was fully human and interbred with *Homo sapiens*—and therefore were *Homo sapiens*. The paleo-experts who classify Neanderthal as *Homo sapiens* freely acknowledge the fact that they displayed unique features not typically seen in modern humans. It is uncontested in the paleo-community that Neanderthals share a cluster of traits that are unusual. What is contested is whether or not those distinctive traits are sufficient grounds to justify classifying Neanderthal as a separate, sub-human species. How paleo-experts answer that question largely depends on their philosophical perspective on what "species" means.

The biological species concept (BSC) is the most widely accepted definition of a species, and was developed by Ernst Mayr. The BSC states that if members of the same or different populations are able to interbreed and produce fertile progeny, then they are considered the same species. However, since Neanderthals are no longer living, the BSC did not seem directly applicable. That changed when scientists were able to recover Neanderthal DNA. Apart from BSC, the next best way to determine whether Neanderthals are a separate human species is to use the morphological species concept (MSC). As the name suggests, the MSC emphasizes morphologically distinctive traits as the basis for defining a new species. Using the MSC, it was traditionally believed that the anatomical features characteristic of Neanderthals were indicators of their complete reproductive isolation from *Homo sapiens* (and therefore separateness as a species). Paleo-experts Cartmill and Smith write, *"most advocates of separate species status for H. neanderthalensis believe that the anatomical peculiarities of Neanderthals are a sign of their reproductive isolation."*[28] They then go on to say, *"But the leap from the MSC to the BSC seems unwarranted."* In other words, just because Neanderthal skeletons display certain unique features, it does not mean that they must therefore have been incapable of interbreeding with anatomically modern *Homo sapiens*. That the MSC model of species is wrong is easily seen by examining different people groups living today— who show striking morphological differences, yet are clearly all *Homo sapiens*. The same can be said about the striking difference between various breeds of dogs— which are likewise obviously all the same species.

The MSC model (i.e., the assumption that superficial morphological differences indicate reproductive isolation and hence justify separate species status) has been

27. Diamond J., Great Leap Forward, *Discover* (May 1989) pp.50-60.
28. Cartmill M. and Smith F.H., *The Human Lineage*, Wiley-Blackwell, Hoboken, NJ, p. 411, 2009.

thoroughly falsified by the recent sequencing of Neanderthal DNA. This DNA evidence provides compelling evidence for gene flow (inter-fertility) between modern *Homo sapiens* and Neanderthals. Thus, in keeping with the BSC standard of species, Neanderthals and anatomically modern humans are, by definition, all *Homo sapiens*. This vindicates the paleoanthropologists who are "lumpers," and who have for decades been arguing that Neanderthals should be reclassified as *Homo sapiens* (or *Homo sapiens*, sub-species *neanderthalensis*).[29]

Neanderthal Features Seen in Modern Humans

Human individuals living today display classic Neanderthal features.[30] If the same traits can be found in modern humans as well as in early modern *Homo sapiens* populations, then there is no rational basis for continuing to treat Neanderthal as a separate species.

Figure 6. Nikolai Valuev is a celebrated former boxing champion. In 2011 he was elected to the Russian parliament. He (like many other people alive today) has a sloping forehead and enlarged brow ridges—reminiscent of the Neanderthal skulls. Human skulls come in many shapes and sizes yet we are all *Homo sapiens*.

The former world-champion boxer, Nikolai Valuev, also a member of the Russian parliament, happens to display Neanderthal-like features in the skull. He has a sloping forehead and heavy brow ridges characteristic of Neanderthal (Figure 6). His chin is modern, but if his skullcap were found as an isolated bone in the fossil record (as most Neanderthal skullcaps are found), a "splitter" might misclassify him as a separate species. Like a large part of the human race, Mr. Valuev carries Neanderthal DNA.

29. Tattersall I., *The Last Neaderthal*, Nevraumont Publishing Company, New York, p.10, 1995.
30. Trinkaus E. *et al.*, An early modern human from the Pestera cu Oase, Romania, *Proc Natl Acad Sci*, USA 100(20):11231-11236, 2003.

Cartmill and Smith write:

> The most persuasive empirical reason for doubting that complete reproductive isolation occurred in this case is the existence of specimens with mixed morphology. Some of these are fossils of early modern humans found in or at the edges of the Neandertal homeland, which exhibit features of the skeleton otherwise characteristic of Neandertals.[31]

Neanderthal features that can be observed in early modern humans are seen in the postcranium (below the neck) as well as in the skull.[32] There is no clear definition of what constitutes a modern human skull. There are always aberrant human skulls that fall outside the proposed ranges of human morphology. As Cartmill and Smith write, *"most of the definitions of "modern human" that have been proposed are either too vague to be useful or too narrow to encompass the range of modern human variation.... an all-encompassing definition may be impossible."*[33] In spite of these difficulties, generally accepted features of the modern human skull are as follows: rounded high-vertical forehead, reduced or absent brow ridge, projecting chin, smoothly curved occipital bone (lacking a protrusion at the rear of the skull), and less projecting lower face.[34] Paleo-experts have attempted to distinguish *Homo sapiens* on the basis of these commonly shared traits, and have used these traits to exclude Neanderthal from *Homo sapiens*. The problem with this characterization of *Homo sapiens* is that it is too narrow. There are a number of modern human skulls that fall outside the "accepted" human range. For instance, there are a number of Australian aboriginal skulls that do not meet the typical standard of "modern" human crania, yet no one doubts they are fully human.

Thomas Huxley was the first to compare Australian aboriginal skulls to Neanderthals in 1863. He noted the skulls displayed a number of morphological similarities to Neanderthals.[35] Decades later in the *Journal of Anatomy* (1922),[36] anatomists dubbed an aboriginal skull "Neanderthaloid" which showed so-called "primitive features" characteristic of Neanderthals, such as an "extremely low sloping forehead" and a pronounced brow ridge.

Other skulls attributed to *Homo sapiens* have been found that display Neanderthal features (Figure 7). For example, three fairly complete skulls were excavated from

---

31. Cartmill M. and Smith F.H., *The Human Lineage*, Wiley-Blackwell, Hoboken, NJ, p. 412, 2009.
32. Day M.H., *Guide to Fossil Man*, University of Chicago Press, Chicago, p.131, 1985. Considering Amud remains from Israel, Michael Day describes the specimen as *"displaying a mixture of morphological characters most of which are best compared with those of 'classic' Neandertalers whilst some are reflected in later human material."* The skulls show "affinities to the Skhul and Qafzeh remains."
33. Cartmill M. and Smith F.H., *The Human Lineage*, Wiley-Blackwell, Hoboken, NJ, p. 412, 2009.
34. Day M. and Stringer C.B., A reconsideration of the Omo-Kibish remains and the erectus-sapiens transition. In: de Lumley M. (ed.), *L'Homo erectus et la place de l'homme de Tautavel parmi les hominidés.* Nice: CNRS, pp. 814-846, 1982.
35. Curnoe D., A 150- Year Conundrum: Cranial Robusticity and Its Bearing on the Origin of Aboriginal Australians, *International J Evol Biol* vol. 2011, Article ID 632484, 18 pages, 2011. DOI:10.4061/2011/632484
36. Burkitt A.N. and Hunter J.I., The description of a Neanderthaloid Australian skull, with remarks on the production of the facial characteristics of Australian skulls in general, *J Anat* 57:31–54, 1922.

a cave located in Es Skhul, on the slope of the Mt. Carmel region of northern Israel in the 1930s. Some skulls displayed elongated and low lying vaults, forward projecting faces, pronounced brow ridges, and a reduced chin. Skhul IV and Skhul IX in particular are described in the *American Journal of Physical Anthropology* as aligning closer to Neanderthals than to modern humans, even though the skulls were found buried together with other anatomically modern human skulls that are themselves clearly *Homo sapiens* (dated as 100,000 years old).[37] A paleo-expert in a separate study published in the same journal took note of the overlapping variation in skulls from Israel saying, *"the morphological variability within sites ...makes a separation between Neandertals and Homo sapiens in these localities impossible and demonstrates a great range of variation within a unique population."*[38] Moreover, because of their "archaic" looking features, the skulls were cited by other researchers as evidence of interbreeding between *Homo sapiens* and Neanderthals. The sample from Mt. Carmel was further noted for its extensive degree of anatomical variation. The researchers who excavated the remains made the following observation:

> We are of the opinion that the variability found amongst the fossil people of Mount Carmel is greater in degree and in kind than is to be observed in any local community of modern times. Had the Mount Carmel people been discovered—not collectively, in one place, but separately, in diverse localities, each excavator would have been convinced that a new and separate form of humanity had been unearthed, so great does one Carmelite individual differ from another.[39]

They acknowledge that if the bones had not been found together, they would likely have been classified as belonging to separate species. It is too easy to underestimate the extent of variation in the human form, and thereby exclude certain skull types from their rightful human status.

Nearby, in Jabel Qafzeh, two complete skulls were recovered from a cave in the 1930s that dated to approximately 92,000 years old. Among the remains were found many animal bones, several fire hearths, stone tools, and red ochre (a natural pigment made into a cosmetic). The skulls were classified as *Homo sapiens*, yet they exhibit Neanderthal features such as a projecting lower face and robust brow ridges. Qafzeh VI clearly displays a Neanderthal morphology (Figure 7).[40]

One final example worth noting is the Mladeč remains recovered from a cave in the Czech Republic in the late 1800s and early 1900s. Nearly 140 skeletal remains were found in total, however, only a few survived the destruction caused by World War II. Among the salvaged remains were several skulls. They have been dated to just

37. Corruccini R.S., Metrical Reconsideration of the Skul IV and IX and Border Cave 1 Crania in the Context of Modern Human Origins, *Am J Phys Anthropol* 87:433-445, 1992.
38. Arensburg B, From sapiens to Neandertals: rethinking the Middle East, *Am J Phys Anthropol* 12:44, 1991.
39. McCown T. and Keith A., *The Stone Age Man of Mount Carmel: The Fossil Human Remains from the Levalloiso-Mousterian*, Oxford University Press, New York, 1939.
40. Corruccini R.S., Metrical Reconsideration of the Skul IV and IX and Border Cave 1 Crania in the Context of Modern Human Origins, *Am J Phys Anthropol* 87:433-445, 1992.

over 30,000 years old. In the journal *Nature*, evolutionary paleo-experts state that the remains are universally accepted as belonging to *Homo sapiens*. Nevertheless, the male skulls in particular display a number of Neanderthal features (listed by the researchers), including the shape of the skull, pronounced brow ridges, occipital bulge at the rear skull, and other traits typical of Neanderthals.[41] The postcranial remains were also briefly noted for their robust features such as "articular hypertrophy"—a description of the joint surfaces. They were enlarged like that of Neanderthals. In a separate publication in the journal *Humanities*, evolutionary archaeologist Robert Bednarik confirmed the many Neanderthal features are seen in the Mladeč skulls.[42] He described the following traits: thick projecting brow ridges, low laying vaults, large cranial capacities typical of Neanderthals (e.g., 1650 cm^3 for Mladeč 5), inclined foreheads, angled occipital region, and more.

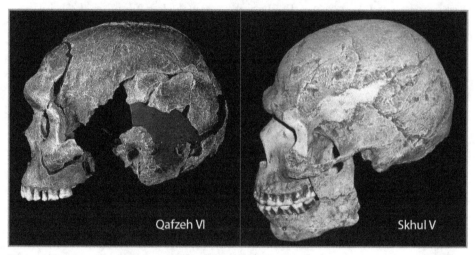

Figure 7. *Homo sapiens* skulls from Qafzeh (left) and Es Skhul (right) caves in northern Israel display a combination of Neanderthal and anatomically modern traits.

Huxley correctly suspected at the time of Darwin that the morphological boundary used to distinguish *Homo sapiens* and Neanderthal skulls was arbitrary. Even today paleo-experts debate about whether certain skulls should be classified as *Homo sapiens* or Neanderthals because they are not readily distinguishable.[43] Many *Homo sapiens* skulls (including those of people living today; see Figure 6) display the very same features that are used to classify Neanderthals. Examples like these demonstrate that Neanderthals and *Homo sapiens* are members of the same species, just as the "lumper" paleo-experts have always maintained. The generally accepted criteria used to classify hominin skulls are too narrow and do not encompass the full range of human variation. Thus, one cannot reasonably

41. Wild E.M. *et al.*, Direct dating of Early Upper Paleolithic human remains from Mladeč, *Nature* 435:332-335, 2005. DOI: 10.1038/nature03585.
42. Bednarik R.G., The origins of human modernity, *Humanities* 1:1-53, 2012. DOI: 10.3390/h1010001.
43. Minugh-Purvis N. and Radovcic J., Krapina A: Neandertal or Not? *Am J Phys Anthrop*, Suppl. 12, p. 132, 1991.

exclude Neanderthals as *Homo sapiens* on the basis of their skull morphology.

Extensive Coexistence with *Homo sapiens* in the Fossil Record

One of the clearest evidences that Neanderthals and *Homo sapiens* are one and the same species is their extensive overlap in time and space. *Homo sapiens* and Neanderthals occupied the same territory of western Eurasia for at least 60,000 years (according to conventional dating methods) so there would clearly have been co-mingling of their cultures. The contact between *Homo sapiens* and Neanderthals is described as *"extensive and long-lasting."*[44] Cartmill and Smith note, *"such a broad hybrid zone would cast doubt on whether the morphs involved really should be thought of as separate species."*[45] Evolutionary studies have estimated geographic separation between sub-populations must endure for at least 1 million years before a speciation event can occur. They go on to say, *"it is doubtful that the isolation went on long enough for complete reproductive isolation to occur."*[46]

"Pit of Bones"—Neanderthals, Erectus, and *Homo sapiens*

In 1992 a team led by Juan-Luis Arsuaga of the Complutense University of Madrid discovered a "pit of bones" (Sima de los Huesos) hidden within a complex of caves in the Sierra de Atapuerca of northern Spain.[47] It was located at the bottom of a 43-foot deep vertical shaft, where at least 28 hominin individuals were found, including three well-preserved skulls. The site was dated as 430,000 years old. The individuals appear to have been deliberately disposed of, as opposed to accidentally falling to their death.[48] What is most intriguing about this discovery is the extreme variation seen in the skulls. In the journal *Nature*, paleo-expert Chris Stringer listed numerous features that are characteristic of the three major *Homo* species—including Erectus (chapter 4), Neanderthals, and *Homo sapiens*. The extent of variation seen in the Sima de los Huesos sample encompasses all of the so-called "archaic" humans. "Archaic" humans include those, who cannot be neatly categorized as either Erectus or Neanderthals because they share qualities of both (e.g., *Homo heidelbergensis*). Stringer decided to classify all of the diverse skeletons as Neanderthals, though he admits that by doing so, there is no longer any good reason why those species should be split. He writes, *"In spite of all the variation they display, they get sucked in with the Neanderthals. Once that happens, it becomes very difficult to prevent the rest of the European material from getting sucked in as well."*[49] This is consistent with what "lumpers" have always maintained—that Erectus, Heidelbergensis, Neanderthals, and *Homo sapiens* all belong to the same

44. Cartmill M. and Smith F.H., *The Human Lineage*, Wiley-Blackwell, Hoboken, NJ, p. 412, 2009.

45. Cartmill M. and Smith F.H., *The Human Lineage*, Wiley-Blackwell, Hoboken, NJ, p. 411, 2009.

46. Cartmill M. and Smith F.H., *The Human Lineage*, Wiley-Blackwell, Hoboken, NJ, p. 412, 2009.

47. Arsuaga, J.L., Martinez I., *et al.*, Three new human skulls from Sima de los Huesos Middle Pleistocene site in Sierra de Atapuerca, Spain, *Nature* 362: 534-537, 1993.

48. http://www.msn.com/en-us/news/technology/prehistoric-skull-with-puncture-wounds-could-be-worlds-first-murder-mystery/ar-BBkjj9A

49. Shreeve J., Infants, Cannibals, and the Pit of Bones, *Discover* 15(1):39, Jan 1994.

interbreeding species. For instance, Milford Wolpoff (a well-known "lumper") wrote in 1994 that the Sima de los Huesos sample *"shows that all that variation is normal for the population"* and further states, *"[a]ll Caucasians, are carrying around quite a bit of the Neanderthal genetic legacy."*[50] This insightful observation would not be confirmed until 20 years later with the sequencing of the Neanderthal genome. The "Pit of Bones" demonstrates that all three major hominin "species" (Erectus, Neanderthals, and *Homo sapiens*) coexisted in the same place at the same time, and can be arranged into a morphological continuum, reflecting diversity within a single, interbreeding population. In 2016 Meyer *et al.* reported in *Nature* an analysis of a small segment of nuclear and mitochondrial DNA extracted from five bone samples from within the pit (presumably different individuals).[51] The nuclear DNA suggested they were Neanderthal, yet the mitochondrial DNA indicated a Denisovan ancestor.[52] This supports the interpretation that they had different genetic histories yet could all interbreed, and are all one species—*Homo sapiens*.

DNA Analysis Confirms Neanderthals Interbred with *Homo sapiens*

The discovery of the first "Neanderthal Man" in 1856 sparked a century-and-a-half long debate surrounding the question of whether Neanderthals were fully human or a separate sub-human species. Much of the debate has centered on the question of whether or not they interbred with early modern humans. Corroborating evidence has been cited for the likelihood of interbreeding. This includes: bones displaying a mixture of Neanderthals and anatomically modern traits; cultural evidence showing Neanderthals had integrated with modern human populations; fossil evidence showing Neanderthals and modern humans were buried together in the same gravesites; and controversial mitochondrial DNA analysis of the first bones recognized as "Neanderthal" from Düsseldorf. However, the results of mitochondrial DNA analyses were argued to be inconclusive evidence of interbreeding.[53] Most paleo-experts dug their heels in and argued against the possibility of gene exchange and assumed complete reproductive isolation between Neanderthals and modern humans. However, a milestone study published in the prestigious journal *Science* in 2010 and a number of subsequent DNA analyses seem to have settled the debate once and for all.

Sweedish geneticist Svante Pääbo, current director of the Department of Genetics at the Max Planck Institute of Evolutionary Anthropology in Leipzig Germany, is the world's foremost authority on Neanderthal DNA sequencing. In 2010, Pääbo and his international team of researchers published the first-ever nearly complete Neanderthal genome.[54] It is arguably the most significant accomplishment in the

50. Shreeve J., Infants, Cannibals, and the Pit of Bones, *Discover* 15(1):39, Jan 1994.
51. Meyer M. *et al.*, Nuclear DNA sequences from the Middle Pleistocene SIMA de los Huesos hominins, *Nature* 531:504-507, 2016. DOI: 10.1038/nature17405
52.Callaway E., Ancient DNA pinpoints dawn of Neanderthals, *Nature* 531:286, 2016.
53. Green R.E. *et al.*, A Draft Sequence of the Neanderthal Genome, *Science* 328(5979):710-722, 2010.
54. https://www.eva.mpg.de/neandertal/press/presskit-neandertal/pdf/PR_NIH.pdf

history of paleoanthropology research. Pääbo writes:

> Many would say that a species is a group of organisms that can produce fertile offspring with each other and cannot do so with members of other groups. From that perspective we had shown that Neanderthals and modern humans were the same species.[55]

The Neanderthal DNA was extracted from a well-preserved Neanderthal specimen from Vindija Cave in Croatia. The sequence was then aligned with the DNA from five modern humans from various geographic locations, as well as with the chimp genome. The human and Neanderthal samples were so similar that investigators were concerned any contamination between the two would go undetected. The researchers concluded, *"Neanderthals fall within the variation of present day humans for many regions of the genome..."* In a press release, the National Human Genome Research Institute commented on the results of the study stating, *"Neanderthal DNA is 99.7 percent identical to present-day human DNA."*[56] These findings confirmed earlier suspicions based on cultural and fossil evidence that Neanderthals interbred with the ancestors of modern day Europeans and Asians. In the *Proceedings of the National Academy of Sciences* (2016), researchers confirm, *"Neanderthals did contribute to the modern human gene pool, with all humans who trace their ancestry beyond sub-Saharan Africa carrying Neanderthal DNA making up around 1-4% of their genome..."*[57] Based upon these new findings, some museums have replaced their now outdated sub-human representations of Neanderthals with very human-looking ones, featuring light eyes, pale skin (with freckles) and red hair (Figure 4)—genetic traits indicated by DNA analyses published in *Science*.[58,59]

Small segments of Denisovan genomes have also been sequenced, revealing that they interbred with Neanderthal and *Homo sapiens*.[60] Present-day Europeans and Asians as far south and east as Polynesia contain traces of Denisovan DNA. Svante Pääbo observed that *Homo sapiens*, Neanderthals, and Denisovans were part of a large, interconnected network of people (which he calls a "metapopulation") who exchanged genes with one another. In *Nature Reviews Genetics* (2015) Pääbo explains:

> The multiple instances of gene flow now documented among hominin groups show that modern humans were part of what one could term a 'hominin metapopulation'—that is, a web of different hominin populations, including

---

55. Pääbo S., *Neanderthal Man: In Search of Lost Genomes*, p. 237, Kindle Edition (Kindle Location 4273). Basic Books, New York, 2014.

56. https://www.eva.mpg.de/neandertal/press/presskit-neandertal/pdf/PR_NIH.pdf

57. Roebroeks W. and Soressi M., Neandertals Revised, *Proc Natl Acad Sci, USA* 113(23): 6372-6379, 2016.

58. Lalueza-Fox C. *et al.*, A Melanocortin 1 receptor allele suggests varying pigmentation among Neanderthals, *Science* 318(5855):1453-1455, 2007.

59. Ledford H., Some Neanderthals were red-heads, *Nature*, 25 October 2007; http://www.nature.com/news/2007/071025/full/news.2007.197.html

60. Browning S. et al., Analysis of Human Sequence Data Reveals Two Pulses of Archaic Denisovan Admixture, *Cell*, 173:53-61, 2018; https://doi.org/10.1016/j.cell.2018.02.031

Neanderthals, Denisovans and other groups, who were linked by limited, but intermittent or even persistent, gene flow.[61]

Clive Finlayson, evolutionary paleo-expert and Director of the Gibraltar Museum describes the significance of these findings, stating, *"The irony is that the scientific community is going to have to come round to the acceptance that the Denisovans and the Neanderthals also belonged to the species which we call Homo sapiens."* He goes on to say:

> Put together, this evidence shows us that humans formed an interwoven network of populations with varying degrees of gene flow between them. Some humans may have looked quite different from each other, revealing a combination of adaptation to local environments and genetic drift, but it does seem as though those differences were not large enough to prevent genetic interchange. ... I have suggested that humans, at any point in time in our evolutionary history, behaved as a polytypic species; they consisted of an array of regional populations clustered into geographical races which had not achieved independent species status—they could exchange genes when they met. And this is not a new idea either. The great evolutionary biologist Ernst Mayr proposed it for the human species as far back as 1950! An obsession with turning each new fossil into a distinct species has clouded the biological reality that we are now retrieving.[62]

Archaeology Confirms Neanderthals Had Modern Human Intelligence

For a long time, the paleoanthropology community has incorrectly assumed Neanderthal was an intellectually inferior species with a limited cultural inventory. However, more recent archaeological evidence recovered over the past few decades has prompted many paleo-experts to reevaluate the cognitive competency of the Neanderthal people. It turns out that the presumed intellectual inferiority was derived from evolutionary preconceptions, rather than actual evidence.

There is a common general principle used by the paleo-community that is deeply flawed. If a particular people group has a fairly sparse cultural inventory, then they are written-off as having below-average intelligence and are therefore "not really human." This assumption is invalid, as there are modern-era people groups, such as aboriginal Tasmanians or nomadic tribes living today in Africa, who until recently, have had a very limited cultural inventory—arguably less advanced than that of Neanderthals. If their limited cultural inventory had been found in the fossil record, evolutionary paleo-experts might assume they belonged to a sub-human species. Thus, even if Neanderthals did have a less impressive cultural inventory than *Homo sapiens,* it does not necessarily follow that they must belong to a sub-human species. More reasonably, their "inferior" cultural inventory is a reflection of their hunter-gatherer lifestyle (or possibly due to a loss of technology as seen with the Tasmanians) rather than a reflection of their cognitive abilities.

---

61. Pääbo S., The diverse origins of the human gene pool, *Nature Reviews* 16:313-314, 2015.
62. Clive Finlayson, BBC News, December 30, 2010; http://www.amren.com/news/2011/01/all_change_theo/

Ironically, there is now mounting evidence from archaeology that reveals a very impressive Neanderthal cultural inventory. The perceived cultural gap between Neanderthals and "modern humans" is rapidly closing with every new discovery.

The time period known as the Upper Paleolithic has traditionally represented an era of technological leaps associated with the arrival of modern humans in western Eurasia dated around 40,000 years ago.[63] Evolutionary paleo-experts had assumed that the Middle Paleolithic culture of the Neanderthals was inferior to that of the later-arriving modern humans. Paleolithic archaeologist Paola Villa, curator at the University of Colorado Museum of Natural History, argues that the comparison of technology between the Upper Paleolithic and Middle Paleolithic cultures is *"like comparing the performance of Model T Fords, widely used in America and Europe in the early part of the last century, to the performance of a modern-day Ferrari and conclud*[ing] *that Henry Ford was cognitively inferior to Enzo Ferrari."*[64] Paleo-expert Finlayson agrees and casts further doubt on the presumed intellectual and cultural inferiority of Neanderthals:

> So the Neanderthals weren't stupid apes but humans, and they interbred with our own ancestors ... But in spite of the evidence there are those who will resist. A hallmark, for the archaeologists, of modern humanity has been the Upper Paleolithic technology. In recent years the boundary between this technology and its makers has become increasingly diffuse and I would argue that technology can no longer be used as a proxy for human taxa.[65]

Finlayson and collaborators cite additional evidence in the *PLOS ONE* journal that Neanderthals made for themselves items of personal adornment that signify symbolic behavior, which *"assigns unprecedented cognitive abilities to these hominins. ... Our results, providing clear evidence that Neanderthal cognitive capacities were comparable to those of Modern Humans, constitute a major advance in the study of human evolution."*[66] Johansson in the *Wiley Interdisciplinary Review of Cognitive Science* affirms their evaluation—writing, *"There is now good evidence that Neanderthals were cognitively sophisticated, displaying many of the cognitive traits that were traditionally regarded as proxies for modern human cognition, notably including language."*[67]

63. Villa P. and Roebroeks W., Neanderthal Demise: An Archaeological Analysis of the Modern Human Superiority Complex, *PLOS ONE* 9(4):e96424, 2014. DOI: 10.1371/journal.pone.0096424. The researchers note that the limited cultural inventory of Neanderthals has been used as a *"discriminant factor between the Upper and Middle Paleolithic and therefore between AMH and Neanderthals... Into the 1980's many paleoanthropologists argued that the Neandertals had evolved into modern humans (or modern Europeans) and that the upper Paleolithic derived from the Middle Paleolithic Neandertal culture...Prior to the last decade the cultural attributes listed above were generally considered as exclusive manifestations of the western Eurasian Upper Paleolithic, as the result of a major behavioral revolution compared to the preceding Middle Paleolithic."*
64. Quote spoken by Paola Villa based on *PLOS ONE* study at http://colorado.edu/today/2014/04/30/neander-thals-were-not-inferior-modern-humans-says-cu-bolder-study, accessed 11/30/16.
65. Finlayson C., All Change: Theories of Human Ancestry Get an Overhaul, *BBC News*, 2010.
66. Finlayson C. *et al.*, Birds of a Feather: Neanderthal Exploitation of Raptors and Corvids, *PLOS ONE* 7(9):e45927, 2012. DOI: 10.1371/journal.pone.0045927.
67. Johansson S., The thinking Neanderthals: what do we know about Neanderthal cognition?, *Wiley Interdiscip Rev Cogn Sci* 5(6):613-620, 2014. https://www.ncbi.nlm.nih.gov/pubmed/26308868

In the past, researchers have listed a number of attributes indicative of modern human cognition that were assumed to be beyond the intellectual reach of Neanderthals. Evolutionary paleo-experts Paola Villa and Wil Roebroeks review some of these major "defining characteristics" of modern human cognition that are inferred from archaeological evidence, including: complex symbolic communication systems; capacity for innovation; efficient hunting abilities; sophistication in weaponry; highly varied diet; use of traps and snares; large social networks, etc. (see Table 1 in Villa *et al.* for a full list). Previous to recent findings, these abilities were thought to be found exclusively in modern humans. However, Villa and Roebroeks disagree and provide compelling evidence that Neanderthals were just as capable as anatomically modern humans (AMH) from the Upper Paleolithic. In fact, Neanderthals appear to showcase some skillsets superior to those of modern humans.[68] Villa and Roebroeks conclude in an article published in *PLOS ONE* (2014): *"In our study none of the explanations listed in the introduction and in Table 1 proved to be supported by adequate archaeological data… We have found no data in support of the supposed technological, social, and cognitive inferiority of Neandertals compared to their AMH* [anatomically modern human] *contemporaries."*[69] The Neanderthal archaeological record *"was not different enough to support the purported cognitive "gap" between them and their contemporary modern humans."* In a separate article, Villa states, *"The evidence for cognitive inferiority is simply not there. What we are saying is that the conventional view of Neanderthals is not true."*[70]

Other paleo-experts have suggested that Neanderthals became culturally sophisticated through the spread of ideas from modern humans, who arrived in Eurasia later. In other words, it is assumed that Neanderthals did not have the capacity to innovate, at least not on a level equal with modern humans, so they had to borrow from their "superior" modern human neighbors. However, Villa *et al.* have contested this claim as well. Recent archaeological findings indicate that Neanderthals were capable of harnessing equally sophisticated technologies long before the arrival of modern humans in Eurasia. Neanderthals were apparently fully capable of modern human-level innovation:

> In the recent past, much debate has been generated from the observation that Neandertals began to produce a richer archaeological record, including bone tools, personal ornaments and use of manganese and ochre, at the time when AMH [anatomically modern humans] started colonizing Europe. Some interpreted this change in the record as the result of Neandertal absorption of ideas and techniques from the incoming AMH. ... However, as reviewed here, use of ochre, of personal ornaments, production of specialized bone tools and

68. Soressi M. *et al.*, Neandertals made the first specialized bone tools in Europe, *Proc Natl Acad Sci*, USA 110(35):14186-14190, 2013.
69. Villa P. and Roebroeks W., Neandertals Demise: an archaeological analysis of the modern human superiority complex, *PLOS ONE* 9(4):e96424, 2014.
70. http://www.colorado.edu/today/2014/04/30/neanderthals-were-not-inferior-modern-humans-says-cu-boulder-study

complex hafting techniques were part of the Neandertal repertoire already before the arrival of AMH in western Eurasia.[71]

In fact, rather than Neanderthals borrowing from anatomically modern humans, it appears to have been the other way around in some cases. Marie Soressi and her team of collaborators cite evidence in the *Proceedings of the National Academy of Sciences* (2013) that Neanderthals used specialized bone tools that were previously thought to be exclusive to modern humans.[72] In this case, however, the researchers note that Neanderthals used those specialized bone tools prior to their use by AMH. The researchers note that this finding may be *"evidence for the cultural diffusion from Neanderthals to modern humans"*.[73]

One of the most impressive technologies employed by Neanderthals, dating as far back as 200,000 years ago, is their ability to synthesize pitch from birch bark through the controlled use of fire. Neanderthals used birch bark pitch as a type of adhesive to haft tools and weapons (e.g., fixing flint flakes to a wooden handle). Unlike natural forms of "glue" which can be taken directly from a tree (such as sap), birch bark pitch must be carefully produced through a complex process involving distillation in the absence of oxygen and the careful regulation of temperature (between 340–400°C). Experimental archaeologists have attempted to produce birch bark pitch without the use of modern technology. For instance, after many trials, German archaeologist Friedrich Palmer was able to produce small amounts of pitch through this process. Wil Roebroeks, an accompanying archaeologist, commented on the feat in wonder. He remarked that the know-how required of Neanderthals to perform this task *"goes to show that they were very capable pyrotechnologists. We're still learning how they did it a quarter of a million years ago."*[74] Another team had great difficulty as well, but with a thermometer, they were able to do it on the first try. Paleo-archeologists are hard pressed to know how exactly Neanderthals were able to perform a sophisticated process recognized today by chemists as "dry distillation." Villa *et al.* note, *"Experimental studies show that production of pitch in the absence of air-tight pottery containers requires a high degree of technical knowledge."*[75] A number of Neanderthal sites have provided evidence of this technology.

Listed below are additional behavioral practices and abilities associated with Neanderthals that are indicative of modern human cognition:

71. Villa P. and Roebroeks W., Neanderthal demise: an archaeological analysis of the modern human superiority complex, *PLOS ONE* 9(4):e96424, 2014. DOI:10.1371/journal.pone.0096424.
72. Soressi M. *et al.*, Neandertals made the first speciaized bone tools in Europe, *Proc Natl Acad Sci, USA* 110(35):14186-14190, 2013.
73. Soressi M. *et al.*, Neandertals made the first specialized bone tools in Europe, *Proc Natl Acad Sci, USA* 110(35):14186-14190, 2013.
74. Hadingham E., Neanderthals Defy Stereotypes, Jan 9, 2013, NOVA. http://www.pbs.org/wgbh/nova/evolution/defy-stereotypes.html
75. Villa P. and Roebroeks W., Neanderthal Demise: An Archaeological Analysis of the Modern Human Superiority Complex, *PLOS ONE* 9(4):e96424, 2014. DOI: 10.1371/journal.pone.0096424.

- Cordage/knot-making
- Controlled use of fire
- Manufacture of pitch
- Drying of fresh meat
- Tailored clothing & footwear
- Sewing
- Wind breaks/shelters
- Living floors
- Personal adornment (jewelry)
- Cosmetics (red ochre)
- Care for injured/weak/elderly
- Ceremonial burial (spirituality)
- Abstract thinking
- Human language
- Fireplace hearths
- Strategic hunting (large game)
- Planning/foresight
- Cooking/filleting
- Sophisticated stone/bone tools
- Multipart weapons (hafted)
- Symbolic communication
- Art/sculptures
- Musical instruments (bone flutes)
- Highly varied diet

Arguably the most compelling archaeological evidence for the fully human status of Neanderthals (in addition to their beautiful sculptures, use of cosmetics[76], jewelry, musical instruments, care for the elderly and weak[77], manufacture of sophisticated stone and bone tools, etc.) is the ceremonial burial of their loved ones—a defining aspect of what it means to be human. As Stanford University anthropologist Richard Klein notes, *"Neanderthal graves present the best case for Neanderthal spirituality or religion."*[78] Out of a total of nearly 500 Neanderthal sites, 258 represent intentional burials in caves or rock shelters.[79] Neanderthal skeletons have been found in a manner suggesting they were carefully laid in graves—some adorned with valuable artifacts (sculpted flint artifacts, flowers, deer antlers, etc.), which evolutionary paleo-experts consider to be "grave goods."[80] It is clear that they believed in an afterlife or some sense of life apart from the grave (see Figure 8). Neanderthals and anatomically modern humans have been found together in the same gravesites such as Skhul Cave, Israel; Qafzeh, Israel, and Sima de los Huesos, Spain.[81] Marvin Lubenow, lifetime researcher of human evolution comments on the significance of these findings, stating: *"That Neanderthals and anatomically modern humans were buried together constitutes strong evidence that they lived together, worked together, intermarried, and were accepted as members of the same family, clan, and community."*[82]

76. Rifkin R.F., Processing ochre in the Middle Stone Age: testing the inference of prehistoric behaviours from actualistically derived experimental data, *J Anthropol Archaeology* 31(2):174-195, 2012. *"The habitual use of red ochre is a defining aspect of 'modern' human behaviour."* DOI: 10.1016/j.jaa.2011.11.004

77. Trinkaus E., Lebel S., *et al.*, Comparative morphology and paleobiology of Middle Pleistocene human remains from the Bau de l'Aubesier, Vaucluse, France, *Proc Natl Acad Sci, USA* 98(20):11097-11102, 2001; *"These human populations therefore had achieved a level of sociocultural elaboration sufficient to maintain debilitated individuals and to provide the motivation to do so."*

78. Klein R.G., *The Human Career: Human Biological and Cultural Origins*, The University of Chicago Press, Chicago, p.236-237, 1989.

79. Lubenow M.L, *Bones of Contention*, Baker Books, Grand Rapids, Michigan, p. 276, 2004.

80. Arsuaga J.L., *The Neanderthal's Necklace In Search of the First Thinkers*, Trans. A. Klat., Four Walls Eight Windows Publishing, New York, pp. 271-72, 2002.

81. Arsuaga J.L., *The Neanderthal's Necklace: In Search of the First Thinkers*, Trans. A. Klat., Four Walls Eight Windows Publishing, pp. 272-73, 2002. *"It is not even necessary to discuss the question of Neanderthal burial, not least because I have spent years arguing their ancestors at the Sierra de Atapuerca engaged in funerary behavior 300,000 years ago as the find at Sima de los Hueso [sic] establishes."*

82. Lubenow M., In: Mortenson T., *Searching for Adam*, p. 277, Master Books, Green Forest, AR, 2016.

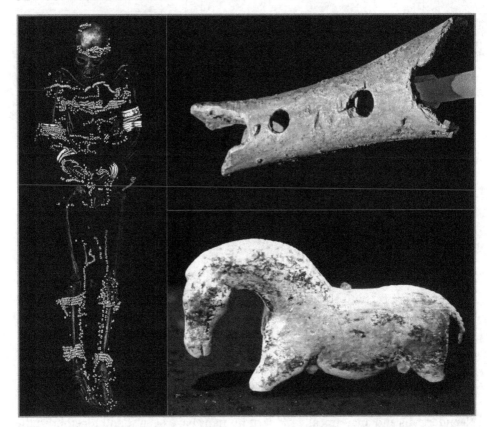

Figure 8. (Left) An elaborate burial of a presumed 28,000-year-old Neanderthal found at Sungir, Russia. The 60-year-old male was decorated with hundreds of mammoth ivory beads sewn onto leather, mammoth tusk ivory bracelets, necklaces, and pendants of shell and animal teeth. He wore a leather cap, pants, and knee-high boots. Two children buried nearby were also extravagantly adorned. (Upper Right) The Divje Babe flute was discovered in a cave in Slovenia in 1995. It is regarded as the world's oldest musical instrument. Using conventional dating methods (ESR), the Neanderthal flute is believed to be over 50,000–60,000 years old. It was made from a cave bear's thighbone. However, some paleo-experts find it hard to believe Neanderthals were so sophisticated to play music. They argue the "instrument" is really just a bone chewed on by hyenas.[83,84] Yet other researchers dismiss the hyena hypothesis. Musicologists have found that the spacing of the holes reflects a recognizable musical scale. These researchers find it hard to believe they were formed by accident: *"Its technological perfection points to high cognitive abilities of Neanderthals."*[85] Reconstructions of the Neanderthal flute make a beautiful sound. (Bottom Right) An impressive figurine carving of a horse recovered from Volgerherd Cave in Germany in 1931. Other figurines found include ice age mammals: bison, reindeer, lion, mammoth, woolly rhino, panther, and a snow leopard. Radiocarbon-14 analysis suggests the site is 30,000–40,000 years old. The elegant figurines have traditionally been attributed to early modern humans. However, a more recent study published in *Nature* casts doubt on these earlier claims and raises *"the possibility that the figurative art found at Vogelherd was produced by Neanderthals."*[86,87]

83. http://news.nationalgeographic.com/2015/03/150331-neanderthals-music-oldest-instrument-bones-flutes-archaeology-science/
84. http://rsos.royalsocietypublishing.org/content/2/4/140022
85. Turk M. *et al.*, Neanderthal Flute From Divje Babe I: Old and New Findings, *Opera Institute Archaeological Slovenia*, 251-265, 2011.
86. Gugliotta G., Study Finds Craftsmen Might be Neanderthal: Archaeologists Reexamine Bones from Ancient Cave, Washington Post, July 8, 2004. http://www.washingtonpost.com/wp-dyn/articles/A35315-2004Jul7.html Date accessed: April 04, 2017.
87. Conard N.J. *et al.*, Unexpected recent dates for human remains from Vogelherd, *Nature* 430:198-201, 2004.

Conclusion—Neanderthal was Fully Human

Since the time of Darwin, Neanderthals have been proclaimed to the world as a separate sub-human species, unworthy of the classification *Homo sapiens*. However, there is now compelling evidence, from numerous sources, that Neanderthals were fully human and should be classified as *Homo sapiens*. Neanderthal anatomy is overwhelmingly modern—as the paleo-community now universally concedes. The most notable differences are confined to the skull; however, those same features are seen in certain skulls belonging to *Homo sapiens* from various sites throughout Europe (e.g., Israel, Spain, and the Czech Republic). Thomas Huxley and many contemporary paleo-experts have further noted that Neanderthals and *Homo sapiens* can be arranged into a morphological continuum, which argues against their separateness as a species. Not surprisingly, "lumpers" have insisted that Neanderthals should be reclassified as *Homo sapiens*. Famous sites such as the "Pit of Bones" in Spain show that it is possible for a single population to display features characteristic of all major hominin species in the genus *Homo* (Erectus, Heidelbergensis, Neanderthals, and *Homo sapiens*). This proves that all these people coexisted and were part of a diverse, interbreeding population. In 2010, the sequencing of the Neanderthal genome confirmed that Neanderthals (and Denisovans) are members of our own species, *Homo sapiens*. Neanderthal burial sites corroborate what the DNA evidence is now showing—*Homo sapiens* and Neanderthals lived together in the same communities, intermarried, worked together, and were buried together. Finally, archaeological evidence recovered over the last few decades has refuted the myth that Neanderthals were intellectually inferior to modern humans. In conclusion, the evidence from paleontology, archaeology, and modern genetics all dramatically confirm that the Neanderthal people were in every respect, fully human. Neanderthal is us!

CHAPTER 4

Homo erectus
Upright "Ape-man" or Fully Human?

Does Homo erectus exist as a true taxon or should it be sunk into Homo sapiens?[1]

Paleoanthropologist Michael Day, Professor of Anatomy at University of London

New Species or Anatomical Variation within *Homo sapiens*?

Certain bones have been classified as *Homo erectus* (we will usually refer to these bones simply as "Erectus"), meaning "upright man." These bones are claimed to represent an extinct transitional form between the australopithecine apes and modern humans, and are used as one of the primary arguments for human evolution. There is growing evidence that indicates that what has been called Erectus is fully human, just as a significant number of paleo-experts have always maintained. Erectus is essential to the ape-to-man story, and so textbooks, museums, and TV programs still insist that Erectus is less than human. Their primary argument is based upon the fact that Erectus had an atypical skull (very similar to Neanderthal), however (unlike Neanderthal), Erectus had reduced brain volume. In addition, some Erectus bones indicate reduced body size and other pathologies. There is evidence that these traits can best be understood as being the result of reductive selection, inbreeding and genetic degeneration.

We, the authors, stand with the paleo-experts who lump *Homo erectus* with *Homo sapiens*. In our view, they are both erect, and they are both intelligent; they are clearly human.

While Erectus is clearly human, it is not a normal human. Erectus was very much like Neanderthal—but displaying evidence of various pathologies. Many Erectus skulls are disturbing—showing diverse abnormalities and asymmetries. It is said that Erectus skulls have certain "primitive" (ape-like) features. These phenotypic differences seem to have been exaggerated and are not so much "primitive" as they are degenerant. The most striking features of Erectus are small body size and reduced brain volume. These features do not seem to be so much ape-like, as they

---

1. Day M.H., *Guide to Fossil Man*, University of Chicago Press, Chicago, 1986.

seem to reflect pathology. Even these pathological features fall within the range of variation seen within *Homo sapiens*.

In this chapter we will show that hunter-gatherer groups that are subject to inbreeding and reductive selection are prone to developing abnormal skulls. Hunter-gatherer groups can survive for many generations in small, geographically isolated tribes, resulting in severe inbreeding and accelerated mutation accumulation (see chapter 13).[2] Erectus was clearly such a population—being a hunter-gatherer people that lived in isolation over many generations, in remote places such as the Indonesian islands of Java and Flores. Under such conditions, distinctive skeletal features are expected to arise and become established in small populations.

We will discuss how both genetic and non-genetic influences can produce Erectus-like features in modern *Homo sapiens*. This evidence supports the interpretation that Erectus is more appropriately a variant (a degenerate form) of *Homo sapiens*, and is not a transitional form between apes and man.

Background and Discovery of Erectus

In 1891, the Dutch anatomist Eugène Dubois discovered the first fossil remains that are currently classified as *Homo erectus*. Charles Darwin's newly published works inspired Dubois, and so he set off to the Indonesian island of Java in search of a "missing link" between apes and humans.[3] Along the banks of the Solo River near the village of Trinil he found a tooth, a skullcap and a femur bone (Figure 1). The femur was unmistakably human but the skullcap had some unusual features, in particular a low forehead with heavy brow ridges. Dubois interpreted the skullcap as having ape-like qualities and assigned the bones to a new species that he named *Pithecanthropus erectus*. The Greek/Latin name translates as "upright ape-man"—in accordance with Dubois's firm belief that humans evolved from ape-like creatures. These bones came to be popularly recognized by the general public as "Java Man," a name still used today. Since then, numerous bones from Java and China have been found and reassigned to *Homo erectus*—considered to be the immediate ancestor to *Homo sapiens*. However, as is typical in the field of paleoanthropology, experts disagree about how to interpret this fossil. "Lumpers" view these bones as an early form of *Homo sapiens*. These researchers challenge the *erectus* species designation,[4] and would classify these bones as *Homo sapiens*.

Worldwide, there have been about 300 Erectus finds—most often consisting of an isolated skullcap and/or a few broken bones or teeth. These remains have been found in Indonesia (Java Man), China (Peking Man), and also in Europe,[5] Africa,

2. Lynch M., Mutation and Human Exceptionalism: Our Future Genetic Load, *Genetics* 202:869-875, 2016.
3. Morwood M.J. and van Oosterzee P., *A New Human: the discovery of the Hobbits of Flores*, Smithsonian Books, Washington DC, p.124, 2007. Dubois believed there was only one transitional species, and he was determined to find it.
4. Stringer C., *Lone Survivors*, Times Books, Henry Holt and Company LLC, New York, p. 15, 2012.
5. Including Austria: http://www.pasthorizonspr.com/index.php/archives/12/2013/ochre-hand-imprint-homo-erectus-revealed

and possibly India.[6] The African form of *Homo erectus* is often referred to as *Homo ergaster*. Until very recently, only one nearly complete Erectus skeleton has been recovered, which was dubbed "Turkana Boy." It was found in Kenya in 1984, and is the only *Homo erectus* (or *H. ergaster*) skeleton where the skull has been found clearly associated with the rest of the body. Before the discovery of Turkana Boy previous Erectus remains primarily consisted of isolated, broken bones. These included individual teeth, skullcaps, fragmented skulls and jaws, and one intact femur mixed with numerous broken femurs.[7] Two prominent paleo-experts, Ian Tattersall and Jeffery Schwartz, noted that the general absence of other Erectus bones confounded the analysis of Turkana Boy:

> Although it is truly remarkable just how much of a single individual's skeleton could be recovered, this amazing find also presented a dilemma because, *H. erectus* or not, most of it couldn't be compared with anything else closely related to it because the comparable parts weren't known![8]

In terms of age, the earliest Erectus remains have been dated to 1.9 million years old. The species is thought to have persisted until about 500,000–140,000 years ago,[9] but some studies have suggested they may have lived as recently as 20,000

Figure 1. The first bones assigned to the species Erectus. Inspired by Darwin's recently published works, Dutch anatomist Eugène Dubois journeyed to the Indonesian island of Java in search of the "missing link" between ape and man. In 1891 Dubois came across a tooth, thighbone, and skullcap. He named his finding "*Pithecanthropus erectus,*" which literally translates as "upright ape-man." The bones were given the nickname "Java Man." Today the species is recognized as *Homo erectus* or *Homo sapiens*. Note that the femur has pathological deformities.

6. Kennedy K.A.R. *et al.*, Is the Narmada Hominid an Indian *Homo erectus*? *Am J Phys Anthropol* 86: 475-496, 1991.

7. Tattersall I. and Schwartz J., *Extinct Humans*, Westview Press, New York, p. 132, 2000.

8. Tattersall I. and Schwartz J., *Extinct Humans*, Westview Press, New York, p. 132, 2000.

9. http://smithsonianscience.si.edu/2011/07/scientists-show-that-modern-humans-never-co-existed-with-homo-erectus/ Accessed: October 12, 2015.

years ago.[10] Thus, the estimated time when Erectus lived would have spanned roughly two million years—about one third of the six million years during which an ape population is said to have evolved into modern man.

Description of the Basic Erectus Morphology

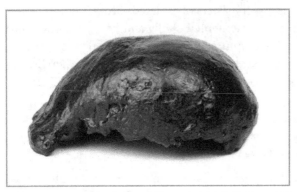

Figure 2. A cast of the skullcap (designated Trinil 2) discovered by Eugène Dubois in 1891 at Trinil near the Solo River on the Indonesian island of Java. Trinil 2 is considered the defining specimen of the hominin species Erectus.

The Java skullcap discovered by Eugène Dubois is the "type specimen" or "defining specimen" of the *H. erectus* species. Being the "type specimen" (the first-found specimen) means it is the reference point for assessing all other fossils that might belong to the same species.[11] This is problematic, since it is essentially just a skullcap (Figure 2). On the other hand, "Turkana Boy" is the most complete Erectus skeleton, and would arguably be the better choice for a type specimen (discussed later).[12] Since the Java skullcap is the type specimen, it is important to describe its basic morphology and some notable features. Tattersall and Schwartz offer a careful description,[13] summarized as follows. It has low braincase with a long, sloping forehead. The brow ridges are pronounced and continue straight across. For its small size the skull is fairly elongated. In frontal view the skull is wide with a slight depression on either side of the midline. In side view the rear of the skull, known as the occipital region, is V-shaped. The cranial capacity is estimated to be approximately 940 cm³, considerably larger than apes but overlapping with the lower end of human variation.[14]

Generally speaking these features—large brow ridges, sloping foreheads, and small cranial capacities—are characteristic of most Erectus specimens. In skulls that preserve the face, they typically exhibit marked prognathism (a forward projecting jaw) and lack a distinct chin. However, it is important to realize there is considerable variation in the skulls assigned to this species. Leading paleo-experts have pointed out that Erectus includes highly variable skull types that look

10. Major J., Kow Swamp remains are re-dated to more than 20,000 years old, *UniNews* (a University of Melbourne publication) 13(3), March 8-22, 2004. http://archive.uninews.unimelb.edu.au/news/1255/ Accessed: October 19, 2015.
11. Tattersall I. and Schwartz J., *Extinct Humans*, Westview Press, New York, p. 140, 2000.
12. Brown F. *et al.*, Early *Homo erectus* skeleton from west Lake Turkana, Kenya, *Nature* 316:788-792, 1985.
13. Tattersall I. and Schwartz J., *Extinct Humans*, Westview Press, New York, p. 140, 2000.
14. Schultz A.H., The Physical Distinction of Man; In McKern T.W and Cliffs E. (eds), *Readings in Anthropology*, Prentice-Hall, NJ, 1966.

significantly different from the Trinil 2 type specimen.[15] A figure from a paper recently published in *Science* (2014) displays the extent of variation in Erectus, reflecting an ongoing debate within the paleoanthropological community (Figure 3). Note that many Erectus skulls appear deformed and asymmetrical, even after correcting for postmortem fossil damage. This is consistent with the idea that these individuals suffered from pathologies (as will be discussed).

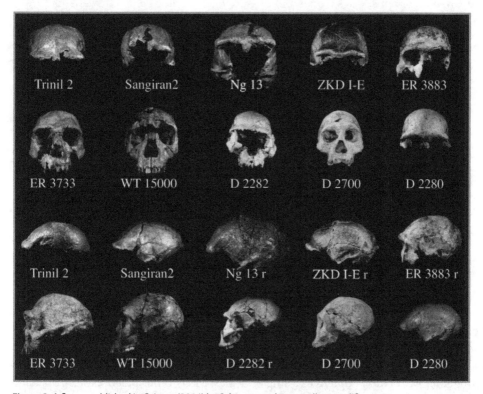

Figure 3. A figure published in *Science* (2014) by Schwartz and Tattersall exemplifies an ongoing controversy in the paleo-community. Paleo-experts disagree on whether all or any of the skulls typically attributed to the species Erectus are in fact Erectus. Splitters like Schwartz and Tattersall emphasize certain anatomical differences to argue there are multiple species included in this assemblage. In their paper they describe the array of *"supposed Erectus specimens"* as a *"visually and morphologically incoherent assemblage."* Aside from "Turkana Boy" (KNM-WT 15000), none of these skulls were found with a coherent skeleton. This has confounded the ability of paleo-experts to make clear taxonomic assignments to many of the fragmentary skulls generally regarded as Erectus.

To "splitters," the variant skull types could signify different species.[16] Paleo-experts do not agree on which skulls belong to Erectus and which skulls do not. For instance, five skulls discovered in Dmanisi, Georgia, exhibited a marked degree of variation in size and shape. Researchers noted that if the skulls had been found

15. Schwartz J.H. and Tattersall I., Comment on "A complete skull from Dmanisi, Georgia, and the evolutionary biology of early *Homo*," *Science* 344:360a, 2014.
16. Tattersall I. and Schwartz J., *Extinct Humans*, Westview Press, New York, p. 141, 2000.

separately they would have been considered different species.[17] But because they were found in close proximity to one another and dated to the same age, it was argued that they belonged to a single evolving lineage, *Homo erectus*. As Dmanisi team leader David Lordkipanidze noted:

> If you found the Dmanisi skulls at isolated sites in Africa, some people would give them different species names. But one population can have all this variation. We are using five or six names, but they could all be from one lineage.[18]

Not surprisingly, other paleo-experts disagree, and insist the skulls be viewed as different species that lived side by side (because they look too different to be the same species). This type of controversy in the field is common.[19] The bottom line is that there is no clear-cut criterion for what constitutes Erectus morphology.[20] Paleoanthropologists have long acknowledged that the morphological boundary between Erectus and *Homo sapiens* is arbitrary and *"not clearly demarcated."*[21] As researchers have noted, *"No longer is Homo erectus a clearly definable taxon temporally, morphologically or even geographically."*[22] The allowable extent of variation is highly subjective and debated among paleo-experts. This has led to taxonomic ambiguity and has opened the door for australopith (ape) skulls to be wrongly interpreted as Erectus. There is at least one possible example of this in the Dmanisi site (skull D4500). However, as we will demonstrate in this chapter, most of the remains attributed to Erectus are fully human and should therefore be reclassified as *Homo sapiens*, as the "lumpers" in the field advocate.

Prominent Paleo-experts Agree—*Homo erectus* is *Homo sapiens*

The evolutionary paleo-experts known as "lumpers" have insisted for decades that the variation found within Erectus specimens overlap extensively with modern humans.[23,24] On that basis, such "lumpers" agree that Erectus should be grouped together with *Homo sapiens* as a single species. Many other paleo-experts object to this and claim Erectus exhibits a distinct morphology that merits its classification as a separate species. While it is true Erectus exhibits some distinctive traits, it does not logically follow that they must therefore be viewed as a separate, sub-human species. Human skeletons come in many different shapes and sizes. In

17. Charles C.Q., Were Earliest Humans All 1 Species? Oddball Skull Sparks Debate, *LiveScience* 2013. http://www.livescience.com/40505-earliest-humans-one-species.html Accessed October 05, 2015.
18. Sample I., Skull of *Homo erectus* throws story of human evolution into disarray, *The Guardian* October 17, 2013. http://www.theguardian.com/science/2013/oct/17/skull-homo-erectus-human-evolution
19. Tattersall I. and Schwartz J., *Extinct Humans*, Westview Press, New York, p.141, 2000.
20. Sigmon B.A. and Cybulski J.S. (eds.), *Homo erectus*: Papers in Honour of Davidson Black, University of Toronto Press, 1981. *"Indeed, one may well wonder whether agreement will ever be reached as to which fossils do belong to or represent the taxon, and on what morphological-cum-phylogenetic grounds fossil hominids are or are not to be regarded as Homo erectus."*
21. Rightmire G.P., *The Evolution of Homo erectus*, Cambridge Univ. Press, Cambridge, p. 181, 1990.
22. Day M.H., *Guide to Fossil Man*, University of Chicago Press, Chicago, p. 409, 1986.
23. Jelinek J. (ed.), *Homo erectus* and His Time. Contributions to the Origin of Man and his Cultural Development Vol. II, *Anthropologie (Brno)* 19(1): 3-96, 1981.
24. Thoma A, New evidence for polycentric evolution of *Homo sapiens*, *J Hum Evol* 2(6):529-536, 1973.

modern populations distinct traits in the face and cranium serve as recognizable people groups. Forensic scientists are able to identify which people group a particular modern skull belonged to, by looking at diagnostic traits.[25] However, no scientist today would claim that the distinctive skull features in modern people groups proves they belong to a different species. Instead traits that are distinctive to different people groups simply reflect the incredible amount of natural variation found within the human family. With this in mind, "lumpers" maintain that "splitters" fail to recognize the extensive variation within the human population. As Gabriel Lasker, the internationally known evolutionary paleo-expert from Wayne State University conceded:

> *Homo erectus* is distinct from modern man (*Homo sapiens*), but there is a tendency to exaggerate the differences. Even if one ignores transitional or otherwise hard to classify specimens and limits consideration to the Java or Peking populations, the range of variation of many features of *Homo erectus* falls within that of modern man.[26]

Paleo-expert Milford Wolpoff, recipient of the Darwin Lifetime Achievement Award, agrees with this view, as do his colleagues Alan Thorne and Wu Xin Zhi. They note that the differences between the two are arbitrary and should be regarded as the same species:

> In our view, there are two alternatives. We should either admit that the *Homo erectus/Homo sapiens* boundary is arbitrary and use nonmorphological (i.e., temporal) criteria for determining it, or *Homo erectus* should be sunk [into *Homo sapiens*].[27]

Other leading experts in the field have raised similar concerns.[28] Evolutionary paleo-expert Michael Day in *Guide to Fossil Man* asks, "*Does Homo erectus exist as a true taxon or should it be sunk into Homo sapiens?*"[29] To "sink" means to combine into a single species. Sinking *Homo erectus* into *Homo sapiens*, would mean simultaneously folding in other very similar "species" such as *Homo heidelbergensis*, *Homo rhodesiensis*, *Homo antecessor*, *Homo ergaster*, and all other so-called "archaic humans."[30] The paleo-experts who hold the separate species view need to demonstrate that the distinctive traits found in Erectus do not occur in *Homo sapiens*.

25. Stringer C., *Lone Survivors*, Times Books, Henry Holt and Company LLC, New York, p.189, 2012.
26. Lasker G.W., *Physical Anthropology*, Holt, Rinehart and Winston, Inc., New York, 284 pp., 1973.
27. Wolpoff M.H. *et al.*, Modern *Homo sapiens* Origins: A General Theory of Hominid Evolution Involving the Fossil Evidence from East Asia; in Smith F.H. and Spencer F. (eds), *The Origins of Modern Humans*, Alan R. Liss, New York, pp. 465-466, 1984.
28. Sigmon B.A. and Cybulski J.S. (eds.), *Homo erectus*: Papers in Honour of Davidson Black, University of Toronto Press, 1981. *"Indeed, one may well wonder whether agreement will ever be reached as to which fossils do belong to or represent the taxon, and on what morphologicalcum-phylogenetic grounds fossil hominids are or are not to be regarded as Homo erectus."*
29. Day M.H., *Guide to Fossil Man*, University of Chicago Press, Chicago, p. 408, 1986.
30. Lubenow M.L., *Bones of Contention*, Baker Books, Grand Rapids, Michigan, p. 184, 2004.

Erectus Skeleton Indistinguishable from Modern Humans

Since the time of Dubois (1891), it has been claimed that the "Java Man" type (Erectus) is a sub-human ancestor. Yet almost a century passed before any substantial Erectus skeleton was found. This happened with the discovery of Turkana Boy in 1984.[31] Prior to that time, almost no non-skull (postcranial) bones were recovered—just a severely diseased and distorted partial skeleton from Kenya with no analytical value (KNM-ER 1303), a partial pelvis,[32,33] one complete femur, and other bone fragments. As *Nature* reports in the discovery paper detailing the anatomy of Turkana Boy:

> Previous *H. erectus* postcranial material has been either fragmentary, not definitely associated, disputed as to species or diseased. From Trinil, Indonesia, there are several fragmentary and one complete (but pathological) femora. Despite the fact that it was these specimens that led to the species name, there are doubts as to whether they are *H. erectus* with the most recent consensus being that they probably are not. Until recently the only *H. erectus* postcranial bones from China were from Zhoukoudian and these were very fragmentary, with no complete lengths or articular [joint] surfaces.[34]

Other Erectus material had been found at Olduvai Gorge, Tanzania and East Turkana, Kenya prior to the discovery of Turkana Boy. However, those remains are equally fragmentary, and also diseased. With the exception of a single specimen, none of the remains were "*complete enough to be absolutely certain of attribution* [to Erectus]."[35] Nevertheless, even before 1984 it had become apparent to researchers that the post-cranial anatomy of Erectus was virtually indistinguishable from that of modern humans. For example, leading paleo-experts F. Clark Howell and Bernard Campbell offered their evaluation of the postcranial anatomy of Erectus stating:

> His bones were heavier and thicker than a modern man's, and bigger bones required thicker muscles to move them. These skeletal differences, however, were not particularly noticeable. "Below the neck," one expert had noted, "the differences between *Homo erectus* and today's man could only be detected by an experienced anatomist."[36]

The Institute of Human Origins founded by Donald Johanson posted an article affirming this assessment. They note that aside from being more heavily built, in every other respect they share "striking similarities" with modern *Homo sapiens*.[37]

---

31. Brown F. *et al.*, Early *Homo erectus* skeleton from west Lake Turkana, Kenya, *Nature* 316:788-792, 1985.

32. Leakey R., New hominid fossils from the Koobi Fora formation in Northern Kenya, *Nature* 26:574-576, 1976.

33. Rose M.D., A Hominin Hip Bone, KNM-ER3228, from east Lake Turkana, Kenya, *Am J Phys Anthropol* 63:371-378, 1984.

34. Brown F. *et al.*, Early *Homo erectus* skeleton from west Lake Turkana, Kenya, *Nature* 316:788-792, 1985.

35. Brown F. *et al.*, Early *Homo erectus* skeleton from west Lake Turkana, Kenya, *Nature* 316:788-792, 1985.

36. White E. and Brown D.M., *The First Men*, Time-Life Books, New York, p. 14, 1973.

37. Institute of Human Origins, *Homo erectus*. http://www.becominghuman.org/node/homo-erectus-0 Accessed: October 18, 2015.

The discovery of Turkana Boy in 1984 only helped to validate these earlier evaluations. Kamoya Kimeu, assistant of the famous paleontologists Richard and Meave Leakey, discovered the bones 3 miles west of Lake Turkana along the banks of the Nariokotome River in northern Kenya. Kimeu spotted skull fragments (frontal lobe) that were found scattered across the excavated area.[38] A volcanic tuff underlying the bones was potassium-argon dated to 1.6 million years old. Turkana Boy is recognized as the most complete Erectus skeleton ever found, only missing parts of the skull, and much of the hands and feet. Finally, paleo-experts were able to perform a complete analysis of the postcranial skeleton, and provide a confident reconstruction of Erectus. Upon examining the bones it was immediately obvious that Erectus was anatomically human (Figure 4). Seddon, human evolution researcher and author of *Humans: From the Beginning* notes, *"Turkana Boy was unquestionably human."*[39] Mariette DiChristina, editor-in-chief of *Scientific American*, lists a suite of anatomical features that she refers to as *"Hallmark traits of the human body."*[40] In her assessment, Turkana Boy exhibits all major postcranial features characteristic of modern human anatomy. These include low shoulders, barrel-shaped rib cage, strong wrist, long thumb, long flexible waist, twisted humerus, forwardly placed opening for spinal cord, short broad pelvis, enlarged femur head, strong knee joint, arched foot, and short toes.[41] John Reader, distinguished expert on human origins, also noted the striking modernity of the skeleton: *"...is he a missing link? The answer must be no. Not as a being who stood halfway between the apes and modern humans—the skeleton is too human-like for that."*[42]

No paleo-expert doubts that the overall size and body proportions of Turkana Boy are anatomically modern. Dental evidence and unfused growth plates suggest he was an adolescent no older than 12–13 years of age. At the time of death he would have stood 5 ft. 3 in., but had he lived to adulthood he could have grown to 6 ft. 1 in. in height. All of these features demonstrate Turkana Boy was fully human from the neck down (and as we will see, this is also true of the skull). It is for this reason that leading experts acknowledge *Homo erectus* represents the *"emergence of the modern body"*[43]—this is a clear admission that Erectus is anatomically human. It has been noted, *"From the neck down, the skeleton is virtually indistinguishable from that of a modern Kenyan bushman."*[44] It is no wonder a bishop from Kenya is calling on locals to demand the Turkana Boy display be removed from Kenya's

38. Brown F. *et al.*, Early *Homo erectus* skeleton from west Lake Turkana, Kenya, *Nature* 316:788-792, 1985.
39. Seddon C., (2014-03-03). *Humans: from the beginning: From the first apes to the first cities* (Kindle Locations 13892-13893). Glanville Publications. Kindle Edition.
40. DiChristina M. (ed.), What makes us special, *Sci Am* 311:60-61, September 2014.
41. Turkana Boy lacks the bones of the hands and feet, but these can be reasonably inferred based on the overall bipedal anatomy of the preserved skeleton and footprints fossilized from Ileret, Kenya.
42. Reader J., *Missing Links*, Oxford University Press, New York, p. 146, 2011.
43. Tattersall I. and Schwartz J., *Extinct Humans*, Westview Press, New York, Chapter 5, 2001.
44. Sodera V., *One small Speck to Man: the evolution myth*, 2nd ed., Vija Sodera Productions, p.337-345, 2009.

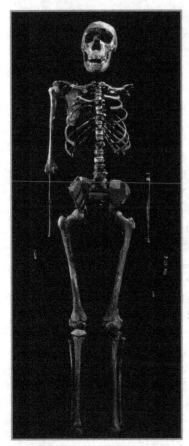

Figure 4. The nearly complete skeleton of Turkana Boy was discovered in northern Kenya, 3 miles west of Lake Turkana. Turkana Boy represents the most complete Erectus skeleton recovered to date (also classified as *Homo ergaster*). Paleo-experts were surprised to find that the best representative skeleton of Erectus displays remarkably modern human anatomy.

national museum to be properly buried.[45] Other researchers have noted that Turkana Boy's body proportions happen to be *"almost identical to those of the tall Dinka people of southern Sudan, who live about 124 miles (200 kilometers) west of Nariokotome River"* and that *"his body, apart from his skull, is surprisingly like our own."*[46] The most obvious difference seen when Turkana Boy was compared to modern humans was the size and shape of his braincase, which was characteristic of other Erectus skulls (discussed later in this chapter).

If paleo-experts openly acknowledge that Erectus exhibited a postcranial anatomy almost identical to modern humans, on what grounds can they insist it was a sub-human species? With respect to the postcranial anatomy, the vertebral canal is one of the few noticeable features (at least if you're a trained anatomist) that have been emphasized by paleo-experts to set Erectus apart from *Homo sapiens*. Seddon reiterates the claim originally put forth by MacLarnon and Hewitt:[47]

> The Turkana Boy had a much narrower thoracic vertebral canal than a modern human. The vertebral canal is the space in the vertebral column through which the nerve-bearing spinal cord passes, and the thoracic vertebrae are those located between the neck and the base of the rib cage. The nerves passing through this region control breathing, and he might therefore have lacked fine breathing control necessary for modern speech.[48]

In suggesting this, researchers are trying to find a possible reason to downgrade *Homo erectus* to a sub-human species (some paleo-experts refuse to accept Erectus as being human). In seeking to demote Erectus, there seems to have been a tendency to rely on minutiae such as the exact size of the vertebral canal. Realistically, there

45. Mitchell A., Ancient skeleton focus of modern debate, 2 Feb. 2007. http://www.nbcnews.com/id/17029155/#.WNwSOGPV1Qs

46. Bahn P. (ed), *Written in Bone*, p.65-71, 2003. http://planet.uwc.ac.za/nisl/scientific_methods/attachments/bahn_turkana_boy.pdf

47. MacLarnon A. and Hewitt G., The evolution of human speech: the role of enhanced breathing control, *Am J Phys Anthropol* 109:341-363, 1999.

48. Seddon C., (2014-03-03). *Humans: from the beginning: From the first apes to the first cities* (Kindle Locations 13892-13893). Glanville Publications. Kindle Edition.

is no way to tell if a slightly narrowed vertebral canal would affect speech. Ella Been, expert in spinal anatomy and pathology from Tel Aviv University does not believe Turkana Boy would have had any difficulty breathing because of the small vertebral canal.[49] Dr. Sodera, a prominent surgeon from the UK agrees, saying:

> ...this is pure speculation since the spinal cord contains a vast number of nerve fibers, only a small portion of which are related to the control of the muscles of the rib cage and diaphragm. We can be sure that a narrower spinal canal is of no relevance to defining whether or not Turkana boy could or could not speak since 3-year-old children are well able to speak;[50]

He goes on to say that even parakeets with a vertebral canal *"only a few millimeters in diameter can mimic speech with fidelity."* There is no reason to believe Turkana Boy would have had any problems with fine breathing or speech. If this is the level of minutiae that defines whether a specimen is human or sub-human, then one would have no choice but to relegate many modern humans to a sub-human species as well. This would include bones belonging to North American Indians. The evolutionary anatomist Owen Lovejoy has acknowledged that it is easy to make this mistake. In a 1000-year-old North American burial site containing Native American skeletal remains, Lovejoy observed many features that seemed to exceed the normal range of human variation. As Reader notes:

> The Amerindian collection on which Lovejoy works undoubtedly represents a population belonging to the species *Homo sapiens*, yet it includes many unusual bones that probably would have been assigned to a different species, or even a different genus, if they had been discovered as individual fossils...[51]

The extent of anatomical variation found in modern human skeletons is very substantial. This fact must be kept in mind when analyzing the remains attributed to Erectus and other *Homo* types.

Erectus Skull Morphology Found in Modern Humans

The most distinctive features of Erectus are seen in the skull. Erectus specimens are typically identified based upon a smaller braincase than the average modern human, a heavier brow ridge, a more sloping forehead, a reduced chin, more constricted temples, larger teeth, and a more forward-projecting jaw (prognathism). These characteristics are commonly discussed as if they are unique to the Erectus type. The evolutionary justification for the establishment of Erectus as a sub-human species is built around the assumption that the same traits are not found in modern humans. However, there are a number of modern examples of human skulls exhibiting classic Erectus features that discredit this assumption

49. Personal communication, 2015.
50. Sodera V., *One small Speck to Man: the evolution myth*, Vija Sodera Productions, p. 380, 2009.
51. Reader J., *Missing Links: The hunt for earliest man*, Little Brown and Company, Boston, p. 232, 1981.

such as "post-Erectus" archaic humans from East Asia and Australia.[52,53,54]

In addition to normal variations in skull type, abnormal skulls (especially reduced brain volume) can arise due to pathologies. This is seen in the case of the Zika virus, which is spread by the *Aedes* mosquito.[55] This virus is believed to have originated in the Zika forest of Uganda (about 300 miles from where Turkana Boy was found). The first reported human case was in 1952. This virus has now spread globally and has infected a large number of people. When pregnant woman become infected with this virus, their child can be born with severe microcephaly—resulting in reduced brain volumes comparable to Erectus.[56] Microcephaly can produce constricted temples, prognathism, pronounced brow ridges, abnormally small braincases, and a V-shaped occipital region (features commonly seen in Erectus skulls). It is possible some examples of Erectus could have arisen in a similar way.

Microcephaly can also be caused by mutations. This is especially relevant to Erectus—a people that lived in small, genetically isolated hunter-gatherer groups. Intermarriage between closely related members of a group, over many generations, should increase mutation rates. Geneticist Michael Lynch recently reported in the journal *Genetics* that hyper-mutation is especially likely to occur if mutations arise in genes encoding DNA repair enzymes.[57] This would increase the risk of rare developmental disorders that could result in abnormal features similar to those found in microcephalics (the effects of inbreeding will be discussed in more depth later). Microcephaly can also be caused by malnutrition (diets lacking sufficient nutrients—as expected in hunter-gatherer lifestyles), as well as overexposure to toxic chemicals and ionization radiation. Interestingly, the bones of *Homo erectus* are often found in caves where they sought shelter. Caves are known to be hotspots for natural sources of radiation. Thus it is conceivable that radiation-induced diseases, comparable to microcephaly, produced some of the anomalous skull shapes found in Erectus specimens. It is now known that a very large portion of the human genome codes for brain development and function—and brain development affects skull shape. Therefore any type of genetic disruption of brain development will tend to lead to deformities of the skull.

Healthy modern humans can also display Erectus-like features. Rampasasa pygmies from the island of Flores are prone to prognathism and a receding chin. Other unique-looking people groups, such as the Eskimos and Aleuts, have been noted to share features with Asian Erectus specimens. Anthropologist William Laughlin of the University of Connecticut made note of these similarities in the

52. Day M.H., *Guide to Fossil Man*, University of Chicago Press, Chicago, p. 409, 1986.
53. Wolpoff M.H. *et al.*, Modern *Homo sapiens* Origins: A General Theory of Hominid Evolution Involving the Fossil Evidence from East Asia; in Smith F.H. and Spencer F. (eds), *The Origins of Modern Humans*, Alan R. Liss, New York, pp. 465-466, 1984.
54. Swisher C.C. *et al.*, *Java Man*, Scribner, New York, p. 211, 2000.
55. Centers for Disease Control and Prevention, http://www.cdc.gov/zika/about/index.html
56. Centers for Disease Control and Prevention, http://www.cdc.gov/zika/pregnancy/question-answers.html
57. Lynch M., Mutation and Human Exceptionalism: Our Future Genetic Load, *Genetics* 202: 869-875, 2016.

journal *Science*. He concluded that in light of the extensive variation found in the human form, *Homo erectus* should be included within the single species *Homo sapiens*:

> When we find that significant differences have developed, over a short time span, between closely related and contiguous peoples, as in Alaska and Greenland, and when we consider the vast differences that exist between remote groups such as Eskimos and Bushmen, who are known to belong within the single species of *Homo sapiens*, it seems justifiable to conclude that *Sinanthropus* (Peking Man) [later renamed *Homo erectus*] belongs within this same diverse species.[58]

Leading proponents of the Multiregional Continuity Model have noted striking similarities between Erectus skulls (crania) and those belonging to Australian *Homo sapiens* who lived in the relatively recent past. This has been reported in the journal *Nature*. The remains of approximately 50 Aboriginal people were found in a burial site in the Kow Swamp region of Northern Victoria, Australia. Thorne and Macumber identified a suite of traits *"not seen in recent Aboriginal crania"* that overlap extensively with classic Erectus morphology. These include a receding forehead, heavy brow ridges, large teeth, prognathism, absent chin, vault thickness, and other traits normally regarded by evolutionists as sub-human or "archaic." They write:

> This article describes the first extensive collection of late Pleistocene human remains from Australia. Analysis of the cranial morphology of more than thirty individuals reveals the survival of *Homo erectus* features in Australia until as recently as 10,000 years ago.[59]

In a later publication in the *American Journal of Physical Anthropology*, Thorne and Wolpoff refer again to the Kow Swamp series. This time they focus on an Erectus cranium from Java known as Sangiran 17. The specimen was described by the researchers as sharing a number of features with the Aboriginals from Kow Swamp. They note, *"... in no other region can a specimen* [referring to *Homo erectus* skull, Sangiran 17] *be found that combines so many features that seem unique or at least of high frequency in Pleistocene Australians."*[60] The similarities can be most clearly seen in a side-by-side comparison with the Kow Swamp 1 (KS-1) cranium (Figure 5). The Australian *Homo sapiens* K-S1 cranium is not significantly different from the Java *Homo erectus* specimens. It may be argued that if the Kow Swamp series had not been radiocarbon-dated to such a recent age, they could have easily been classified as an Erectus population that migrated to Australia. Not surprisingly, this has actually been proposed to explain the retention of Erectus features in the Kow Swamp sample—a view that is still held by paleoanthropologists today. Darren

---

58. Laughlin W.S., Eskimos and Aleuts: Their Origins and Evolution, *Science* 142 (3593):633-645, 1963.
59. Thorne A.G. and Macumber P.G., Discoveries of Late Pleistocene Man at Kow Swamp Australia, *Nature* 238:316-319, 1972.
60. Thorne A.G. and Wolpoff M.H., Regional continuity in Australasian Pleistocene hominid evolution, *Am J Phys Anthropol* 55(3):337–349, 1981.

Curnoe summarizes these views in *International Journal of Evolutionary Biology*.[61] According to one recently developed model, Erectus from Java (*Homo erectus soloensis*) migrated to Australia around 130,000–150,000 years ago to become the robust Australian type, which preserved the Erectus-like features of the cranium. This event was followed by a later colonization of *Homo sapiens* from Africa that merged to form a single population through "genetic mixing"—the interbreeding between the two species.[62] In this model the Kow Swamp specimens exhibiting Erectus-like skull features are the remnant of this earlier interbred population. It is noteworthy that according to the most widely accepted definition of a species (the biological species concept) if two populations are able to interbreed they are considered the same species.[63] Therefore if Erectus and *H. sapiens* interbred, they are by definition the same species.

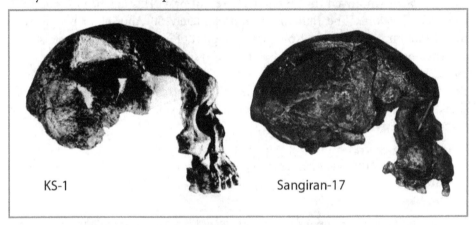

KS-1   Sangiran-17

Figure 5. A skull dated to be 10,000 years old, from the Kow Swamp region of Australia (left). Sangiran-17 is an Erectus specimen from Java (right). The relatively recent Australian skull clearly falls within the broad morphological range of Erectus skulls. Paleo-experts Thorne and Macumber describe a suite of Erectus features seen in the Kow Swamp sample in their paper. They suggested that inbreeding might adequately explain the emergence of archaic-looking traits. Researchers in a separate paper published in the *Journal of Human Evolution* reiterated the same explanation, *"Genetic isolation caused by climatically-induced population decline may explain the robust skeletal morphology of the Kow Swamp people."*[64] Note: specimens not shown to scale.

Other scientists reject the interpretation that the Kow Swamp *Homo erectus* features are due to interbreeding. What these researchers have found is that many of the Erectus-like features have low to moderate heritability. They argue it is biologically unrealistic to assume every subtle variation in skull shape has an underlying genetic basis that affects reproductive success. This has challenged the traditional view that robust cranial features—such as those found in the Kow Swamp series—arose through an evolutionary mechanism of mutations and natural selection. A growing

61. Curnoe D., A 150- Year Conundrum: Cranial Robusticity and Its Bearing on the Origin of Aboriginal Australians, *Int J Evol Biol* Volume 2011, Article ID 632484, 18 pages. DOI: 10.4061/2011/632484
62. Webb S.G., *The First Boat People*, Cambridge University Press, Cambridge, UK, 2006.
63. Mayr E., *What Evolution Is*, Basic Books, New York, ch. 8, pp. 161-173, 2001.
64. Stone T. and Cupper M.L., Glacial Maximum ages for robust humans at Kow Swamp, southern Australia, *J Hum Evol* 45:99-111, 2003.

number of researchers believe many of the traits in common between Erectus and the Kow Swamp samples are due to non-genetic influences known as phenotypic plasticity—morphologies that are shaped by *"developmental interactions among cells, tissues and their environments"* called epigenesis.[65] As Curnoe affirms, *"Most characters [of the cranium] are unlikely to be independent units, being integrated in their development and influenced by a complicated set of epigenetic interactions."*[66]

The Kow Swamp analysis conducted by Thorne and Macumber became even more problematic after a subsequent discovery of modern-looking Aborigine skulls in the neighboring region of Lake Mungo dated to 40,000 years ago. The new findings suggested *Homo sapiens* with anatomically modern human skulls existed *before* the "archaic" Erectus–looking skulls of the Kow Swamp people, an evolutionary paradox, because the bones of modern *Homo sapiens* should not significantly predate their alleged progenitors. A University of Melbourne publication summarizes the results of researchers investigating this problem:

> The riddle surrounds the robust physical characteristics of the Kow Swamp people that some experts suggest links them to earlier more 'archaic' humans such as *Homo erectus* found in Indonesia. How could people with such archaic traits exist only 9000–15,000 years ago when more modern-looking and gracile people had been at Lake Mungo in south-west NSW 40,000 years ago?[67]

In an attempt to resolve this, University of Melbourne geochronologists Stone and Cupper re-dated the Kow Swamp site to no younger than 19,000 years old.[68] And in place of the controversial claim that the Kow Swamp population was a late surviving form of Erectus, the robust cranial features were attributed to a harsh climate incurred by the last phase of the ice age and genetic isolation (inbreeding). The researchers note:

> Such conditions would have forced Indigenous populations to survive in small groups. The robust skeletal form of the Kow Swamp people probably arose from the increasing physical and hence genetic isolation [inbreeding], accentuated by the severity of the LGM [Last Glacial Maximum].[69]

This story does not seem persuasive, and appears to be one more attempt to sweep aside the problem.[70] When the fossil evidence from Kow Swamp conflicted with evolutionary expectations the dates were revised and the narrative was rewritten

65. Curnoe D., A 150- Year Conundrum: Cranial Robusticity and Its Bearing on the Origin of Aboriginal Australians, *Int J Evol Biol* Volume 2011, Article ID 632484, 18 pages. DOI: 10.4061/2011/632484
66. Curnoe D., A 150- Year Conundrum: Cranial Robusticity and Its Bearing on the Origin of Aboriginal Australians, *Int J Evol Biol* Volume 2011, Article ID 632484, 18 pages. DOI: 10.4061/2011/632484.
67. Major J., Kow Swamp remains are re-dated to more than 20,000 years old, *UniNews* (a University of Melbourne production) 13(3):8-22, March 2004, accessed at uninews.unimelb.edu.au/news/1255 on October 28th 2015.
68. Stone T. and Cupper M.L., Last Glacial Maximum ages for robust humans at Kow Swamp, southern Australia, *J Hum Evol* 45:99-111, 2003.
69. Gregson A., Riddle solved, *Riverine Herald*, 12 January 2004. Accessed at https://app.lms.unimelb.edu.au/bbcswebdav/pid-3266399-dt-content-rid-2414359_2/xid-2414359_2.
70. Lubenow M.L., *Bones of Contention*, Baker Books, Grand Rapids, Michigan, 2004.

to make the problem go away.

Erectus Brain Size Overlaps with that of Modern Humans

The reduced cranial capacity commonly found among Erectus skulls is often cited as evidence they were our sub-human ancestors. It is generally believed that before we evolved into modern *Homo sapiens* we had smaller brains and significantly reduced intelligence. The volumes of ape braincases tend to fall in the range of 390 to 540 cubic centimeters (cm³) with male gorillas being at the upper end of the spectrum.[71] Normal human braincase volumes vary greatly, ranging between 800 and 2220 cm³, with an average around 1345 cm³.[72] Erectus cranial capacities are on average 940 cm³ and range anywhere between 700 and 1400 cm³.[73] Turkana Boy is 880 cm³ but could have reached 1000 cm³ in adulthood. If Solo Man specimens from Java are included (which are typically identified as Erectus),[74] cranial capacity ranges up to 1250 cm³—approaching the modern human average.[75] The Vertezollos occipital bone attributed to Erectus reveal an even larger cranial capacity of 1400 cm³.[76] The specimens attributed to the species exhibit a wide range of cranial capacities, just as humans do today. As John Allen writes in *The Lives of the Brain: Human Evolution and The Organ of Mind*:

> Finally, there is *H. erectus*, which spans a considerable period of time and a wide range of cranial capacities. Even after removing *H. ergaster* and *H. heidelbergensis*, *H. erectus* cranial capacities range from a low 727 cc for OH12 from east Africa to over 1,200 cc for the largest Chinese specimens (Holloway et al. 2004a).[77]

Did Erectus have sub-human intelligence? Erectus had smaller brain volumes, but were they less intelligent than modern man? Not necessarily—brain size varies according to body size and does not clearly correlate with intelligence. Erectus was typically much smaller than an average human today, and would naturally have a smaller brain. The average woman has a smaller brain, when compared to men—but this reflects over-all body size, and does not mean women are less intelligent. Whales have enormous brains but it doesn't mean they're smarter than humans. Neanderthals had larger brains than the average modern human (averaging 1487 cm³).[78] It is for this reason Thomas Huxley (remembered as "Darwin's

---

71. Kappelman J., The evolution of body mass and relative brain size in fossil hominids, *J Hum Evol* 30:243-276, 1996.

72. Molnar S., *Human Variation: Races, Types, and Ethnic Groups*, 5th Edition, Prentice Hall, New Jersey, p.189, 2002.

73. The five skulls found in Dmanisi Georgia may reduce this lower estimate to 600 cm³, excluding skull 5 which may actually belong to an ape.

74. Some paleoanthropologists split these specimens into *Homo soloensis*, see Allen J.S., *The Lives of the Brain: Human Evolution and the Organ of Mind*, Belknap Press, Cambridge, MA, USA, 2009.

75. Holloway R.L. *et al.*, The Human Fossil Record Volume 3, Appendix 1, John Wiley & Sons Inc., 2004. http://www.columbia.edu/~rlh2/PartII.pdf

76. Wolpoff M.H., Some Notes on the Vertesszollos Occipital, *Am J Phys Anthropol*, 47:357-364, 1977.

77. Allen J.S., *The Lives of the Brain: Human Evolution and the Organ of Mind*, Belknap Press, Cambridge, MA, USA, p. 62, 2009.

78. Holloway R.L. *et al.*, *The Human Fossil Record* Volume 3, Appendix 1, John Wiley & Sons Inc., 2004. http://www.columbia.edu/~rlh2/PartII.pdf

Bulldog") regarded Neanderthals as fully human.[79,80] Neurologists now know that when it comes to intelligence, brain organization is more important than brain size. Paleoanthropologists have recognized this for some time. As psychologists Willerman and colleagues have noted in the journal *Intelligence*, "*There is no strong direct relationship between brain size and intelligence among modern humans.*"[81]

Moreover, there are documented cases of modern humans with cranial capacities far lower than the average. Traditional thinking would assume these individuals had a lower IQ than normal. Anatole France was the winner of the 1921 Nobel Prize for literature. His cranial capacity was 933 cm³—the same size as many Erectus specimens such as Java Man and Turkana Boy.[82] A man named Daniel Lyon had a cranial capacity of 660 cm³, yet he lived a normal life and worked for the Pennsylvania Railway Terminal for twenty years in the late 1800's. Lyon was able to read and write and had no signs of mental deficiency.[83] These examples and others demonstrate that brain size should not be used to support the evolutionary assumption that Erectus was a sub-human species.

The Impressive Cultural Inventory of Erectus

Many have expressed opinions of the low intelligence level of Erectus, generally based upon evolutionary preconceptions, not actual physical evidence. For instance, it has been claimed that Erectus was only capable of the most "*rudimentary human speech*" and was not capable of using words.[84] Claims like this are inherently speculative.[85]

One of the strongest pieces of evidence for the fully human status of Erectus is their extensive cultural inventory. But before we examine the cultural evidence, it is important to address a widespread evolutionary misconception. It is common practice among cultural anthropologists to associate a lack of sophisticated tools with sub-human status. Yet there are examples of present-day tribes that use stone tools, and lack modern technological capabilities.[86] In these cases, it would obviously be a mistake to assume that using crude stone tools reflects sub-human intelligence. Consider the Tasmanians of Australia. According to anthropologists, Tasmanians are viewed as the "*most primitive people still alive in recent centuries.*" Anthropologist Jared Diamond describes the Tasmanians as having "*the simplest*

79. Johanson D. and Shreeve J., *Lucy's Child,* William Morrow and Company, New York, p. 49, 1989.
80. Klein R.G., Darwin and the recent African origin of modern humans, *Proc Natl Acad Sci*, USA 106(38): 16007–16009, 2009.
81. Willerman L. *et al.*, In vivo brain size and intelligence, *Intelligence* 15: 223–228, 1991.
82. Skoyles J.R., (1999) Human Evolution Expanded Brains to Increase Expertise Capacity, Not IQ, Psycoloquy: 10,#2 Brain Expertise (1), http://psycprints.ecs.soton.ac.uk/archive/00000637/
83. Anderson D., Turkana Boy—getting past the propaganda http://creation.com/turkana-boy-getting-past-the-propaganda#txtRef10 Accessed: October 10, 2015.
84. White E. and Brown D.M., *The First Men,* Time-Life Books, New York, p. 18, 1973.
85. Bednarik R.G., Seafaring in the Pleistocene, *Camb Archaeol J* 13:1, 41-66, 2003. It is based on the sheer assumption proposed by Darwin in Descent of Man (1871) that "*language was a gradually selected capability that emerged from more primitive forms of communication evident in animals.*" p. 57.
86. Leakey M.D., Primitive Artifacts from Kanapoi Valley, *Nature* 5062:579-581, 1966.

technology of any recent people on Earth." He writes:

> Unlike mainland Aboriginal Australians Tasmanians couldn't start a fire; they had no boomerangs, spear throwers, or shields; they had no bone tools, no specialized stone tools, and no compound tools like an axe head mounted on a handle; they couldn't cut down a tree or hollow out a canoe; they lacked sewing to make sewn clothing, despite Tasmania's cold winter climate with snow; and, incredibly, though they lived mostly on the seacoast, the Tasmanians didn't catch or eat fish. How did those enormous gaps in Tasmanian material culture arise?[87]

The sparse cultural inventory of the Tasmanians had nothing to do with evolution (or lack thereof), but is instead attributed to cultural degeneration leading to loss of technology. During the ice age, the southern Australian mainland was connected to the Tasmanian island via a land bridge. At that time there would be interbreeding and cultural exchange between the two populations—allowing for a rich cultural inventory. However, when the land bridge was submerged at the end of the ice age, contact was lost between the Tasmanians and the mainland Australians. Consequently, technologies such as the controlled use of fire, bone tools for sewing clothes, fishing capabilities, and other skills were lost. The Tasmanians' primitive lifestyle in no way indicates they were anything less than fully human. In circumstances like this, cultural degeneration and loss of technology explain the "primitive" nature of isolated people groups. The same logic applies to Erectus—limited technology should not be used as evidence that they were a sub-human species.

Now, contrary to long-held assumptions, we are finding that Erectus had an impressive cultural inventory, richer in fact, than that of Tasmanians and some other isolated tribes living today. A striking piece of evidence in support of the fully human status of Erectus is their inferred ability to sail—a finding that has stunned evolutionary paleoanthropologists.

Just east of Java are the islands of Wallacea. On one of those islands (the island of Flores), archeological remains were discovered dating 800,000 years old, and have been attributed to Erectus. Paleoanthropologists in the journal *Nature* explain that there are 3 deep-water straits between the Sunda continental shelf and Flores (Figure 6). They note:

> Even at times of lowest sea level during the last glacial maximum, these straits required sea crossings of at least 19 km [approximately 12 miles]. ... We conclude that *Homo erectus* in this region was capable of repeated water crossings using watercraft.[88]

87. Diamond J., Why Did Human History Unfold Differently On Different Continents for the Last 13,000 years? *Edge*, April 22, 1997. Accessed on November 02, 2015: http://edge.org/conversation/jared_diamond-why-did-human-history-unfold-differently-on-different-continents-for-the
88. Morwood M.J. *et al.*, Fission-track ages of stone tools and fossils on the east Indonesian island of Flores, *Nature* 392:173-176, 1998. Note: the most distant strait is roughly 15 miles.

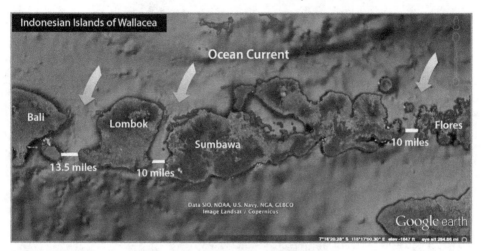

Figure 6. To get to the island of Flores, Erectus would have had to have navigated across at least three deep-water straits (10-15 miles each). This type of sea-travel would have required sailing vessels, planning, navigation, etc.

Discover magazine discussed the significance of Morwood and colleagues' findings:

> What kind of brain does it take to build a boat and steer it across 15 miles of choppy seas and strong currents? Could a chimp do it? Not likely. "It's a pretty formidable water crossing," Morwood says. ... Presumably they didn't swim. Nor does Morwood think they could have crossed the strait in any significant numbers by accident, hanging on to logs or crude rafts. "I think you need directed watercraft," he says. "You'd have to have some means of steering, and some means of propulsion. If you try to put a few logs together and jump on it, you're probably going to die." ...To make such a voyage, it has been argued, requires quintessentially modern skills—not just technical ones but the ability to plan, to work as a group, even to talk.[89]

Successfully navigating rough, choppy waters against an ocean current would require sophisticated seafaring abilities. A prominent paleo-archeologist, Robert Bednarik, led the First Mariners Project. He pointed out:

> Armchair archaeologists, who think that sea crossings are a piece of cake, really ought to try doing this on drifting vegetation flotsam.[90]

Leading paleo-expert Chris Stringer takes note of these talented sailors and admits it is strong evidence Erectus *"was more human, just like us."*[91] In light of these and other findings, the researchers in their *Nature* report call upon the paleo-community to reconsider the cognitive capabilities of Erectus. Evolutionary paleoarchaeologist Robert Bednarik states forcefully, *"The proposition is advanced that hominid cognitive and cultural evolution during the Middle and early Late Pleistocene have been severely misjudged. The navigational*

89. Kunzig R., Erectus Afloat, *Discover* 20(1):80, 1999.
90. Bednarik R.G., Seafaring in the Pleistocene, *Camb Archaeol J* 13:1, 41-66, 2003.
91. Sarfati J., *The Greatest Hoax on Earth*, Creation Book Publishers, Atlanta, GA, p.161, 2010.

feats of Pleistocene seafarers confirm the cultural evidence of sophistication available from the study of palaeoart.[92] Bednarik associates seafaring abilities not only with careful craftsmanship and navigational skills, but also with foresight and planning. He argues that in order to accomplish such a feat Erectus was most certainly capable of *"sophisticated communication, most probably in verbal form (speech) or some other suitable mode of language."*

Additional evidence could be cited to argue for the fully human status of Erectus. For the sake of brevity, Erectus–associated artifacts and skills are summarized below:

- Watercraft assembly and sailing against an ocean current
- Language, speech, communication
- Reasoning, foresight, planning, ingenuity
- Bead and pendant manufacture/necklaces
- Cordage/knot-making
- Manufacture of diverse stone and bone implements
- Controlled use of fire and hearths of stones (fire places)[93]
- Catching, skinning, and cleaning fish
- Cooking food[94,95]
- Occupational floors/living spaces[96]
- Petroglyphs, figurines, paint (red ochre), art[97]
- Woodworking[98,99]
- Coordinated hunting
- Butchering, skinning, and transporting large game
- Manufacturing clothing from skins (possibly sewing)
- Production of fibers and resins
- Kinship/family structure
- Care for old and weak individuals[100,101]

There can be no doubt that Erectus exhibited an array of sophisticated abilities requiring fully human cognition. Artifacts found in association with Erectus clearly speak of mental capacity that overlaps with that of modern man.

92. Bednarik R.G., Seafaring in the Pleistocene, *Camb Archaeol J* 13:1, 41-66, 2003.

93. Berna F. *et al.*, Microstratigraphic evidence of in situ fire in the Acheulean strata of Wonderwerk Cave, Northern Cape province, South Africa, *Proc Natl Acad Sci*, 2012.

94. Wrangham R., *Catching Fire: How Cooking Made Us Human*, Basic Books, New York, 2009.

95. Organ C. *et al.*, Phylogenetic rate shifts in feeding time during the evolution of *Homo*, *Proc Natl Acad Sci*, USA 108:14555–14559, 2011.

96. Alperson-Afil N. *et al.*, Spatial Organization of Hominin Activities at Gesher Benot Ya'aqov, Israel, *Science* 326:1677-1680, 2009.

97. Bednarik R.G., Exograms, *Rock Art Res* 31(1):47-62, 2014.

98. Dominguez-Rodrigo M. *et al.*, Woodworking activities by early humans: a plant residue analysis on Acheulian stone tools from Pening (Tanzania), *J Hum Evol* 40:289-299, 2001.

99. Dominguez-Rodrigo M. *et al.*, Woodworking activities by early humans: a plant residue analysis on Acheulian stone tools from Peninj (Tanzania), *J Hum Evol* 40:289–299, 2001.

100. http://humanorigins.si.edu/evidence/human-fossils/species/homo-erectus

101. Walker A. and Shipman P., *The Wisdom of the Bones: in Search of Human Origins*, Alfred A. Knoff Publishing, New York, p. 167, 1996.

Does Erectus Show Evidence of Genetic Degeneration?

While Erectus appears to be fully human, Erectus populations are now extinct, and they appear to have been highly inbred and genetically compromised. Although Erectus brain volume overlaps with modern brain volumes, it is consistently on the lower end of the spectrum. Similarly, the Erectus cultural inventory is distinctly human, but is on the low end of the spectrum. There seems to be an element of degeneration and pathology inherent in these populations. Many paleoanthropologists acknowledge that populations such as Neanderthal and Erectus would have existed in very small, isolated populations, where inbreeding and genetic drift would result in genetic decline and genetic pathologies. We know that highly inbred populations become progressively compromised—eventually leading to extinction. Depending on the extent of inbreeding, such a population may range from only slightly compromised to being on the verge of extinction.

A modern example of this type of small population would be the pygmies of central Africa and the San (Bushmen) of South Africa. These remnant populations have, until recently, lived in extreme isolation for many generations. The average life expectancy of the Bushmen is 45–50 years and 16–24 years for the pygmies. Adult male African pygmies are on average, no taller than 4 feet 9 inches in height (adult females are even shorter).[102]

Hunter-gatherer groups must live in small bands to survive. This leads to a very serious problem associated with genetic inbreeding. Populations of less than 100 individuals will, over many generations, always show evidence of inbreeding, resulting in many types of genetic pathologies. In such an inbred group, many non-adaptive genetic features and various pathologies will quickly drift to fixation. This can be expected to eventually create morphological abnormalities unique to that group of people.

In addition to the expected genetic degeneration associated with small population sizes, it is widely recognized that reduction in physical size (especially brain size) can arise due to what is called "reductive evolution." Reductive evolution is when natural selection favors the reduction, or shrinkage of a species' body size or capabilities. This can lead to reduced energy requirements, favoring survival.

A tribe with a hunter-gatherer lifestyle will tend to be chronically undernourished, facing repeated cycles of starvation, which should create strong selection pressure for reductive evolution. It is well established that reduced size in general, but especially reduced brain size is adaptive in undernourished populations (Figure 7). Remarkably, in these types of populations there can be strong natural selection favoring smaller brain size. Paleo-expert Susan Anton points this out in *Yearbook of Physical Anthropology* journal:

> As has been widely noted, the brain is an extremely costly organ from a nutritional

---

102. Encyclopædia Britannica: Pygmy. Britannica.com. https://www.britannica.com/topic/Pygmy

perspective, consuming about 16 times as much energy as does muscle by weight. Thus sustaining trends in brain size increase requires additional energetic resources and a clear selective advantage for the organism involved.[103]

Reductive evolution would explain both the reduced height and the reduced brain volume of Erectus. As we will see, the same logic can be applied to Hobbit and Naledi. Selection for smaller brain size due to limited resources should not be mistaken for forward evolution. This type of "reductive evolution," is really evolution going backwards—it is counterproductive in terms of long-term evolutionary advance. Depending on the location and the specific tribe, we seem to be seeing snapshots of people groups at different stages of degeneration.

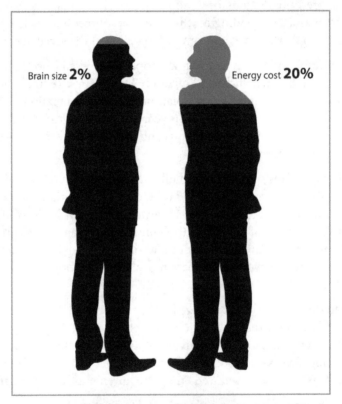

Brain size **2%**

Energy cost **20%**

Figure 7. The human brain is an energetically costly organ. It constitutes only 2% of the body's total weight yet it consumes 20% of its energy. Erectus lived in small hunter-gatherer populations in extreme isolation with limited resources and low-calorie diets. Yet their demanding lifestyles required a high calorie intake. Aware of this, paleo-experts have proposed that selective reduction in brain size would be favored under such conditions. Reduced brain size is not an example of true forward evolution. It is actually "reductive evolution"—which is evolution in reverse and fits with our alternative model for how the various Homo-types arose (see chapter 14).

103. Anton S.C., Natural History of *Homo erectus*, *Yearbook Phys Anthropol* 46:126-169, 2003. (p.155)

Conclusion—Erectus was Fully Human

There is strong evidence that the bones commonly referred to as *Homo erectus* are fully human individuals who suffered from various pathologies associated with such things as inbreeding, mutation, teratogens (developmental abnormalities), etc. Claims that Erectus was a sub-human species are clearly contested among leading evolutionary paleo-experts. While some insist Erectus was morphologically distinct from modern man, others point out that Erectus morphology overlaps extensively with modern humans—and so Erectus should be reclassified as *Homo sapiens*. While some claim they were our progenitors, others acknowledge that they coexisted and interbred with anatomically modern *Homo sapiens*.[104,105] While some attribute the differences in skull shape of Erectus and modern man to progressive evolution, others would attribute the Erectus skull morphology to multiple factors, including reductive evolution.

The ability of Erectus to sail (across 10–15 mile wide deep-water straits against strong ocean currents) speaks powerfully of human intelligence. Likewise, the controlled use of fire, sophisticated language, and paleo-art reveal a human mind and soul. Moreover, the overall morphology of Erectus overlaps extensively with modern humans—as paleoanthropologists freely confess. The Erectus postcranial skeleton is indistinguishable from that of modern *Homo sapiens*, apart from subtle differences detectable only through the eyes of a trained anatomist. Indeed, most of the classic features attributed to Erectus—including those found in the skull and face—have been found in modern humans. For all these reasons, evolutionary paleo-experts known as "lumpers," acknowledge that Erectus is a variant form of *Homo sapiens*. We agree!

104. Curnoe D., A 150- Year Conundrum: Cranial Robusticity and Its Bearing on the Origin of Aboriginal Australians, *Int J Evol Biol* Vol. 2011, Article ID 632484, 18 pages. DOI: 10.4061/2011/632484
105. Webb S.G., *The First Boat People*, Cambridge University Press, Cambridge, UK, 2006.

CHAPTER 5

Homo floresiensis
Is "Hobbit" a New Species?

Flores LB1 [Hobbit] *may represent a congenitally abnormal individual drawn
from a small bodied population of H. sapiens.
...results from founder effects, genetic isolation and a high inbreeding coefficient.*[1]

Paleoanthropologist Lee Berger, University of the Witwatersrand

Discovery of "Hobbit"

In 2003 a team of paleoanthropologists led by Michael Morwood and Peter Brown
were exploring a limestone cave known as Liang Bua (which means "cold cave"), on
the Indonesian Island of Flores in Southeast Asia (Figure 1). To their surprise they
discovered a nearly complete skull and partial skeleton, formally designated LB1.[2]
The skeleton included leg bones, hands, feet, a partial pelvis, and other fragmentary
remains (Figure 2). A complete lower jawbone was also found belonging to a second
individual, designated LB2. The skull of LB1 was very small (Figure 3), maybe one
third the size of an average human, and had a cranial capacity of 380 cm^3 (later
revised to 420 cm^3).[3] Their initial reaction was that it was a child. However, its
fully emerged wisdom teeth, brow ridges, and other features suggested it was a
female adult which stood about 3 feet 6 inches tall.[4] Brown thought it might be
a diseased human with some type of growth disorder, but soon decided it was a
new species entirely.[5] The basis for naming it as a new species had to do with a
combination of abnormal features such as small stature, tiny cranial capacity, short
femur bones, disproportionately flat feet, and asymmetry of the facial features.[6] In

---

1. Berger L.R. *et al.*, Small-bodied humans from Palau, Micronesia, *PLOS ONE* 3(3):e1780, 2008.
2. Brown P. *et al.*, A new small-bodied hominin from the Late Pleistocene of Flores, Indonesia, *Nature* 431:1055-1061, 2004.
3. Kubo D. *et al.*, Brain size of *Homo floresiensis* and its evolutionary implications, *Proc Roy Soc B* 280: 20130338, 2013.
4. Stringer C., Small remains still pose big problems, *Nature* 514:427-429, 2014. [*Nature Collections, Homo floresiensis* 2014: The 'hobbit'—ten years on, p. S8-S10, 2014.]
5. Callaway E., Tales of the hobbit, *Nature* 514:422-426, 2014.
6. Henneberg M. *et al.*, Evolved developmental homeostasis disturbed in LB1 from Flores, Indonesia, denotes Down syndrome and not diagnostic traits of the invalid species *Homo floresiensis, Proc Natl Acad Sci,* USA 111(33):11967-11972, 2014.

2004, they reported in the journal *Nature* that they had discovered a new human species that lived 18,000 years ago, based on carbon-14 dating of the surrounding limestone.[7] The researchers called the new species *Homo floresiensis*, but nicknamed it "Hobbit" because of her diminutive size. Shortly after, a number of bones of at least eight other individuals were recovered from the same site.[8] By 2009, this number increased to a total of 14 individuals, though LB1 remains the most complete skeleton recovered to date. The researchers were uncertain as to whether Hobbit was a modern offshoot of *H. erectus*, *H. habilis*, or even *Australopithecus*.[9,10] Despite its uncertain origin the authors remain convinced it was a new species, distinct from *Homo sapiens*.

Figure 1. Liang Bua—a beautiful limestone cave located on the Indonesian island of Flores where the remains of the reputed hominin species *Homo floresiensis* ("Hobbit") were first discovered in 2003.

However, many other paleoanthropologists (including some members of the discovery team,) adamantly insist that Hobbit is not a new species, but is fully human (*Homo sapiens*). They cite evidence that these bones represent modern humans suffering from a complex of serious pathologies, and that they lived no more than 3,000 to 4,000 years ago.

7. Brown P. *et al.*, A new small-bodied hominin from the Late Pleistocene of Flores, Indonesia, *Nature* 431:1055-1061, 2004.
8. Morwood M.J. *et al.*, Further evidence for small-bodied hominins from the late-Pleistocene of Flores, Indonesia, *Nature* 437:1012-1017, 2005.
9. Argue D. *et al.*, *Homo floresiensis*: microcephalic, pygmoid, *Australopithecus* or *Homo*?, *J Hum Evol* 51(4):360-374, 2006.
10. Lieberman D.E., *Homo floresiensis* from head to toe, *Nature* 459:41-42, 2009.

New Species or Diseased Modern Human?

Even now, intense debate continues to rage within the paleo-community. Paleo-expert, Chris Stringer, noted a decade after the discovery, *"Controversy about this species continues to this day, including whether it belongs in Homo."*[11] *Scientific American* published an article at the same time titled, *"Human or Hobbit? The arguments over an ancient skeleton just won't die."*[12] Paleo-researchers describe the two competing views in the *Académie des Sciences* (2016):

> From the beginning, two schools of thought prevailed, and this situation persists today. One purports that the Liang Bua human series belongs to a local modern human (*Homo sapiens sapiens*) with anatomical particularities or pathologies that may be due to insular isolation/endogamy. The second argues in favour of the existence of a new species that, depending on the authors, is either a descendant of local *Homo erectus*, or belongs to a much more basal taxon, closer to archaic *Homo* or to australopithecines.[13]

The paleo-experts who insist the Flores Hobbit is a legitimate new species, distinct from humans, originally claimed the hominin was present on the island of Flores as early as 92,000 years ago and disappeared 12,000 years ago.[14] However, a more recent study published in *Nature* offered a revised timespan, from 190,000–50,000 years ago, possibly surviving long after. This paper indicates the Hobbit may have lived alongside *Homo sapiens* who arrived on the island between 55,000–35,000 years ago.[15] A separate 2016 study reported additional fossil findings suggesting the Hobbit might have lived on the island much earlier (700,000 years ago).[16,17] So at this point the age for these bones could range anywhere from 1,000 to 1 million years old, based on conventional dating methods. Whatever its age, proponents of the new species hypothesis regard the Hobbit as a miniaturized descendant of Erectus that arrived on the island perhaps 1 million years ago. Some have considered the idea that Hobbit evolved directly from *Australopithecus*. To support their view, these researchers claim the Hobbit displays an "evolutionary mosaic" of *Australopithecus* and *Homo* traits.[18] However, many other leading paleo-experts

11. Stringer C., Small remains still pose big problems, *Nature* 514:427-429, 2014. [*Nature Collections, Homo floresiensis* 2014: p. S8]

12. Wong K., Human or Hobbit? *Sci Am* 311:28-29, 2014.

13. Zeitoun V. *et al.* Phylogenetic analysis of the calvaria of *Homo floresiensis*, C.R. Palevol Académie des Sciences, 2016. http://dx.doi.org/10.1016/j.crpv.2015.12.002.

14. Morwood M.J. *et al.*, Further evidence for small-bodied hominins from the Late Pleistocene of Flores, Indonesia, *Nature* 437:1012-1017, 2005.

15. Sutikna T. *et al.*, Revised stratigraphy and chronology for *Homo floresiensis* at Liang Bua in Indonesia, *Nature* 532(7599):366-369, 2016.

16. Gomez-Robles A., The dawn of *Homo floresiensis*, *Nature* 534(7606):188-189, 2016.

17. Brumm A. *et al.*, Age and context of the oldest known hominin fossils from Flores, *Nature* 534(7606):249-253, 2016.

18. Zeitoun V. *et al.*, Phylogenetic analysis of the calvaria of *Homo floriensis*, C.R. Palevol Académie des Sciences, 2016. http://dx.doi.org/10.1016/j.crpv.2015.12.002. *"The new species hypothesis promoted by several authors (Aiello, 2010; Argue et al., 2009; Brown and Maeda, 2009; Jungers et al., 2009a&b) is mainly based on the fact that the Liang Bua specimens arguably posses both derived and primitive characters which were produced by mosaic evolution..."*

reject those dates and completely reject the "new species" designation. Instead, they highlight a number of skeletal features shared by the modern pygmy *Homo sapiens* population that actually still lives in the neighborhood of the cave. Leading evolutionary paleo-experts (including Alan Thorne, Bob Eckhardt, Teuku Jacob, Maciej Henneberg, and others) have reported this in the *Proceedings of the National Academy of Sciences*:

> ...if this population [*Homo floresiensis*] had been isolated genetically up until the very recent past, how can identical anatomical features shared by members of the putative new taxon and subsequent *H. sapiens* [i.e., the Rampasasa pygmies that live near Liang Bua Cave] be explained? Alternatively, if contact and interbreeding did occur, how could separate species status for *H. floresiensis* be justified?[19]

Interestingly, the paleo-experts who named Hobbit as a new human species (Morwood, Brown, and colleagues) never compared its skeletal features to the very small human beings who now populate that region of the island. These researchers explain that if they had done so, they would have noticed the obvious similarities to the modern Rampasasa pygmies who live close to the cave. Instead, comparisons were made with modern humans from other parts of the world (primarily Europe).

These and other researchers liken the skeletal LB1 abnormalities (e.g., asymmetry of the skull) to known human diseases. These paleo-experts have insisted that Hobbit is a modern human which suffered from microcephaly,[20] which is a well-known developmental disorder that results in a misshapen skull with a reduced braincase. Other possible developmental disorders have also been suggested in the scientific literature, including cretinism[21], Laron syndrome[22], and Down's syndrome.[23] Paleoanthropologist Maciej Henneberg, the lead author of the paper published in *Proceedings of the National Academy of Science* (2014), explains:

> About two and a half years ago, it all clicked. I could see that all signs of the bones were compatible with Down's syndrome. There are about 20 or so characteristics that are matching. There is not a single characteristic of LB1 that doesn't match.[24]

In support of the diseased modern human interpretation, they note in their paper that the skeletal features of LB1 were *not* found in the skeletal remains belonging

19. Jacob T. *et al.*, Pygmoid Australomelanesian *Homo sapiens* skeletal remains from Liang Bua, Flores: Population affinities and pathological abnormalities, *Proc Natl Acad Sci*, USA 103(36):13421-13426, 2006.

20. Vannucci R.C. *et al.*, Craniometric ratios of microcephaly and LB1, *Homo floresiensis*, using MRI and endocasts, *Proc Natl Acad Sci*, USA 108(34):14043-14048, 2011.

21. Obendorf P.J. *et al.*, Are the small human-like fossils found on Flores human endemic cretins?, *Proc Roy Soc B.* 275:1287-1296, 2008.

22. Hershkovitz I. *et al.*, Comparative skeletal features between *Homo floresiensis* and patients with primary growth hormone insensitivity (Laron syndrome), *Am J Phys Anthropol* 134(2):198-208, 2007.

23. Henneberg M. *et al.*, Evolved developmental homeostasis disturbed in LB1 from Flores, Indonesia denotes Down syndrome and not diagnostic traits of the invalid species *Homo floresiensis*, *Proc Natl Acad Sci*, USA 111(33):11967-11972, 2014.

24. Callaway E., Hobbit mystery endures a decade on, *Nature News*, 22 October 2014. DOI:10.1038/nature.2014.16204.

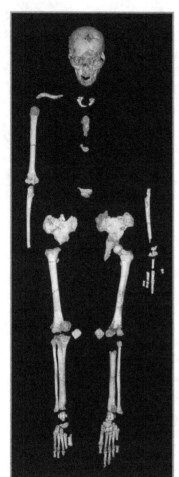

Figure 2: LB1 is the type specimen of the reputed new species, *Homo floresiensis*. LB1 is the most complete skeleton recovered to date. It belongs to an adult female who is estimated to have stood 3 ft. 6 in. tall.

to the eight other individuals recovered from the dig site at that time. They criticize Brown and his team for basing their new species interpretation on a single partial skeleton. They report:

> Specimen LB1 from Liang Bua Cave is unusual, but craniofacial and postcranial characteristics originally said to be diagnostic of the new species are not evident in the other more fragmentary skeletons in the sample that resemble other recent small-bodied human populations in the region (including the Andaman Islands, Palau, and Flores itself).[25]

Other paleoanthropologists disagree with this interpretation, and insist that Hobbit did not have any of the diseases mentioned above. Morwood and colleagues point out similarities in overall size and morphology between LB1 and the bones of the other individuals found at Liang Bua. For instance, the two jaws recovered from Liang Bua both lacked projecting chins. Brown and Morwood list chins as a distinguishing feature of *Homo sapiens*.[26,27] Brown notes: *"You can't have a colony of microcephalics going through time. That's crazy."*[28] They claim that shared features among other individuals are evidence that *"LB1 is not aberrant, but is instead representative of a long-term, morphologically unique, small-bodied population with a configuration of features never recorded in normal or pathological H. sapiens."*[29] These paleo-experts argue that pathology is an unconvincing explanation for the asymmetrical shape of the skull and other abnormal features.

There was an embarrassing mistake made soon after the fossil remains were recovered. The late Teuku Jacob (1929–2007), former

25. Henneberg M. *et al.*, Evolved developmental homeostasis disturbed in LB1 from Flores, Indonesia denotes Down syndrome and not diagnostic traits of the invalid species *Homo floresiensis*, *Proc Natl Acad Sci, USA* 111(33):11967-11972, 2014.

26. Brown P. *et al.*, A new small-bodied hominin from the Late Pleistocene of Flores, Indonesia, *Nature* 431:1055-1061, 2004.

27. Morwood M.J. *et al.*, Archaeology and age of a new homonin from Flores in eastern Indonesia, *Nature* 431:1087-1091, 2004.

28. Dalton R., Fossil finders in tug of war over analysis of hobbit bones, *Nature* 434:5, 2005. [*Nature Collections, Homo floresiensis*, pp. s16-s17, 2014.]

29. Morwood M.J. *et al.*, Further evidence for small-bodied hominins from the Late Pleistocene of Flores, Indonesia, *Nature* 437:1012-1011, 2005.

head of Indonesia's national paleoanthropology institute, insisted that his institute owned the fossil remains, and took them to his own laboratory for further research. Apparently, while attempting to make molds, the fossils were damaged beyond repair.[30] Brown explained that the un-fossilized bones were like mush and could easily become a *"pile of mashed potato"* if they weren't treated carefully.[31] The bones were extremely fragile, too soft to be made into casts.[32] *Nature* writer, Rex Dalton, replays the unfortunate events:

> The researchers believe that efforts to make casts at Jacob's lab, along with the trauma of transport, led to significant damage. Parts of the skull were pulled off, they say, and a jaw was broken between the front two teeth, splintering an area crucial for future analysis... There was even an attempt to force the pieces back together with glue, he says, and the pelvis of LB1 was crushed.[33]

As paleoanthropologist Peter Brown lamented, *"It is an outrage. It is now impossible for future scholars to verify my work. The pelvis was whole; now it is 100 crumbs."*[34] Pictures and measurements are all that is left for further study of the damaged bones. This has made it difficult for researchers to discern whether the abnormalities of LB1 (particularly the asymmetry of the skull) are legitimate anatomical features, or simply recent damage of the bones. Teuku Jacob subsequently returned most of the remains except for the femur bones and portions of the rib that he sent to the Max Planck Institute for Evolutionary Anthropology in Germany where researchers were probing for intact DNA. If the fossil remains had yielded viable DNA that could be sequenced, it would resolve the status of *Homo floresiensis* once and for all. However, there have been no publication about Hobbit DNA to date, so the attempt must have been unsuccessful. Even before Jacob had access to the fossils, damage had already been done to the bones during the excavation process. The most recent damage has only complicated things, making analysis of the remains

Figure 3. The skull of LB1 is small, approximately 420 cm³ (about one third the size of the average modern human). The skull shares some similarities with Erectus and is classified within the human genus *Homo*. CT scans of the interior of the braincase confirm Hobbit had a human brain.

30. Morwood M. and van Oosterzee P., *A new human: The startling discovery and strange story of the "Hobbits" of Flores*, Indonesia, Smithsonian Books, Harper Collins, 255 pp, 2007.
31. Callaway E., Hobbit mystery endures a decade on, *Nature News*, 22 October 2014. DOI:10.1038/nature.2014.16204.
32. Brown P. *et al.*, A new small-bodied hominin from the Late Pleistocene of Flores, Indonesia, *Nature* 431:1055-1061, 2004.
33. Dalton R., Looking for the ancestors, *Nature* 434:432-434, 2005. [*Nature Collections*, 2014, p. S12-S14.]
34. Dalton R., Looking for the ancestors, *Nature* 434:432-434, 2005. [*Nature Collections*, 2014]

even more challenging.[35,36] Researchers holding to the new species interpretation have insisted that the asymmetrical features of the skull can be better explained by damage during excavation that removed part of the brow ridge, nasal region, and eye socket.[37,38]

Endocast Scans Reveal Cognitively Modern Human Brain

What can we gather from all this confusion? Is Hobbit a legitimate new hominin species or simply a unique people group belonging to the human race? As with Erectus and Naledi the question is: "is it human, or just nearly human?" An evaluation of cognitive capabilities is one of the most informative lines of evidence to consider. If Hobbit shows evidence of the features of creativity, complex language, forethought, design, craftsmanship, and other advanced mental processes unique to modern man, it would be difficult to deny its humanity.

Initially, paleoanthropologists suspected Hobbit must have had the intellect of a chimpanzee, since its cranial capacity was of similar size—approximately 420 cm^3.[39] But when it comes to brains, bigger isn't necessarily better, as mentioned in the previous chapter. In 2005, paleoneurologist Dean Falk and a group of evolutionary paleo-experts published a paper in the journal *Science* describing LB1's brain shape. The shape of Hobbit's brain was digitally reconstructed by taking CT scans of the interior of the braincase. The researchers compared Hobbit's brain shape to that of chimpanzees, *Homo erectus*, a modern woman, and a modern human who suffered from microcephaly. Their comparative analysis revealed that Hobbit looked most similar to *Homo erectus*—only smaller.[40,41] Since Erectus has been recognized by paleoanthropologists as having advanced cognition, this came as a surprise to the researchers. Falk was stunned to find distinct temporal lobes that reveal Hobbit's cognition was just as advanced as modern humans.[42,43,44] In describing the endocast results in her book *The Fossil Chronicles*, Falk writes:

> It was clear to us that the wide temporal lobes of Hobbit were a feature that was evolutionarily advanced toward the human condition, which was unexpected

35. Brown P. *et al.*, A new small-bodied hominin from the Late Pleistocene of Flores, Indonesia, *Nature* 431:1055-1061, 2004.

36. Jacob T. *et al.*, Pygmoid Australomelanesian *Homo sapiens* skeletal remains from Liang Bua, Flores: Population affinities and pathological abnormalities, *Proc Natl Acad Sci*, USA 103 (36):13421-13426, 2006.

37. Brown P. *et al.*, A new small-bodied hominin from the Late Pleistocene of Flores, Indonesia, *Nature* 431:1055-1061, 2004.

38. Nogrady B., Did the 'Hobbit' have Down syndrome?, *ABC Science*, August 5, 2014. http://www.abc.net.au/science/articles/2014/08/05/4060550.htm

39. Falk D. *et al.*, The brain of LB1, *Homo floresiensis*, *Science* 308:242-245, 2005.

40. Falk D., (2011-10-03). *The Fossil Chronicles: How Two Controversial Discoveries Changed Our View of Human Evolution* (Kindle Locations 1941-1942), University of California Press. Kindle Edition.

41. Falk D. *et al.*, The brain of LB1, *Homo floresiensis*, *Science* 308:242-245, 2005.

42. Forth G., Hominids, hairy hominoids and the science of humanity, *Anthropology Today* 21(3):13-17, 2005.

43. Falk D. *et al.*, The brain of LB1, *Homo floresiensis*, *Science* 308:242-245, 2005.

44. Balter M., Small but Smart? Flores Hominid shows signs of advanced brain, *Science* 307:1386-1387, 2005.

(even unprecedented) in such a small brain.[45]

Falk and her team found evidence of an organ known as Brodmann's area 10 (BA 10) or the frontopolar cortex. It is a region of the brain activated during numerous cognitive tasks, such as multitasking, devising plans, making judgements, recalling specific events, imagining future events, day-dreaming, and switching between *"internally generated thoughts and those stimulated by external events."*[46] The expanded BA 10 region, as well as other features shown by the endocast scans suggests that Hobbit was capable of advanced mental processes typical of modern man. As Falk concludes, *"...these regions are especially important for higher cognition in modern humans, and it's a good guess that they were for hobbits too."*[47] It is evident that Hobbit was capable of complex decision-making, reasoning, creativity, and even language. Corroborating evidence for this is based on advanced tools and artifacts found in the same strata as Hobbit's remains at Liang Bua.[48,49] Evolutionists have noted that the stone artifacts associated with Hobbit exhibit a level of sophistication on par with those of human craftsman: *"H. floresiensis is said to have manufactured implements that exhibit a level of sophistication elsewhere associated exclusively with H. sapiens."*[50] Paleoanthropologist Michael Morwood, who led the Hobbit discovery team, similarly reported in the journal *Nature*, *"The cognitive capabilities of early hominins, however, should not be underestimated, as indicated by the technology of stone artifacts associated with Hobbit at Liang Bua."*[51] Some of the sophisticated tools found by excavators include awls, micro-blades, carefully sharpened spear heads, large blades, and other artifacts needed to hunt, transport, and butcher large animals living on the island—such as adult Stegodons (dwarfed elephants), which weighed up to half a ton (the remains of which have been found at the Liang Bua Cave). Geochronologist and discovery team member Richard Roberts has noted that hunting and transporting large mammals must have involved coordinated group activity requiring language.[52,53]

The mounting evidence that supports the fully human status of the Hobbit is hard to ignore. Among the excavated remains were found charred bones and a circular hearth of stones revealing controlled use of fire and cooking. Morwood writes in *Nature*: *"Use of fire by hominins is indicated by charred bone and clusters of*

45. Falk D., (2011-10-03). *The Fossil Chronicles: How Two Controversial Discoveries Changed Our View of Human Evolution* (Kindle Locations 1941-1942), University of California Press. Kindle Edition.
46. Falk D., (2011-10-03). *The Fossil Chronicles: How Two Controversial Discoveries Changed Our View of Human Evolution* (Kindle Locations 1941-1942), University of California Press. Kindle Edition.
47. Falk D., (2011-10-03). *The Fossil Chronicles: How Two Controversial Discoveries Changed Our View of Human Evolution* (Kindle Locations 1941-1942), University of California Press. Kindle Edition.
48. Wong K., A mini species, *Sci Am* 291:34, 2004.
49. Brumm A. *et al.*, Early stone technology on Flores and its implication for *Homo florensiensis*, *Nature* 441:624-628, 2006.
50. Wong K., The Littlest Human, *Sci Am* 292:56-65, 2005.
51. Morwood M.J. *et al.*, Archaeology and age of a new hominin from Flores in eastern Indonesia, *Nature* 431:1087-1091, 2004.
52. Wong K., The Littlest Human, *Sci Am* 292:56-65, 2005.
53. Forth G., Hominids, hairy hominoids and the science of humanity, *Anthropology Today* 21(3):13-17, 2005.

reddened and fire-cracked rocks."[54] Commenting on these findings, geochronologist Roberts remarked, *"There are also circular clusters of burnt stones, akin to 'hearth' arrangements. If you go to the effort of making a tidy fireplace, it's not a huge step to have a barbecue."*[55]

Hobbit Sailed to the Island of Flores?

Another problem for those who have tried to argue that Hobbit was a pre-human species is Hobbit's arrival on the Flores Island (which was never accessible through a land bridge, even during the ice age when sea levels were lower). Citing Morwood *et al.*, Robin Denell *et al.* acknowledge this in *Quaternary Science Review* (2014):

> The question of how *H. floresiensis*—or its predecessors—arrived on Flores is an important one because Flores would always have been an island that was at least 19 km from other islands on the Sunda Shelf, even when sea levels were over 100 m lower than today (Morwood *et al.*,1998; Morwood and Jungers, 2009).[56]

How then did the ancestors of Hobbit arrive on the island of Flores? There are really only two possibilities—one of which seems unlikely. Paleoanthropologists have suggested the possibility that it *"arrived accidentally on natural rafts of vegetation that had been swept out to sea following a cyclone or tsunami."*[57] This is far-fetched because while it could happen to a stray individual, it would be extremely unlikely to transport a viable breeding population. The more reasonable alternative is that Hobbit arrived by sailing (as Dennell puts it, *"purposeful navigation"*). This has been suggested by a number of evolutionary paleoanthropologists who believe the ancestors of Hobbit were *H. erectus.*[58,59] Building and navigating boats would clearly prove that both Erectus and Hobbit were fully human. Transportation via a watercraft across a strait of 19 km against an ocean current is not as easy as it might sound. Morwood was astounded as he imagined their journey while taking a ferry ride to Flores from Lombok over rough waters. He asked in disbelief, *"Do you think you could make it across here in a raft?"*[60] Sailing from Bali to Flores would require careful planning, navigation skills, steering, and some type of propulsion— abilities only seen in *Homo sapiens*. The underlying reason why some paleo-experts have preferred the accidental-tsunami-rafting interpretation is because of the notion that Hobbit was too primitive, lacking the mental prowess necessary for sailing. As evolutionary human origins author Christopher Seddon writes, *"...the construction of a suitable watercraft and the navigational skills required to make a*

54. Morwood M.J. *et al.*, Archaeology and age of a new hominin from Flores in eastern Indonesia, *Nature* 431:1087-1091, 2004.
55. Hopkin M., The life of a hobbit, *Nature* 437:935, 2005. [Bert Roberts quoted]
56. Dennell R.W. *et al.*, The origins and persistence of *Homo floresiensis* on Flores: biogeographical and ecological perspectives, *Quaternary Sci Rev* 96:98-107, 2014.
57. Dennell R.W. *et al.*, The origins and persistence of *Homo floresiensis* on Flores: biogeographical and ecological perspectives, *Quaternary Sci Rev* 96: 98-107, 2014.
58. Bednarik R.G., Seafaring in the Pleistocene, *Camb Archaeol J* 13:1, 41-66, 2003.
59. Stringer C., Small remains still pose big problems, *Nature* 514:427-429. [*Nature Collections* S9]
60. Dalton R., Looking for the ancestors, *Nature* 434:432-434, 2005. [*Nature Collections* s13]

voyage across the open sea are generally accepted to have been beyond the abilities of early humans."[61] And Stringer similarly says, *"If the ancestors of H. floresiensis really made watercraft to reach the island, this would be surprising, because such behavior is usually considered to be exclusive to our species."*[62] The assumption that Hobbit's ancestors were incapable of sailing is based on an evolutionary presupposition, ignoring actual evidence. Putting preconceptions aside and considering the evidence at face value (endocast scans, stone tools, artifacts, etc.), everything we can reasonably infer about the Flores Hobbit suggests they were fully human. The other skeletal abnormalities, such as reduced chins, can be found in other people groups including the nearby Rampasasa pygmies, or can otherwise be explained by a process known as insular dwarfism.[63]

The Island-Dwarfing Hypothesis

Mainland Elephant

Pygmy Stegodon

Figure 4. Butchered Stegodon fossils of an extinct pygmy elephant (*Stegodon florensis insularis*) were found in the same cave where the Hobbit was excavated. An adult Stegodon would have stood about 4 feet tall, half the size of their mainland counterparts.

Insular dwarfism is a well-documented phenomenon: mammals living on an island can become smaller over generations. This is typically seen in island-dwelling species with access to a limited food supply. Such dwarfed populations are reproductively isolated many generations, and must survive for long periods, undernourished and in very small populations. Under these conditions severe inbreeding occurs, as well as selection for reduced body size and brain volume (see chapter 4). Deleterious mutations accumulate in the population and drift to fixation, causing changes in skeletal proportions and various other malformations. An example of this is an endangered population of pygmy elephants living on the Southeast Asian island of Borneo. They are genetically distinct, smaller in size (around two meters tall), and rounder in shape, compared to their mainland ancestors in Asia (Figure 4). Historical records and long-held beliefs

---

61. Seddon C., (2014-03-03), *Humans: From the Beginning: from the first apes to the first cities*, (Kindle Locations 2034-2056). Glanville Publications. Kindle Edition. 2014.

62. Stringer C., *Lone Survivors*, Times Books, Henry Holt and Company LLC, New York, p. 84, 2012.

63. Jacob T. *et al.*, Pygmoid Australomelanesian *Homo sapiens* skeletal remains from Liang Bua, Flores: Population affinities and pathological abnormalities, *Proc Natl Acad Sci*, USA 103 (36):13421-13426, 2006.

among the locals suggest the Borneo elephants originated from Java. A *National Geographic* article tells of an ancient Javanese ruler who sent elephants to the sultan of Sulu as a gift.[64] While diminutive elephants no longer inhabit the island of Java, the fossil remains can still be found. Excavations at Liang Bua, the cave where the Hobbit was discovered, reveal the remains of butchered Stegodons—a dwarfed elephant species. The fossil remains of other dwarfed elephants no larger than one meter in height have been found on other islands such as Sicily, Malta, and Crete.[65]

Since island dwarfing is well known among mammals, there is no reason why a small, genetically isolated human population would not undergo the same types of changes. A number of paleo-experts have suggested this is the best explanation for the Hobbit's diminutive size and unique traits. This includes Morwood himself, who is credited with being the *"driving force behind the Hobbit discovery."*[66] He and his team first proposed the insular dwarfism hypothesis in their paper published in *Nature*, saying: *"If early hominin populations survived long-term on these islands, they would have been subject to the same insular speciation pressures evident in H. floresiensis."*[67] Morwood advanced this as a case for why Hobbit was so small, suggesting Hobbit was a pre-human species—however the same process would obviously happen just as easily within *Homo sapiens*.

Similarly, Berger and colleagues provide evidence for insular dwarfism in their analysis of skeletal remains from Palau, Micronesia that are only 940–2,890 years old. Those bones clearly belong to *Homo sapiens* and are described as *"small in body size even relative to* [smaller] *"pygmoid" populations from Southeast Asia and Indonesia, and thus may represent a marked case of human insular dwarfism."* The researchers go on to say:

> A number of individual traits observed in the Palauan sample are seen also in specimens from Flores (although the form of these traits may differ in the Palauan sample), some of which have been argued to support the unique taxonomic status of *H. floresiensis*: small body size, reduction of the absolute size of the face, pronounced supraorbital tori, non-projecting chins, relative megadontia, expansion of the occlusal surface of the premolars, rotation of teeth within the maxilla and mandible, and dental agenesis. These last two features are not argued to be taxonomic markers, but their occurrence in specimens from both Palau and Flores is notable, as they may be parallel results from founder effects, genetic isolation and a high inbreeding coefficient...This finding would be consistent with the argument that Flores LB1 may represent a congenitally abnormal individual drawn from a small bodied population of *H. sapiens*.[68]

64. Roach J., "Hobbits" were pygmy ancestors, not new species, study says, *National Geographic*, August 21, 2008. http:// news.nationalgeographic.com/news/2006/08/060821-hobbits.html
65. Lahr M.M. and Foley R., Human evolution writ small, *Nature* 431:1043-1044, 2004. See also: http://en.wikipedia.org/wiki/Insular_dwarfism
66. Roberts R.G. and Sutikna T., Michael John Morwood (150-2013), *Nature* 500:401, 2013.
67. Morwood M.J. *et al.*, Archaeology and age of a new hominin from Flores in eastern Indonesia, *Nature* 431:s3, 2004.
68. Berger L.R. *et al.*, Small-bodied humans from Palau, Micronesia, *PLOS ONE* 3(3):e1780, 2008.

According to Berger and colleagues, there is very strong morphological evidence that Hobbit was an anomalous population of *Homo sapiens*, suffering from the consequences of genetic isolation, inbreeding, and fixation of deleterious mutations.[69] These researchers argue that the morphological features observed in Hobbit can best be explained by island dwarfing. This undermines the rationale for using the Hobbit's abnormal size and features as evidence of a new species.

Other scientists have objected to the insular dwarfism hypothesis and insist it cannot account for the Hobbit's disproportionately smaller brain-size. Based on models of dwarfism, it is believed that brain-size should scale downward in proportion to reduced body size. But Hobbit's cranial capacity is too small when scaled to equivalent body mass. However, Weston and Lister challenge the assumed scaling argument in the journal *Nature*. In a study on insular dwarfism in hippos, they noted that brain size reduction does not necessarily scale to body size. They report, *"Here we show that the endocranial capacities of extinct dwarf species of hippopotamus from Madagascar are up to 30% smaller than those of a mainland African ancestor scaled to equivalent body mass."*[70] In opposition to the disease hypothesis, Weston and Lister conclude, *"Our findings challenge current understanding of brain-body allometric relationships in mammals and suggest that the process of dwarfism could in principle explain small brain size, a factor relevant to the interpretation of the small-brained hominin found on the Island of Flores, Indonesia."*[71] In a separate article in *Nature*, Morwood and colleagues explain in detail why island dwarfing may be the best explanation for Hobbit's small body and brain size and other skeletal abnormalities:

> Other mechanisms [than diseases like microcephaly] must have been responsible for the small body size of these hominins, with insular dwarfism being the strongest candidate. ... It has been argued that, in the absence of agriculture, tropical rainforests offer a very limited supply of calories for hominins. Under these conditions selection should favour the reduced energy requirements of smaller individuals. .... Dwarfing in LB1 may have been the end product of selection for small body size in a low calorific environment, either after isolation on Flores, or another insular environment in southeastern Asia.[72]

In their published paper, Weston and colleague make a noteworthy observation: *"Anatomical and physiological changes associated with insular dwarfism can be extensive, with dramatic modification of sensory systems and brain size, and certainly exceed what might be predicted by the allometric effects of body size*

69. Dalton R., Pacific "dwarf" bones cause controversy, *Nature News* 452:133, 2008.

70. Weston E.M. and Lister A.M., Insular dwarfism in hippos and a model for brain size reduction in *Homo floresiensis*, *Nature* 459:85-88, 2009.

71. Weston E.M. and Lister A.M., Insular dwarfism in hippos and a model for brain size reduction in *Homo floresiensis*, *Nature* 459:85-88, 2009.

72. Brown P. *et al.*, A new small-bodied hominin from the Late Pleistocene of Flores, Indonesia, *Nature* 431:1055-1061, 2004.

reduction alone.[73] Lahr and Foley concur writing: *"Island dwarfing is well known among mammals. Released from predation pressure or constrained by restricted resources, and limited by population size, the phenomenon can be dramatic..."*[74] Such dramatic changes caused by island dwarfing can easily account for Hobbit's diminutive size, small brain, and unique skeletal traits without the need to claim it was a sub-human species. Again, this is precisely what the discovery team originally reported in their announcement paper published in *Nature* (2004): *"The describers originally proposed that the H. floresiensis was the end product of a long period of isolation of H. erectus or early Homo on a small island, a process known as insular dwarfism."*[75] We have shown that Erectus is just a variant of *Homo sapiens*. Hobbit can be understood as a extreme version of Erectus (more isolated, more inbred, more dwarfed). This is just as paleo-experts have insisted in light of new fossil findings from Mata Menge, Flores.[76] As paleo-experts write in *Académie des Sciences* (2016), *"We also suggest abandoning the name Homo floresiensis to designate small Homo erectus and we recommend putting Homo floresiensis into synonymy with Homo erectus."*[77]

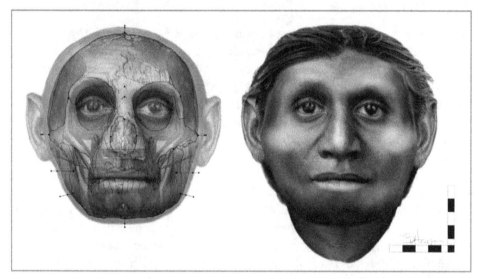

Figure 5. Anthropologist Susan Hayes of the University of Wollongong in Australia used sophisticated forensic techniques to reconstruct the face of the Hobbit (LB1). The reconstruction turned out looking—as *Scientific American* author admits, *"startlingly humanlike,"* particularly to those who are committed to the new species interpretation of the Hobbit. The forensic reconstruction published in *Science* (above) appears far less "ape-like" than the casual artistic renditions more influenced by evolutionary preconceptions than fossil anatomy (e.g., compare with the illustration at http://donsmaps.com/images5/hobbitflores2.jpg)

73. Weston E.M. and Lister A.M., Insular dwarfism in hippos and a model for brain size reduction in *Homo floresiensis*, *Nature* 459:85-88, 2009. [*Nature Collections, Homo Floresiensis*, pp. S49-, 2014]

74. Lahr M.M. and Foley R., Human evolution writ small, *Nature* 431:1043-1044, 2004.

75. Argue D. *et al.*, *Homo floresiensis*: microcephalic, pygmoid, *Australopithecus*, or *Homo*?, *J Hum Evol* 51:360-374, 2006.

76. van den Bergh G.D. *et al.*, *Homo floresiensis*-like fossils from the early Middle Pleistocene of Flores, *Nature* 534:245-248, 2016.

77. Zeitoun V. *et al.*, Phylogenetic analysis of the calvaria of *Homo floresiensis*, *Académie des Sciences*, 2016.

Conclusion—Hobbit was Fully Human

The Hobbit is still surrounded by controversy, and dates for this skeleton are all over the map. However, it seems very clear that Hobbit is human, especially in consideration of the shared features among the Palauan bones and the Rampasasa pygmies living on the island of Flores. Their impressive cultural inventory (an array of sophisticated stone tools), ability to sail the open ocean, endocast scans revealing a modern human brain, and an overall modern human anatomy further confirms their fully human status. To explain their unique features (i.e., asymmetry of the skull, flat-footedness, etc.), paleo-experts have offered a number of plausible explanations, including pathologies seen in modern humans. Their small body size and reduced brain size are quite clearly due to island dwarfism, subsequent inbreeding, and reductive selection. Most paleo-experts would classify Hobbit as either Erectus or *Homo sapiens*. Since *Homo erectus* is recognized by numerous paleo-experts as a variant of *Homo sapiens*, it is entirely reasonable to identify Hobbit as a variant of *Homo sapiens*—one of us!

**Latest Developments

As this book goes to press a paper was published in *Proceedings of the Royal Society B* journal.[78] The findings of José Alexandre and colleagues is almost a point for point confirmation of our assessment of Hobbit in this chapter. The researchers side with "splitters" and maintain that Hobbit is a separate species (on this point we disagree)—yet they concluded from their complex quantitative genetic analysis that the Hobbit could be a dwarfed descendant of Erectus (i.e., *Homo sapiens*) from Indonesia. The researchers made the following points that were in remarkable agreement with our assessment, in addition to citing some of the same studies: 1) Hobbit is a dwarfed descendant of Erectus from Indonesia; 2) Hobbit's small body and brain size was subject to insular dwarfism; 3) Hobbit's small brain is explained by reductive selection; 4) reduced brain size would be advantageous in starvation conditions (because it is energetically costly); 5) dwarfed hippo fossils from Madagascar show how brain size can be reduced more than expected in relation to body size; and 6) this process can occur relatively rapidly in small, isolated populations.

In this chapter we attributed the development of small brain and body size to a process known as "reductive evolution," which is essentially evolution in reverse. It may also be called "adaptive degeneration" because the reduced brain and body size (an adaptation to near-starvation conditions) is achieved via a degenerative process. We propose high levels of inbreeding and mutation accumulation (as expected of isolated populations) would accelerate this process.

In the *American Journal of Physical Anthropology*, paleo-experts Israel Hershkovitz

---

78. Diniz-Filho J.A.F. and Pasquale R., Island Rule, quantitative genetics and brain–body size evolution in *Homo floresiensis*, *Proceedings of the Royal Society B*, 2017. DOI: 10.1098/rspb.2017.1065

et al. suggested a possible mutation that could cause the short stature phenotype of Hobbit.[79] According to their analysis, Laron syndrome patients exhibit many of the features seen in the Hobbit, including small stature and small brain volumes. Laron syndrome (LS) is caused by a defect in the growth hormone (insulin-like growth factor-1) receptor. This means the body does not respond to growth hormone. This is known to be caused by a variety of mutations within a specific gene that specifies the growth hormone receptor protein (GHR). These researchers noted that the Hobbit shares many striking similarities with the local pygmy population, in addition to a suite of characteristics commonly seen in LS patients. These paleo-experts reject the new species hypothesis proposed by Morwood *et al.*, and argue that Hobbit is a small-bodied modern human (*H. sapiens*), possibly drawn from the local pygmy population, that was further subject to mutations in the GHR gene. They write:

> ...patients with Laron Syndrome (LS, primary or classical GH insensitivity or resistance) revealed striking morphological similarities, including extremely small stature and reduced cranial volume. ... In contrast to Morwood's statement (2005) that LB1 manifests a combination of primitive and derived features that dictate exclusion from the species sapiens, we have herein offered evidence to suggest that LB1 is but a local individual in a highly inbred, probably pygmy-like population (of *Homo sapiens*) in whom a mutation of the GH receptor had occurred.

Interestingly, these researchers point out that LS is common in *"consanguineous families and isolates"*, and it has been described in several countries in South East Asia. In other words, LS is most common in highly inbred populations that live in isolation. This is exactly the sort of scenario that would result in the fixation of deleterious mutations. Genetic studies have revealed that there are at least 57 documented mutations affecting this growth hormone receptor, resulting in a wide-variety of short stature body types. Hershkovitz *et al.* write:

> So far 57 mutations have been described in LS patients residing in various parts of the world including South Asia (Rosenfeld et al., 1994; Rosenbloom and Guevara-Aguirre, 1998; Laron, 1999; Shevah et al., 2005). These numerous molecular defects on the GH receptor gene or the postreceptor cascade (Elders et al., 1973; Godowski et al., 1989; Laron et al., 1992; Rosenbloom et al., 1999; Laron, 2004; Woods and Savage, 2004) produce a large variety of short stature phenotypes and a wide spectrum of intellectual abilities and deficits (Shevah et al., 2005), which may also explain the differences between the LS patients and LB1.

Thus a single mutation in the GHR gene is known to produce a suite of traits that have strong anatomical correspondence. For instance, widely flaring ilia—seen in the Hobbit and other *Homo* variants like Naledi—corresponds to longer formal neck, wide lower thorax (ribcage) shape, small stature, etc. Thus a single pathology is sufficient to explain the entire suite of correlated features seen in the Hobbit.

---

79. Hershkovitz I. *et al.*, Comparative skeletal features between *Homo floresiensis* and patients with primary growth hormone insensitivity (Laron syndrome), *Am J Phys Anthropol* 134(2):198-208, 2007.

Section II – Bones of the Ape Type
Introduction to Chapters 6 and 7

The ape-like hominin bones can all be reasonably placed within the genus *Australopithecus*. The genus appears to show a great deal of morphological variation, and so the partitioning of the genus into various species is controversial and unconvincing.[1] The *Australopithecus* species are loosely referred to as the "australopithecines" or "australopiths." Taxonomic "splitters" would like to argue that the australopithecines should be sub-divided into two or more genera, and that *Australopithecus* itself should be divided into several species. Extreme splitters would accept many of the following different australopith-like species: *Ar. ramidus, Au. africanus, Au. afarensis, Au. anamensis, Au. bahrelghazali, Au. garhi, Au. prometheus, Au. sediba.* In addition, they would add the robust (gorilla-like) australopithecines (*Au. aethiopicus, Au. boisei, and Au. robustus*). However, "lumpers" (including ourselves) would argue that these sub-groupings are based upon relatively minor morphological differences (often reflecting less difference, for example, than is seen between the bones of a male and female gorilla). We will consistently use the broader term "australopithecines" to apply to anything similar to the basic *Australopithecus* type.

Most of the bones classified as *Australopithecus* are strikingly similar to the bones of modern apes (chimpanzee, bonobo, gorilla, orangutan, and baboon). However, caution is warranted here. It would be a mistake to assume that 100% of the bones classified as *Australopithecus* were correctly assigned to that group—especially when the bones are found in isolation (separate from an identifiable skeleton) or within mixed bone beds. As we will see, a number of distinctly human-looking bones appear to have been misclassified as australopiths but are in fact true human bones—and need to be distinguished from the *Australopithecus* ape type. In some cases, these misclassified bones have artificially expanded the range of variation within the australopith type well beyond morphologically realistic limits (see chapter 7).

All things considered, we agree with the experts in the field who maintain that *"Australopithecus was a mainly quadrupedal animal, like the living African apes. Even when it came down to the ground, it still spent a lot of time standing and*

---

1. Wood B. and Boyle E.K., Hominin Taxic Diversity: Fact or Fantasy? *Yearbook of Physical Anthropology* 159:S37-S78, 2016.

walking on all fours (Sarmiento 1996, 1998; Sarmiento and Marcus, 2000)."[2]

In this section, we will sometimes need to use the terminology of the splitters when we discuss the bones that are claimed to be separate species or genera. For example, we will discuss a set of bones that were originally classified as *Australopithecus*, but were later reclassified as "*Ardipithecus*" (and given the nickname "Ardi"). The *Ardipithecus* genus includes bones that are extremely ape-like and are very similar to the other australopithecines—as paleo-experts have noted. To keep things simple, we will accept the original designation of Ardi as an australopithecine ape type.

This second section describes the two best known australopiths: *Australopithecus ramidus* (chapter 6), and *Australopithecus afarensis* (chapter 7). *Australopithecus sediba* will be described separately in Section III (Bones of the "Middle" Type).

---

2. Cartmill M. and Smith F.H., *The Human Lineage*, Wiley-Blackwell, Hoboken, NJ, p. 177, 2009.

CHAPTER 6

Ardipithecus ramidus
Oldest Human Ancestor or Extinct Ape?

Where did Ardipithecus and the other early hominin contenders come from?
Are they truly members of the hominin lineage, or simply apes among the
tangled branches that constitute the basal hominine bush?[1]

Paleoanthropologist Terry Harrison of New York University

Background and Discovery of "Ardi"

In the Middle Awash river valley of Aramis Ethiopia, 46 miles away from where the remains of "Lucy" were discovered, fragmentary bones were found and attributed to a new putative species, *Ardipithecus ramidus* (referred to as "Ardi" hereafter). Paleo-expert Tim White and his colleagues recovered approximately 45% of the skeleton. It consisted of broken portions of the skull, a jawbone, a full set of teeth, a few vertebra fragments, broken limb bones, and a crushed hip (Figure 1). These bones were sandwiched between volcanic ash layers that were dated using the argon-argon method to be 4.4 million years old. This is the same questionable method used to date Lucy (see chapters 7 and 12). According to claims made throughout the popular press, Ardi is man's oldest known ape-like ancestor. Based on Ardi's estimated age, it is viewed as the closest hominin species to the "split" (the human/chimpanzee divergence) that allegedly occurred between 5–8 million years ago.[2,3] Headlines promoted Ardi as the *"discovery of the century, triumphing over the famous "Lucy" discovery in 1974."*[4] The finding was said to call into question the long-held evolutionary assumption that humans evolved from a "chimp-

1. Harrison T., Apes Among the Tangled Branches of Human Origins, *Science* 239:532-533, 2010.
2. Patterson N. *et al.*, Genetic evidence for complex speciation of humans and chimpanzees, *Nature* 441:1103-1108, 2006.
3. Langergraber K.E. *et al.*, Generation times in wild chimpanzees and gorillas suggest earlier divergence times in great ape and human evolution, *Proc Natl Acad Sci*, USA 109(39):15716-15721, 2012.
4. Andrew Hill considers "Ardi" to be the discovery of the century, triumphing over the famous "Lucy" discovery in 1974. From: Gibbons A., A New Kind of Ancestor: *Ardipithecus* unveiled, *Science* 326:36-40, 2009. The journal *Science* named the discovery of 'Ardi' the "Breakthrough of the Year 2009". From: Berkely News, Sanders, 2009.

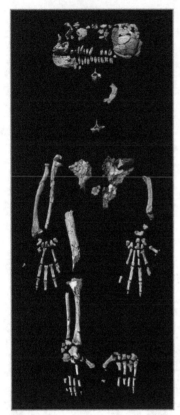

Figure 1. The partial skeleton attributed to the species *Ardipithecus ramidus*, nicknamed "Ardi." The first recovered remains were found in Aramis, Ethiopia in 1992 by Yohannes Haile-Selassie, member of the team led by paleo-expert Tim White. The fragmentary remains were found scattered widely across the excavated area. The photograph is a composite reconstruction consisting of 125 pieces, the most complete (45% of the skeleton) *Ar. ramidus* specimen recovered to date.

like" ancestor.[5,6] It would seem Ardi changed everything. Researchers said textbooks needed to be rewritten (again).[7] The discovery team claimed Ardi was *"a new kind of ancestor"*—not resembling a chimpanzee or a human.[8] It is neither ape nor man, yet somehow *"reveals the surprising ancestry of both."*[9] But if Ardi did not look like a chimpanzee or any other type of living ape, what did it look like? And how could anyone be so sure the poorly preserved remains belonged to an early, ape-like human ancestor as opposed to just another extinct ape? Ardi was originally classified as being in the same genus as Lucy (*Australopithecus*). Later it was re-classified into its own genus (*Ardipithecus*).

Ardi's Pitiful Remains & Artist Imagination

Ardi's bone fragments were discovered in 1992 in the Middle Awash region. A full analysis of the remains was not published until 17 years later, in 2009. The reason why it took almost two decades for researchers to reconstruct the remains and present their findings to the public was because the pieces of bone were scattered over a very wide area, and virtually none of the bones or fragments were connected to each other. The bones were not only very incomplete, but were very poorly preserved. Many bones were crushed and were described as "mush" that crumbled at the slightest touch. Discovery team leader, Tim White, described Ardi's remains as *"road kill."*[10] The pulverized chunks of bone were found eroding out of hillsides, exposed to the elements—rain, weathering, and erosion— presumably for millions of years. Researchers were amazed the bones had not completely

5. Lemonick M.D. and Dorfman A., Ardi is a new piece for the evolution puzzle, *TIME Magazine* Oct. 01, 2009.
6. Though others do not agree: Wood B. and Harrison T., The evolutionary context of the first hominins, *Nature* 470:347-352, 2011: *"However, there are sound logical reasons based on the morphology of their nearest modern out-groups to support the inference that the skeleton of the panin/hominin MRCA would have had more in com-mon with chimpanzees and bonobos than with modern humans."*
7. Zorich, Z., *Ardipithecus*: ape or ancestor? *Archaeology Magazine* 63(1) Jan/Feb, 2010.
8. Gibbons A., A new kind of ancestor: *Ardipithecus* unveiled. *Science* 326:36-40, 2009.
9. White T.D. *et al.*, Neither chimpanzee nor human, *Ardipithecus* reveals the surprising ancestry of both, *Proc Natl Acad Sci*, USA 112(16): 4877-4884, 2015.
10. Gibbons A., A new kind of ancestor: *Ardipithecus* unveiled, *Science* 326:36-40, 2009.

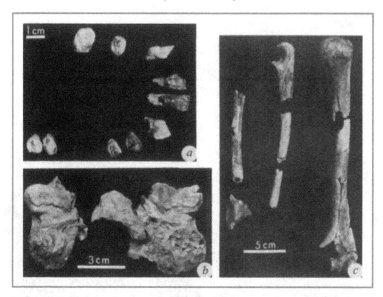

Figure 2. The defining specimen consists of 17 fragmentary bones found between 1992 and 1993. Included among the remains are teeth, a jaw fragment, broken portions of the cranial base, and arm elements. Tim White and colleagues boldly proclaimed in their announcement paper published in *Nature* (1994) that they had discovered the *"long-sought link in the evolutionary chain of species between humans and their African ape ancestors."* As can be seen most of what had been recovered at the time were teeth and broken limb bones.

disintegrated.[11]

Although the bones were incomplete and badly damaged, the researchers immediately assumed they had found the world's oldest human ancestor. Premature conclusions of this type reveal a "treasure hunt" mentality. The strong desire to discover a "missing link" no doubt clouded their ability to be objective. When White and colleagues first proclaimed to the world they had found the oldest human ancestor in 1994 in the journal *Nature*, the only available remains that could be studied at that time consisted primarily of teeth, plus a few broken pieces of the base of the skull, and some arm fragments (Figure 2). The researchers had no way of knowing for sure whether the loose teeth and bone fragments belonged to a single species, let alone a new species, and they had no direct evidence these bones were from an early precursor to man. White acknowledged that out of all the recovered remains, *"no skeletal parts were found articulated."*[12] The remains were completely disconnected and were *"scattered widely across the excavated area."*[13] The initial fragments were as far apart as one mile, and the subsequently recovered bone fragments were spread over a total distance of four miles.[14]

---

11. Yang S., On the Trail of Our Ancestors, Q & A with paleoanthropologist Leslea Hlusko, UC Berkeley News, 01 Oct 2009.
12. White T. *et al.*, *Ardipithecus ramidus* and the paleobiology of early hominids, *Science* 326:75-86, 2009.
13. White T. *et al.*, *Ardipithecus ramidus* and the paleobiology of early hominids, *Science* 326:75-86, 2009.
14. Zorich Z., *Ardipithecus*: ape or ancestor? *Archaeology Magazine* 63(1) Jan/Feb, 2010.

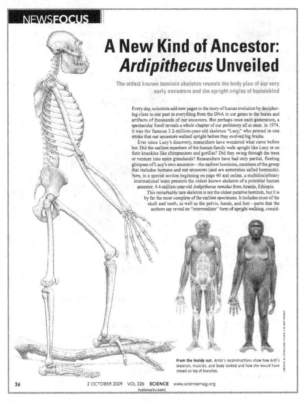

NEWSFOCUS

A New Kind of Ancestor:
Ardipithecus **Unveiled**

The oldest known hominin skeleton reveals the body plan of our very early ancestors and the upright origins of humankind

Every day, scientists add new pages to the story of human evolution by deciphering clues to our past in everything from the DNA in our genes to the bones and artifacts of thousands of our ancestors. But perhaps once each generation, a spectacular fossil reveals a whole chapter of our prehistory all at once. In 1974, it was famous Lucy's discovery, researchers have wondered what came before her. Did the earliest members of the human family walk upright like Lucy or on their knuckles like chimpanzees and gorillas? Did they swing through the trees or venture into open grasslands? Researchers have had only partial, fleeting glimpses of Lucy's own ancestors—the earliest hominins, members of the group that includes humans and our ancestors (and are sometimes called hominids). Now, in a special section beginning on page 60 and online, a multidisciplinary international team presents the oldest known skeleton of a potential human ancestor, 4.4-million-year-old *Ardipithecus ramidus* from Aramis, Ethiopia.

This remarkably rare skeleton is not the oldest putative hominin, but it is by far the most complete of the earliest specimens. It includes most of the skull and teeth, as well as the pelvis, hands, and feet—parts that the authors say reveal an "intermediate" form of upright walking, consid-

From the inside out. Artist's reconstructions show how Ardi's skeleton, muscles, and body looked and how she would have moved on top of branches.

Figure 3. The 2009 discovery paper published in *Science* promoted Ardi as our ancestor with a highly imaginative illustration. Ardi is shown mid-stride with a normal human gait. It is claimed Ardi was as comfortable walking upright along the ground as she was in the trees. The opposable thumb-like toe is being used in an unusual manner. Instead of being used in limb grasping and climbing, as is typical of modern apes, Ardi is shown using her opposable toe to balance on fallen branches as she walked along the forest floor. Many of the claimed features shown in this illustration—the upright human posture, human gait, human lower lumbar, and human-like hip reconstruction—are all based on very fragmentary remains, the reconstructions of which have been heavily criticized by other experts in the field.

The bones were so fragile that they could not generally be collected as found. Ardi's remains had to be hardened with a chemical bonding agent and transported to the lab before they could be digitally reconstructed. An accurate reconstruction of many of these scattered bone fragments into their original anatomical positions was physically impossible (with the exception of a few better-preserved bones of the hands and feet).

What they came up with was a very ape-ish looking creature (but supposedly standing perfectly erect), with inferred hips and spine that were made to appear human. One of the most popular illustrations of Ardi is seen in the 2009 discovery paper published in *Science* (Figure 3).[15] This bizarre interpretation of the bones was strategic to promoting the claim that Ardi was an early human ancestor that evolved not long after the alleged chimp-human lineage split some six million years ago. The image of Ardi reveals an overall ape-like anatomy, however, its upright human posture (lumbar lordosis) and mid-stride human gait give the misleading impression that Ardi was somehow more than an ape, and was undergoing dramatic evolution to become human. To support this notion the discovery team claimed Ardi had a mixture of ape and human traits.

Wherever the skeleton was well preserved, it was clearly an ape, and all parties agreed. This included an ape-sized braincase between 300 and 350 cm³, overall ape-like body proportions with long upper limbs compared to lower limbs, long

15. Gibbons A., A new kind of ancestor: *Ardipithecus* unveiled, *Science* 326:36-39, 2009.

and curved fingers and toes typical of tree-dwelling primates, and ape-like feet with a highly divergent opposable great toe indistinguishable from a chimp's (Figure

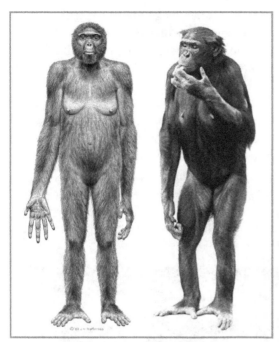

4). This is consistent with paleo-experts who insist that Ardi is nothing more than an extinct ape. So what evidence suggested to the discovery team that Ardi was an early, upright-walking ancestor to man? The evidence is primarily the very poor reconstructions of certain features that made Ardi appear more human, namely the crushed skull, shattered hip, and teeth.[16,17,18] These imaginative reconstructions (skull and hip) were used to justify the very questionable assumption that Ardi had an essentially human spine.[19] However, many paleo-experts did not agree with the discovery team's reconstruction of these poorly preserved bones.

Figure 4. The artist reconstruction of Ardi as shown in the 2009 *Science* announcement paper (left) and an actual photograph of a female bonobo standing upright (right). Notice the overall anatomy, limb proportions, and body size similarities. As paleo-expert David Begun notes, *"It is hard for me to actually find a lot of characteristics that are not chimpanzee-like."* Photograph credit: Frans de Wall and Frans Lanting, *Bonobo: The Forgotten Ape*, University of California Press, 1997. Photograph by Dr. Frans de Waal.

Let's examine each claim separately, and see why leading experts in the field reject the interpretation of White *et al.* that Ardi walked erect and was our ancestor.

Ardi's Ape Skull

A key piece of evidence presented by White *et al.* that Ardi walked upright was the inferred placement of the foramen magnum. This is the hole in the base of the skull that indicates the angle of the head-spine connection. In many apes the foramen magnum is positioned toward the rear of the skull. This allows the spine to project outward at an angle to create the characteristic bent-hip/bent-knee posture of apes. In humans the foramen magnum is positioned directly under the base of the skull, which is conducive for standing and walking upright. This feature

16. White T.D. *et al.*, *Ardipithecus ramidus* and the paleobiology of early Hominins, *Science* 326:75–86, 2009.
17. White T.D. *et al.*, Neither chimpanzee nor human, *Ardipithecus* reveals the surprising ancestry of both, *Proc Natl Acad Sci,* USA 112(16): 4877-4884, 2015.
18. Wood B. and Harrison T., The evolutionary context of the first hominins, *Nature* 470:347-352, 2011.
19. Lovejoy C.O. *et al.*, The Pelvis and Femur of *Ardipithecus ramidus*: The Emergence of Upright Walking, *Science* 326(5949):71-71e6, 2009; DOI: 10.1126/science.1175831.

is traditionally believed to be indicative of habitual bipedal locomotion (walking on two legs like humans).

Ardi's skull was reconstructed to suggest a foramen magnum similar to the human position. On the surface this may sound like a convincing piece of evidence, but there are problems with this interpretation. First, it is important to realize that the researchers were dealing with a skull that was broken into 100 pieces and severely crushed down to 4 cm in height (Figure 5). The remains were in such bad shape that they had to be digitally reconstructed using a CT scanner, and then pieced together like a puzzle. Digital reconstructions are known to involve quite a bit of uncertainty and guesswork compared to physical reconstructions. Evolutionary paleoanthropologist John Hawks acknowledges this, writing:

> On the one hand, a model [referring to the digital reconstruction process employed by the researchers] greatly facilitates the description and comparison of the specimen with other key fossils. But on the other hand, any model comes with a load of assumptions, which may not be explicit when anatomical comparisons are made.[20]

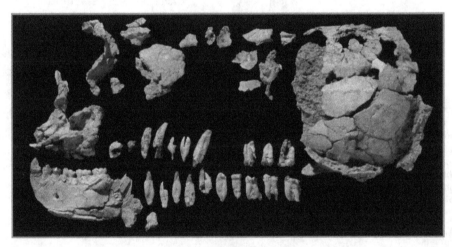

Figure 5. The fragmentary remains of the skull attributed to Ardi were spread widely across the excavation area. The skull was found in 100 pieces, compacted down to 4 cm in height. The researchers described the skull in their *Science* (2009) paper as *"highly fragmented and distorted...many* [recovered elements] *were partially disintegrated by the silty clay sediment, and major structures were fragmentary and variably distorted."* Due to its fragile condition the skull could not be pieced together physically and so its reconstruction was approximated digitally.

Moreover, sizeable portions of the skull were entirely absent. There was certainly a lot of leeway in deciding how the fragmentary remains were pieced together, including the placement of the foramen magnum. In their *Science* report describing the anatomy of the skull, the researchers confess they had to make "allowance"

20. Hawks J., The *Ardipithecus* Pelvis, Hawks Weblog, 2009. Accessed August 25, 2015: http://johnhawks.net/weblog/fossils/ardipithecus-pelvis-2009.html.

Figure 6. Oblique and side views are shown of the digitally reconstructed skull attributed to Ardi (left) and that of a modern chimpanzee (right). Ardi's skull is entirely consistent with short-faced primates including gibbons, monkeys, and the extinct ape *Ramapithecus punjabicus* (a type of orangutan). Note: chimpanzees, as pictured here, have longer projecting lower faces.

for the postmortem (after death) damage of the fossils.[21] The problem is, no one but the digital reconstruction artists know for sure just how much "allowance" was deemed permissible to the "scientific" process of reconstruction. There can be little doubt that interpreter bias played a significant role in assembly. It reportedly took thousands of hours to digitally reconstruct what remained of the skull and it was not until the eleventh reconstruction that the researchers were happy with the outcome. We don't know why the other ten previous versions were not chosen to represent Ardi. Given the severely crushed and fragmentary nature of the skull, it seems any version could have been just as valid as any other. Examination of the skull pieces (Figures 5 and 6) suggests that the base of the skull is not even present (the part of the skull needed to locate the foramen magnum).

For the sake of argument, let's assume the anterior placement of the foramen magnum was accurate. Would it then be a convincing argument that Ardi was a bipedal hominin ancestor? World-renowned evolutionary paleo-experts Bernard Wood and his colleague Terry Harrison adamantly disagreed with the analysis and rationale offered by the researchers regarding Ardi's skull. In the journal *Nature*, Wood and Harrison point out that gibbons and short-faced monkeys have a similarly placed foramen magnum, yet they don't stand erect and have nothing to do with human evolution.[22] They explain that the placement of the foramen magnum at the base of the skull has more to do with features of the face and placement of the head than with upright posture and bipedal locomotion. They note that there is *"a lack of empirical evidence to clearly support a functionally based correlation* [between foramen magnum position and bipedalism]."[23] Consider the foramen magnum position of a newly discovered African monkey species *Rungwecebus kipunji* (Figure 7).[24] It obviously does not denote bipedal locomotion, and it is certainly not evidence that it was our ancestor.

A *Nature News* article summarizes Wood and Harrison's main points:

21. Suwa G. *et al.*, The *Ardipithecus ramidus* skull and its implications for Hominid origins, *Science* 326:68, 68e1-68e7, 2009. DOI: 10.1126/science.1175825.
22. Wood B. and Harrison T., The evolutionary context of the first hominins, *Nature* 470:347-352, 2011.
23. Wood B. and Harrison T., The evolutionary context of the first hominins, *Nature* 470:347-352, 2011.
24. Davenport *et al.*, A New Genus of African Monkey, *Rungwecebus*: Morphology, Ecology, and Molecular Phylogenetics, *Science* 312:1378, 2006.

But, Wood and Harrison say, this interpretation may be too simplistic. The review notes, for instance, that gibbons have foramen magnum that are similar in placement to those of humans—another example of convergence [sharing similar traits apart from common ancestry]. In the case of gibbons, however, the more central placement of the hole is there to allow for different skull characteristics rather than a bent posture. For this reason, the authors suggest that using the foramen magnum as a method for diagnosing bipedal behavior may be misleading.[25]

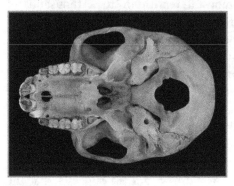

Figure 7. The base of an African monkey skull. Foramen magnum (spinal insertion hole) placement is not a clear indicator of bipedal locomotion nor can it be used to suggest Ardi was a human ancestor. A more anteriorly placed foramen magnum is not a feature exclusive to the human lineage. Gibbons and short-faced monkeys like this newly discovered African monkey species *Rungwecebus kipunji* exhibit this anatomical feature. As paleo-experts Wood and Harrison note in *Nature*, "*it is more broadly associated with differences in head carriage and facial length, rather than uniquely with bipedalism.*"[26]

Regardless of the reconstructed shape of Ardi's skull, there is no question that it is very ape-like. A side-by-side comparison with apes demonstrates this plainly (Figure 6). Moreover, the size of the braincase (between 300 and 350 cm³) was admittedly *"similar to that of bonobos and female chimpanzees and smaller than that of australopithecines...."*[27] All things considered, there is nothing about the skull that indicates that Ardi was an ancestor to man.

Ardi's Ape Hip

The claim that Ardi was an early upright-walking ancestor to man largely rests upon the highly questionable digital reconstruction of the fragmentary hipbone. Anatomist Owen Lovejoy of Kent State University was given the role of digitally reconstructing Ardi's crushed hip. Lovejoy is the same scientist responsible for reconstructing Lucy's hip (see chapter 7). It is quite clear that Lovejoy digitally reconstructed the hip to look the way he imagined—to support the preconceived idea that Ardi walked habitually upright like modern humans.[28]

In consideration of the severely crushed and distorted hip, Lovejoy could have reconstructed it to look any way he wanted (Figure 8). Like the skull, the hip had to be digitally reconstructed using a CT scanner and required just as much imagination. Leading evolutionary paleoanthropologists were skeptical of Lovejoy's analysis. In the *Annual Review of Anthropology*, Craig Stanford, evolutionary

25. Kaplan M., The con of convergence, *Nature News*, 16 February 2011.

26. Wood B. and Harrison T., The evolutionary context of the first hominins, *Nature* 470:347-352, 2011.

27. Suwa G. *et al.*, The *Ardipithecus ramidus* skull and its implications for Hominid origins, *Science* 326:68, 68e1-68e7, 2009. DOI: 10.1126/science.1175825.

28. To watch a Science video digitally modeling the inferred human-like locomotory behavior of Ardi, see UC Berkeley Press Release at the following link: http://www.berkeley.edu/news/media/releases/2009/10/01_ardiskeleton.shtml

paleoanthropologist from the University of Southern California, lists numerous criticisms of the claims made regarding Ardi, including the hip reconstruction:

> The reconstruction by White *et al.* (2009) of the *Ardipithecus* fossils as hominin [a human ancestor], although argued from a variety of morphological traits, ultimately rests on the imaging of the pelvis. As Lovejoy *et al.* (2009b) pointed out, the pelvic remains were so severely crushed that as many as 14 reconstructions via computer tomographic imaging were considered before deciding which morphology was most in line with other data. As Harrison (2010) and Wood and Harrison (2011) have pointed out, a substantial degree of speculation went into the final morphology of the pelvis reconstruction. Subtle changes in the reconstructive process may have yielded a far more ape-like postcranial anatomy.[29]

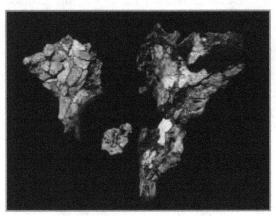

Figure 8. The pelvis included with the Ardi skeleton was severely crushed and distorted. Anatomist Owen Lovejoy digitally reconstructed it with a human-looking anatomy that would have allowed for smooth bipedal locomotion. However, other experts in the field question his reconstruction, noting that because the hip was so poorly preserved and fragmentary, subtle changes would have produced a far more ape-like representation.

Other paleo-experts have been just as wary. William Jungers compares choosing the "correct" pelvis reconstruction to seeing images in an Rorschach inkblot test. Jungers comments in an article in *Archeology Magazine*, "That's [the digital reconstruction of Ardi's hip] *really kind of a 3-D Rorschach test if you ask me. I am still not convinced that it's necessarily completely accurate*."[30] What is a Rorschach test? It is a psychological analysis in which a series of symmetrical inkblots of different random shapes are shown to a subject who is asked to describe what they resemble. The inkblot's form is subject to the interpreter's own imagination and mental state. Jungers offers a fitting analogy for how Lovejoy and colleagues decided which of the 14 digital images best-represented Ardi's hip. The final outcome was very subject to interpreter bias. It was based more on what Lovejoy and collaborators "wanted" to see than what the severely crushed remains were actually capable of revealing. Carol Ward, evolutionary paleoanthropologist and anatomist at the University of Missouri agrees. She notes that because the hip was so badly damaged, any reconstructive

29. Stanford C.B., Chimpanzees and the behavior of *Ardipithecus ramidus*, *Annu Rev Anthropol* 41:139-149, 2012.

30. Zorich Z., *Ardipithecus*: ape or ancestor? *Archaeology Magazine* 63(1), 2010. Accessed 10/22/17: https://archive.archaeology.org/1001/trenches/ardipithecus.html

interpretation could have been argued to be "equivocal."[31] Ward believes the fossil evidence better suggests Ardi walked by shifting its weight side to side like living apes.[32] In short, there is nothing about the hip that demonstrates the capability of Ardi to walk upright like modern humans, or that it was any different from that of an ordinary ape.

Ardi's Ape Spine

Lovejoy *et al.* also claimed Ardi had a human-like spine. This was reported in *Science* (2009): *"He [Lovejoy] also infers from the pelvis that her spine was long and curved like a human's rather than short and stiff like a chimpanzee's. These changes suggest to him that Ar. ramidus has been bipedal [an upright-walker] for a very long time."*[33] Based on his highly speculative reconstruction of the hip, Lovejoy assumed that Ardi must have had a human-like lower spine curvature, called lumbar lordosis.[34] African apes lack lordosis. They have fewer lower vertebrae than humans creating a stiff lower back/hip orientation that forms the characteristic bent-kneed posture of modern apes. Humans have a longer, flexible lower spine that is curved inward to support our upright posture.

In a Discovery TV online broadcast, Lovejoy discusses that since Ardi must have had a human-like lower back, this provides further evidence that Ardi could walk and even run like modern humans. His "evidence" was really just his "assumption" about the spine which was based on the highly questionable human-like reconstruction of the hips (see above).

In the Discovery video, Lovejoy explains that chimpanzees and gorillas have three or four lumbar vertebrae but Ardi probably had six (like modern humans). But there is absolutely no evidence of this in the recovered bones. The lumbar vertebrae are entirely missing! Lovejoy needed lumbar lordosis (lower spine curvature), which would place the center of gravity over the feet, necessary for upright posture and a normal human gait. But as Lovejoy and researchers acknowledge in their papers published in *Science* and in the *Proceedings of the National Academy of Sciences*, none of the lumbar vertebral bones were recovered: *"Although most of her sacrum and lumbar vertebrae were not recovered, parts of both lateral halves of Ardi's pelvis were."*[35] John Hawks, leading paleo-expert and professor of Anthropology notes similarly, *"Unfortunately, Ardipithecus doesn't have any lumbar vertebrae—*

31. Wayman E., Before Lucy, *Earth Magazine*, October 1, 2009. http://www.earthmagazine.org/article/lucy-old-er-hominid-ardi-challenges-thinking-about-human-evolution

32. Gibbons A., A New Kind of Ancestor: *Ardipithecus* Unveiled, *Science NewsFocus* 326:36-40, 2009.

33. Gibbons A., A New Kind of Ancestor: *Ardipithecus* Unveiled, *Science NewsFocus* 326:36-40, 2009.

34. Lovejoy acknowledges lumbar lordosis was an inference based on the pelvis reconstruction. *"The inferred freedom of the lowermost lumbar (or lumbars) in Ar. ramidus, coupled with broadening and more sagittal orientation of the iliac isthmus (fig. S4), would have permitted both lordosis and anterior extension of the lesser gluteals for pelvic stabilization during upright walking (15, 16)."* Lovejoy et al., The Pelvis and Femur of *Ardipithecus ramidus*: The Emergence of Upright Walking, *Science* 326:71e1-71e6, 2009.

35. White T.D. et al., Neither chimpanzee nor human, *Ardipithecus* reveals the surprising ancestry of both, *Proc Natl Acad Sci, USA* 112(16):4877-4884, 2015.

or indeed any sacrum worth reconstructing."[36] In other words, the assumption of lumbar lordosis was merely a casual inference based on the highly questionable reconstruction of the crushed hip remains. Wood and Harrison take issue with this loose assumption in their review paper published in *Nature*:

> Likewise, the claim that *Ardipithecus ramidus* was a facultative terrestrial biped [living in trees and also walking upright on the ground] is vitiated because it is based on highly speculative inferences about the presence of lumbar lordosis and on relatively few features of the pelvis and foot, many of which also occur in the arboreally adapted *Oreopithecus* [an extinct ape].[37]

The assumption that Ardi exhibited a human-shaped lower spine was essential to substantiate their claim that Ardi walked like us. Lovejoy understood this.[38] Therefore, human lordosis was invented to promote Ardi as an upright-walking ancestor to man. But the simple fact is that no lower vertebrae were recovered. This means all the artists' renditions and museum displays that show Ardi with a human-like lumbar curvature (and consequently an upright human posture) have no supporting evidence—they are essentially a fabrication.

Ardi's Ape Teeth

A major justification for the inclusion of Ardi in the human lineage has to do with the size and shape of its canine teeth. Humans have non-threatening, diamond-shaped canines distinct from the larger, sharper canines found in apes. For this reason evolutionists typically regard smaller, less intimidating canines to be a human trait. Since Ardi was found to have considerably smaller canines than most apes, it was used as evidence to support the assertion that it was our evolutionary ancestor. In their published paper in *Science*, the Ardi researchers conclude, *"The Ar. ramidus dental evidence suggests that this occurred as a consequence of selection for a less projecting and threatening male upper canine."*[39] National Geographic repeats this assertion: *"The reduced size of canine teeth is an indication of a shift in social behavior away from male-male aggression, and is one of the hallmarks of the human lineage."*[40]

The so-called "reduced" canines were cited as evidence that Ardi was evolving to become human (Figure 9). As with other exaggerated claims made by the Ardi research team, respected evolutionary paleoanthropologists reject this as a convincing argument for the proposed status of Ardi as an early human ancestor. A major reason for the rejection is that the same dental features have been found

---

36. Hawks J. The *Ardipithecus* Pelvis, Hawks Weblog, 2009. Accessed August 25, 2015: http://johnhawks.net/weblog/fossils/ardipithecus-pelvis-2009.html.
37. Wood B. and Harrison T., The evolutionary context of the first hominins, *Nature* 470:347-352, 2011.
38. Lovejoy C.O. *et al.*, The Pelvis and Femur of *Ardipithecus ramidus*: The Emergence of Upright Walking, *Science* 326:71, 71e1-71e6, 2009. *"A capacity for posturally dependent lower lumbar orientation was a key adaptation to bipedality, an inference made almost a century ago."*
39. Suwa G. *et al.*, Paleobiological implications of the *Ardipithecus ramidus* dentition, *Science* 326:94-99, 2009.
40. National Geographic; http://news.nationalgeographic.com/news/2009/10/photogalleries/oldest-human-skeleton-ardi-missing-link-chimps-pictures/photo2.html

in other species of extinct apes that have nothing to do with human evolution. Sarmiento makes mention of this fact in a response paper published in *Science*:

> Fourteen of the 26 characters in table 1 in (1) [referencing White *et al., Science* 326:64, 2009] common to *Ardipithecus* and *Australopithecus* are in the canine/ premolar complex. However, reliance on the canine/premolar complex to diagnose hominids (in the classic sense) has misdiagnosed Miocene fossil apes (i.e., *Oreopithecus* and *Ramapithecus*) as early human ancestors (12, 13). Character polarity for this complex is not clear-cut with many early hominoids, especially females, often showing a humanlike condition. ... Approximation to the humanlike canine/premolar complex, therefore, does not indicate that *Ardipithecus* is a hominid or ancestral to *Australopithecus* any more than it indicates that *Oreopithecus* and the orangutan-like females of *Sivapithecus*, both of which also share a humanlike premolar/canine complex, are hominids or represent a descendant ancestor continuum.[41]

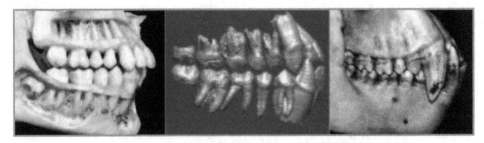

Figure 9. The teeth of a modern human (left), the digital reconstruction of Ardi's teeth (middle), and the teeth of a modern chimpanzee (right). Male chimpanzees in particular exhibit large, sharpened canines. Ardi has considerably smaller canines that lack sharpening against the lower third premolar, typical of apes. This was used as evidence to support the assertion that Ardi was evolving to become more human with "reduced" diamond-shaped canines. However, other researchers note that extinct apes residing outside the human-lineage exhibit reduced canines as well, and they are therefore misleading indicators of hominin ancestry.

Sarmiento points to other extinct apes excluded from the human lineage that have canines and lower third premolars that are very similar to those of Ardi. In the case of the orangutan-like *Sivapithecus* and *Oreopithecus*, the human-like canine and premolars can be misleading to evolutionists who are hoping to find the next "missing link" because they belong to ordinary apes. Wood and Harrison in *Nature* add to the list other extinct apes understood to be outside the human lineage that share this feature:

> ...it is important to recognize that during the late Miocene a number of Eurasian hominids (for example, *Oreopithecus, Ouranopithecus* and *Gigantopithecus*) also developed small canines in conjunction with reduced canine-premolar honing, presumably as a result of parallel shifts in dietary behavior in response to changing ecological conditions. Thus, these changes are in fact not unique to

41. Sarmiento E.E., Comment on the paleobiology and classification of *Ardipithecus ramidus*, *Science* 328:1105-1110, 2010.

hominins [human ancestors]…[42,43,44]

If the same dental features can be found in apes that are understood by paleo-experts to be outside the human lineage, how can they be considered a hallmark of human evolution? As noted, the observed differences among living and extinct apes (including Ardi) in canine size and shape are a reflection of dietary behavior, not evolutionary ancestry.[45,46]

Ardi's Ape Hands and Feet

Ardi is quite clearly an ordinary ape, very similar to the modern chimpanzee (Figure 4). Perhaps this is most clearly seen by examining Ardi's hands and feet. Among the remains that were recovered, the hands and feet were extremely well preserved compared to the rest of the skeleton. For this reason, the hands and feet were the most informative bones in identifying what Ardi was and how it moved around. White, Lovejoy, and colleagues make note of this in the *Proceedings of the National Academy of Sciences* (2015):

> Her [Ardi's] hands and feet are extraordinarily preserved. Less well preserved, but nevertheless nearly complete elements of her teeth, skull, arms, legs and pelvis provide further informative anatomy.[47]

It is interesting that the researchers built their case that Ardi was an early human ancestor almost entirely on those "less well preserved bones"—predominantly the severely crushed skull and hip. On the other hand, the "extraordinarily preserved" bones clearly resembled those of living African apes. For instance, one of the most obvious qualities of the foot, which clearly suggests that Ardi was an ordinary tree-dwelling ape (that also engaged in terrestrial locomotion on all fours like modern apes) was the highly divergent grasping toe. Living apes such as chimpanzees have a great toe called a hallux that is not in line with the other four toes as in humans. Instead, it juts out to the side of the foot and functions like a thumb, as is necessary for limb-grasping. A divergent hallux is one of the clearest indicators of ape anatomy and climbing behavior. So what did Ardi's feet look like? Ardi's feet display a highly divergent grasping toe exactly like modern tree-dwelling apes such as chimpanzee. Even paleo-expert Tim White, the lead member of the Ardi discovery team, couldn't help but notice the specimen's large grasping toe that looks indistinguishable from apes (Figure 10). He notes, *"It really doesn't differ*

---

42. Wood B. and Harrison T., The evolutionary context of the first hominins. *Nature* 470:347-352, 2011.

43. Harrison quoted in: Harmon K., Was "Ardi" not a human ancestor after all? New review raises doubts, *Sci Am*, February 16, 2011.

44. Kaplan M., The con of convergence, *Nature News,* 16 February 2011. DOI: 10.1038/news.2011.98

45. Sarmiento E. and Meldrum D., Behavioral and phylogenetic implications of a narrow allometric study of *Ardipithecus ramidus. J Comp Hum Biol* 62:75-108, 2011.

46. Stanford C.B., Chimpanzees and the behavior of *Ardipithecus ramidus, Annu Rev Anthropol* 41:139-149, 2012. *"… a varied herbivorous diet."*

47. White T.D. *et al.*, Neither chimpanzee nor human, *Ardipithecus* reveals the surprising ancestry of both. *Proc Natl Acad Sci,* USA 112(16):4877-4884, 2015.

from apes, and that's the surprising thing. It is fully apelike."[48] It is for this reason, among others, that William Jungers, anatomist at Stony Brook University, highly doubts Ardi had a form of locomotion any different from that of living apes:

> This is a fascinating skeleton, but based on what they present, the evidence for bipedality is limited at best. Divergent big toes are associated with grasping, and this has one of the most divergent big toes you can imagine. Why would an animal fully adapted to support its weight on its forelimbs in the trees elect to walk bipedally [upright like humans] on the ground?[49]

This is a fair question. Adding to this, Jungers states, *"I see nothing in the foot that suggests bipedality* [upright-walking]."[50] Of course, White and colleagues don't see it this way. Instead of climbing in the trees like an ordinary ape, Ardi is pictured in their 2009 *Science* article as walking along the forest floor using the opposable great toe to balance on fallen tree limbs (Figure 3). The way Ardi is envisioned is bizarre and reckless speculation. The idea of a chimp-like creature using its chimp-like feet to "climb along" branches lying on the ground is quite humorous. The fossil evidence in no way indicates such behavior nor does common sense allow it.

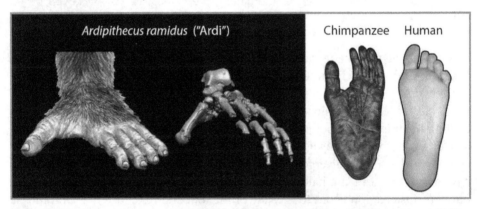

Figure 10. Ardi's feet are indistinguishable from those of living apes and display a prominent "thumb-like" toe that is characteristic of all tree-dwelling primates. This is consistent with the interpretation, held by a number of paleo-experts, that Ardi was merely an extinct ape.

Ardi's hands are also unmistakably ape-like. They are extremely long and curved with short thumbs relative to the other four fingers, a characteristic of all living tree-dwelling apes.[51,52] Sergio Almécija and colleagues in *Nature* (2015) affirm this, stating, *"Ar. ramidus exhibits a shorter thumb (within the gorilla-hylobatid range),*

48. Tim White, University of California Berkeley quoted in: Zorich Z., *Ardipithecus*: ape or ancestor? *Archaeology Magazine* 63(1), 2010.

49. William Jungers, SUNY Stony Brook, quoted in: Shreeve J., Oldest Skeleton of Human Ancestor Found, *National Geographic News*, 28 October 2009: http://news.nationalgeographic.com/news/2009/10/091001-oldest-human-skeleton-ardi-missing-link-chimps-ardipithecus-ramidus.html

50. W. Jungers, quoted in: Zorich Z., *Ardipithecus*: ape or ancestor? *Archaeology Magazine* 63(1), Jan/Feb 2010.

51. Azadeh Ansari, Oldest human skeleton offers new clues to evolution, *CNN*, 2009. http://www.cnn.com/2009/TECH/science/10/01/oldest.human.skeleton.index.html?ref=

52. Almécija S. *et al.*, The evolution of human and ape hand proportions, *Nat Commun* 6:7717 DOI: 10.1038/ncomms8717, 2015

implying limits to its precision grasping capabilities."[53] The morphology of the hand overlaps with those of gorillas and gibbons, and is perfectly suited for limb-grasping. Despite the obvious ape-like anatomy of the hand, White and colleagues still did their best to make Ardi into *"a new kind of ancestor."*[54] One of the key differences between Ardi and modern apes listed by Lovejoy and colleagues is the absence of the locking wrists that afford quadrupedal apes the ability to bear weight on their knuckles like chimps and gorillas.[55] This was cited as evidence that Ardi was not like any living ape, but nevertheless the "surprising" ancestor of both humans and chimpanzees.[56] Yet just because Ardi did not have knuckle-locking wrists typical of chimpanzees, it does not follow that it was an early human ancestor. Most primates are not stiff-wristed knuckle-walkers. Baboons and monkeys walk on their palms (a type of locomotion referred to as palmigrade quadrupedalism) and lack knuckle-locking wrists. Sarmiento and Meldrum acknowledge this in the *Journal of Comparative Human Biology* (2011): *"Ardipithecus wrist joint is that of a palmigrade quadruped..."*[57] Stanford in the *Annual Review of Anthropology* suspects Ardi's locomotory behavior and habitat specialization may have been similar, writing, *"Baboons are plantagrade quadrupeds* [walking with palms flat] *on the ground, but they make extensive use of arboreal substrates."*[58]

Conclusion—Ardi is Fully Ape

A famous advocate of human evolution, Carl Sagan, once said, *"Extraordinary claims require extraordinary evidence."*[59] While the Ardi team has made extraordinary claims, they have certainly not demonstrated extraordinary evidence.

The remains attributed to Ardi and its kind, *Ar. ramidus,* do not represent convincing evidence pointing to an early ancestor to man. All of the major features cited by the discovery team in their attempt to place Ardi in the direct human lineage are based on highly questionable reconstructions and inferences. The quality of the evidence is itself very poor—the bones were unarticulated and loosely scattered across miles of the Afar landscape and were very poorly preserved. The incomplete, disintegrating, and scattered bone fragments made reconstruction an act of faith. The original anatomical orientation of key diagnostic bones, particularly the severely crushed skull and hip were lost forever—too poorly preserved to enable accurate reconstruction. It is no wonder it took nearly 20 years

53. Almécija S. *et al.*, The evolution of human and ape hand proportions, *Nat Commun* 6:7717 DOI: 10.1038/ncomms8717, 2015.
54. Gibbons A., A new kind of ancestor: *Ardipithecus* unveiled, *Science* 326:36-40, 2009.
55. White T.D. *et al.*, Neither chimpanzee nor human, *Ardipithecus* reveals the surprising ancestry of both, *Proc Natl Acad Sci* USA 112(16):4877-4884, 2015.
56. White T.D. *et al.*, Neither chimpanzee nor human, *Ardipithecus* reveals the surprising ancestry of both, *Proc Natl Acad Sci* USA 112(16):4877-4884, 2015.
57. Sarmiento E.E. and Meldrum D.J., Behavioral and phylogenetic implications of a narrow allometric study of *Ardipithecus ramidus*, *HOMO—J Comp Hum Biol* 62:75-108, 2011.
58. Stanford C.B., Chimpanzees and the behavior of *Ardipithecus ramidus*, *Annu Rev Anthropol* 41:139-149, 2012.
59. Carl Sagan (writer/host), "Encyclopedia Galactica", Cosmos, Episode 12 [01:24 minutes in] *PBS*, 1980.

to digitally manipulate the remains to the satisfaction of the discoverers. Many experts in the field have openly questioned Ardi's actual morphology and true manner of locomotion, and have criticized the speculative reconstructions and inferences derived from them.

Leading evolutionary paleo-experts have challenged virtually every claim put forth by the discovery team regarding Ardi. Detailed criticisms have been reported in numerous peer-reviewed scientific journals, including *Science, Nature, Annual Review of Anthropology*, and *Journal of Comparative Human Biology*, as discussed in this chapter. The authors of these papers are respected paleoanthropologists that seem to represent the prevailing view held by the paleo-community. It is unfortunate that the views of these scientists have not been made widely known to the general public and to students. The alterntive view (that Ardi is merely an extinct ape) is not even mentioned in textbooks. Instead, essentially all textbooks now list Ardi as the oldest known human ancestor, arguing that it is another "conclusive proof" of human evolution.

Despite what the discovery team claims, there is no evidence Ardi had a human-like hip. There is no evidence Ardi had a human-like lower lumbar curvature. There is no evidence Ardi's skull and teeth were evolving toward becoming human. Ardi's anteriorly positioned foramen magnum is very questionable and would not warrant its placement in the human lineage. Ardi's limb proportions, hands, and feet are unmistakably that of an ape. There is no legitimate evidence to suggest Ardi walked upright like humans. The traits presented as evidence that Ardi was in the human lineage are the very same features currently seen in living apes—as noted by evolutionary paleo-experts.

**Latest Developments

Ardi was dated 4.4 million years old, and in 1992 was announced to the world as the oldest human ancestor. Despite its proposed status as a human ancestor, Ardi displays an overwhelmingly chimp-like anatomy, including a highly divergent grasping big toe (abducted hallux). A new discovery made in 2017 may be the final nail in the coffin for Ardi. Anatomically modern human footprints from western Crete (dated to 5.7 million years old)[60] further suggests that man has always coexisted with the earliest reputed hominins. The anthropology department at Uppsala University (i.e., Grzegorz Niedzwiedzki, second author of the technical paper) published an article in *Science Daily* stating: *"At approximately 5.7 million years old, they are... more than a million years older than Ardipithecus ramidus with its ape-like feet. This conflicts with the hypothesis that Ardipithecus is a direct ancestor of later hominins."*[61]

---

60. Gierlinski G.D. *et al.*, Possible hominin footprints from the late Miocene (c. 5.7 Ma) of Crete? *Proceedings of the Geologists' Association*, 621:1-14, 2017. DOI: 10.1016/j.pgeola.2017.07.006
61. Uppsala University, Fossil footprints challenge established theories of human evolution, *ScienceDaily*, 2017. Accessed 10/2/17: https://www.sciencedaily.com/releases/2017/08/170831134221.htm

CHAPTER 7

Australopithecus afarensis
Lucy's Kind – The Third View

...the Hadar (and by inference the Sterkfontein) material [Lucy's kind] consists of several distinct species which were previously jumbled together.[1]

Peter Schmid of the University of Witwatersrand and Martin Häusler, University of Zurich

Introduction

"Lucy" is the nickname given to a partial fossil skeleton discovered in 1974 in the Afar region of Ethiopia by famous paleo-expert, Donald Johanson. The bones of Lucy are said to represent a single, individual skeleton (Figure 1). Johanson has claimed that Lucy belonged to an extinct population of similar looking creatures of the same species that once roamed Africa, presumably between 3–4 million years ago based on conventional dating methods. Lucy's bones are said to represent a species which Johanson named as *Australopithecus afarensis* ("Afarensis"). This Latin name means *southern ape from Afar*—because Lucy was found in the Afar region of Ethiopia. Apart from the Lucy skeleton, Afarensis is mostly represented by a loose collection of broken bones (Figure 2). To date, over 400 specimens have been attributed to Afarensis, but nearly all of those consist of isolated bones or bone fragments. Two additional partial skeletons have been found in 2000 and 2005 that preserve nearly as much as Lucy. Lucy is said to preserve 40% of the skeleton (60% is missing). However, the skeleton is only 20% complete if the missing bones

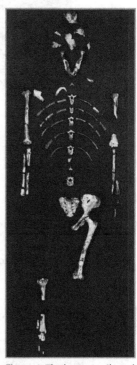

Figure 1. The bones attributed to "Lucy" that were screened from hillside AL 288 in 1974.

---

1. Häusler M. and Schmid P., Comparison of the pelves of Sts 14 and AL 288-1: implications for birth and sexual dimorphism in australopithecines, *J Hum Evol* 29:363-383, 1995.

of the hands and feet are also considered.[2] This is not much, yet Lucy is the most complete Afarensis skeleton yet discovered. The majority of the fossils attributed to Afarensis were discovered during Phase I of the International Afar Research Expedition in the 70s and will be the focus of this chapter. Additional fossils were found during Phase II which began in 1990 and is now called the Hadar Research Project. Excavations in the Hadar region have continued to the present day.

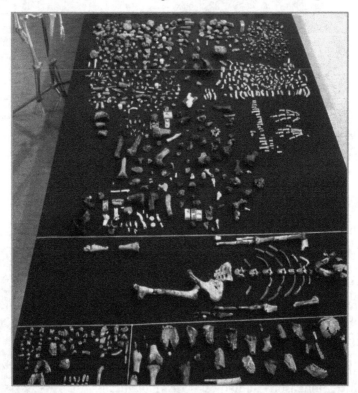

Figure 2. Over 200 isolated bone and bone fragments were recovered during the 1975 field season from the "First Family" site (top). The partial Lucy skeleton is pictured below these bones. Additional mandibular, cranial, and postcranial remains were recovered during the 1973 and 1974 field seasons (bottom right). Mary Leakey's collection of mandibles and dentition recovered from Laetoli in 1974 and 1975 (bottom left). Johanson and White claimed that all 300-plus bones belonged to Lucy's kind, Afarensis. To this day, paleo-experts dispute whether all of these bones belong to a single species or multiple taxa.

The following is an account of the major hominin findings from the 1973-1977 International Afar Research Expedition as well as additional findings from Laetoli, Tanzania that were discovered by the famous paleo-expert, Mary Leakey and her family, during the same time period. Initially, Johanson and the Leakey's had agreed with one another about the taxonomic assignment of their fossils. It was clear to them that their combined fossil assemblage represented multiple species

2. Walker A. and Shipman P., *The Wisdom of the Bones: In Search of Human Origins*, Alfred A. Knoff Publishing, New York, 1996. See also: https://www.scientificamerican.com/podcast/episode/looking-back-on-40-years-of-lucy/

from at least two separate genera—*Australopithecus* and *Homo*. But later, there would be sharp disagreements over Johanson's unilateral decision to reclassify all of his Hadar findings (as well as Mary's findings in Laetoli) as representing his new species, *Australopithecus afarensis*. Their conflicting interpretations of the fossils that they found in Hadar and Laetoli created a divide between them and within the paleo-community, which has lasted to this day. Johanson claimed that Afarensis represented the oldest hominin fossils found, which was the ancestor to all later hominins, including *Homo sapiens*. Johanson's reassessment made him a *"paleoanthropological superstar"*[3] and his beloved Lucy became the most famous hominin fossil ever discovered.

According to his colleagues, Johanson loved the media spotlight and was a *"publicity hound."*[4] He was able to win over the media and influence a sizeable portion of the field as he promoted his own personal interpretation of the Hadar-Laetoli findings. Johanson's personal interpretation of the fossils has been perpetuated throughout education systems and the media ever since—and this has been to the exclusion of all other competing views, even views that are still widely held by the paleo-community. As you will see, many leading paleo-experts have rejected Johanson's claims about Afarensis as a sound species and the ancestor to us all. However, this prevailing model of human origins that is taught in education systems and the media, as popularized by Johanson, is now collapsing as new fossils are found dating to the time of Lucy (see chapter 11). Unfortunately, the public is totally unaware of the shocking full story about how Lucy and the species she is said to represent (Afarensis), became the most famous hominin bones.

A Childhood Dream

Donald Johanson, the discoverer of the famous "Lucy" skeleton, is perhaps the most famous paleoanthropologist. Johanson recounts that since he was a teenager he had always *"dreamed of traveling to Africa and finding a "missing link."*[5] Growing up, he was mesmerized by the expeditions of the famous Louis and Mary Leakey in East Africa that he would read about in National Geographic magazine (the same family that would later reject Johanson's major claims). Johanson's ambition to become a famous fossil hunter eventually led him to the Great Rift Valley, a Y-shaped scar in the earth that cuts through the East African countries of Tanzania, Kenya, and Ethiopia. His first expedition would take place in the Omo River valley in Southern Ethiopia in 1970, under his graduate advisor F. Clark Howell from the University of Chicago. Omo was a famous hominin-bearing site that yielded pig teeth which would later play a pivotal role in calibrating the age and importance of many hominin fossils, including Johanson's famous Lucy fossil.

3. Lewin R., *Bones of Contention*, University of Chicago Press, Chicago, 2nd edition, p. 272, 1997.
4. Johanson D.C. and Edey M.A., *Lucy: The Beginnings of Humankind*, Simon & Schuster, New York, p. 295, 1981.
5. Johanson D.C. and Wong K., *Lucy's Legacy: The Quest for Human Origins*, Crown Publishing Group, New York, p. 3, 2009.

As a graduate student, Johanson spent his summers in the Omo region which gave him valuable field experience.[6] On his return home from a summer expedition in 1971, Johanson stopped in Paris to study chimpanzee skulls in a museum for his doctoral dissertation. It was there that he met Maurice Taieb, a French geologist from the National Center for Scientific Research in Paris. Taieb shared wondrous stories with Johanson about the Hadar region of Ethiopia. Hadar was part of the Afar triangle, a depression formed by the rifting of two plate boundaries that exposed eroding hillsides of sand and ash that were ideal for finding fossils. Taieb described the Hadar region as a land that was littered with fossils. Based on the presumed age of fossil pig teeth, the Hadar region was believed to be over a million years older than the Omo region, which certainly caught the attention of Johanson. At that time, there were only a handful of hominin fossils dating to be 3–4 million years old. The oldest hominin bones were believed to be no older than 2 million years.[7] The thought of finding the oldest hominin fossils yet to be discovered was tantalizing to him. So, when Taieb extended the offer to Johanson to join him on a full-scale expedition to Hadar, he couldn't resist.

A Survey of the Hadar Region (1972)

The stories Maurice Taieb told Johanson were true. In April 1972, Johanson joined Taieb on a month-long reconnaissance of the Hadar region. It was then that Johanson saw with his own eyes a region that fossils hunters could only have dreamed of. He saw what he described as an *"immensely rich concentration of fossil animal bones,"* consisting of *"an astonishing array"* of all types of African species.[8] Many of the species represented by the fossils are still living today—including giraffe, hippo, big cats, tortoises, pigs, antelope, zebras, elephant, horse, rhinoceros, hyenas, apes, baboons, monkeys (lots of them). Johanson writes that he was *"overwhelmed by the array of mammal fossils lying scattered over the ground."*[9] As Johanson drove along in the Land Rover, he would look down and see fossils peppered across the Hadar landscape, extending in all directions for miles. Hadar was a land literally *"oozing with fossils."*[10] Apparently, a widespread catastrophe of volcanism and flooding had caused the mass death of countless African species that were buried in sediments and later exposed as fossils due to continental rifting and erosion. Johanson was sure that he could find hominin fossils somewhere within this mass graveyard of African fauna. Their survey of the Hadar region was a success, to say the least. Their full-scale expedition would begin the following year.

---

6. Johanson spent his summers doing field work in the Omo region from 1970-1972.
7. Skull 1470 was originally dated 2.9 million years old but was challenged and later rejected. See KBS Tuff Controversy in chapter 11.
8. Johanson D.C., Ethiopia Yields First "Family" of Early Man, *National Geographic,* pp. 790-811, 1976.
9. Johanson D. and Johanson L., *Ancestors: In Search of Human Origins*, Villard Books, New York, p. 50-51, 1994.
10. Johanson D.C. and Wong K, *Lucy's Legacy: The Quest for Human Origins*, Crown Publishing Group, New York, p. 12, 2009.

International Afar Research Expedition (1973–1977)

Figure 3. The encampment of the members of the first International Afar Research Expedition in the Middle Awash river valley of Hadar, Ethiopia.

In October 1973, a team of nine French and American scientists arrived in the Awash River valley to commence the first International Afar Research Expedition (IARE), which spanned from 1973 to 1977 (Figure 3). The team was co-led by Donald Johanson, Maurice Taieb, and Yves Coppens—a French paleontologist whom he had also met while he was in Omo. They set up camp in the region of Hadar, named after a tributary stream. For the next several years, major hominin fossil discoveries were made, and along with them, some highly controversial claims about the origin of man. By the end of the Phase I of the IARE in 1977, Johanson and his team had collected a total of 6,000 fossils belonging to 40 different African species. Approximately 240 of those (with more added later) were attributed to what Johanson would later declare to the world as a new hominin species and the ancestor of us all, *Australopithecus afarensis.*[11] As mentioned, most of the Hadar findings consisted of isolated, broken bones. The most impressive specimen was the partial skeleton found during the second field season that was assigned the uninteresting fossil identification number AL 288-1, but to the world it would become known as "Lucy."

First Field Season (1973)—A Knee Joint

Johanson was fresh out of graduate school and had accepted a position as an assistant anthropology professor at Case Western Reserve University in Cleveland,

11. Johanson D., The paleoanthropology of Hadar, Ethiopia, *Human Paleontology and Prehistory*, 16(2):140-154, 2017. doi.org/10.1016/j.crpv.2016.10.005

Ohio. Shortly thereafter, he began his first field season in Hadar in 1973. He would not complete his doctoral dissertation on chimpanzee teeth until August 1974, yet he was about to make a major discovery that would provide the funding his team needed to continue their expeditions in Hadar.

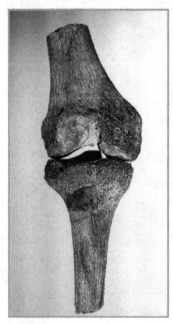

Figure 4. The isolated knee joint (AL 129-1a,b) recovered during the 1973 field season, a year before the discovery of Lucy from a separate location (AL 288).

The first month of fossil hunting was disappointing. Johanson and his team found many fossils of all types of African fauna, but no hominin fossils. But late in the afternoon on October 30th, Johanson spotted a bone protruding from the sand. This was not unusual, most of the fossils were surface finds that could be easily seen. Baboons, monkey, antelope, horse, elephants, pigs, hippos, etc. were common finds. Thinking he had spotted another hippo bone, this time a rib fragment, Johanson picked it up to examine it. He quickly realized that it was the lower end of a thigh bone, and not at all from a hippo. It was quite small, *"most likely a monkey,"*[12] he thought. A few yards away he found the upper end of a shin bone. The two bones fit together to form a perfect knee joint (Figure 4). Yet the knee joint fit together at an angle, not straight up and down like a monkey. Johanson had learned that monkey knee joints meet in a straight line, forming an angle of zero degrees. Modern humans, on the other hand, have a high carrying angle. The two bones of the knee joint meet at an angle to allow for smooth bipedal locomotion. Johanson explains:

What was surprising—astonishing, in fact—was the way they fit together. The thigh and shin bones of monkeys joint to form a straight line. These two bones met at an angle, the femur slanting outward. There was only one living primate endowed with such a knee joint. Human femurs angle outward in order to give balance for walking on two legs. I could scarcely believe the evidence in my hands. If our preliminary dating of the Hadar deposits was correct, I was holding the knee joint of a hominid over three million years old: the earliest record of a bipedal ancestor yet discovered.[13]

As Johanson studied the knee joint, he thought with excitement, *"a manlike knee joint meant manlike walking."*[14] He showed the parts of the knee to his grad student who was with him when he found it. Tom Gray agreed, it was hominin! They were

12. Johanson D. and Johanson L., *Ancestors: In Search of Human Origins*, Villard Books, New York, p. 52, 1994.
13. Johanson D.C. and Shreeve J., *Lucy's Child: The Discovery of a Human Ancestor*, Early Man Publishing, Inc., New York, p. 82, 1989.
14. Johanson D.C. and Edey M.A., *Lucy: The Beginnings of Humankind*, Simon & Schuster, New York, p.156, 1981.

sure that it belonged to a creature that could walk upright in a manner just like modern humans. It was a creature that Johanson had decided must belong in the human lineage, which had diverged from a common ancestor to the African apes. But did the knee joint look more like a human, more like an ape, or something entirely different? According to Johanson, it certainly looked like a modern human knee joint, only much smaller. However, Johanson had specialized in chimpanzee teeth, he was not an expert in postcranial anatomy. For some added assurance, he needed to show his fossil to anatomist and professor Owen Lovejoy from Kent State University.

The problem was, he couldn't take any fossils out of the country without the permission of the Ethiopian government. Johanson needed to show them at a press conference that it was an important fossil, worthy of further study. And the only way he could convince them of that was if he could describe it accurately. Yet he couldn't describe the fossil accurately without a knee joint to compare it with. Johanson writes, *"That left me in quandary. If I described the knee joint incorrectly, I would have botched my first important independent fossil interpretation. But if I did not describe the fossils, I would not be allowed to remove it."*[15] So what did Johanson do? He felt he had no choice but to disturb (raid) one of the graves of the local Afar people. Fearful that they would be caught, and possibly shot, Johanson and his grad student snuck over to the burial mound and retrieved a thigh bone. Johanson shares what happened in his book *Lucy: The Beginnings of Humankind*:[16]

Johanson: *There's an Afar burial mound out there.*

Grad student: *Wait a minute. We've been getting along fine with these people. You're going to rob one of their graves?*

Johanson: *I just want to look at it.*

Grad student: *I don't. … What if they catch us?*

Johanson: *It's late. They won't notice.*

Grad student: *They'll shoot us. They'll run us off.*

Johanson: *I have to have a femur.*

Author (Johanson): *By that time we had arrived at the burial mound. It was a loosely made dome of boulders and was probably a good many years old, because one side had fallen away. I looked in. There was a large heap of bones inside—a family burial place. Lying on the top, almost asking to be taken, was a femur. Tom took it. We looked around. There was no one in sight. Tom put the bone in his shirt and carried it back to camp. That night I compared it with the fossil. Except for size, they were virtually identical.*

---

15. Johanson D.C. and Edey M.A., *Lucy: The Beginnings of Humankind*, Simon & Schuster, New York, p.158, 1981.
16. Johanson D.C. and Edey M.A., *Lucy: The Beginnings of Humankind*, Simon & Schuster, New York, p.158-159, 1981.

Despite Johanson's ethical breach, the stolen femur proved useful to him, in that it gave him certainty that his knee fossil was identical to the knee joint of a modern human. Johanson was granted permission to take the knee joint fossil out of the country for further study. Years later in 1981, Johanson published his book *Lucy*, where he confessed to this grave robbery incident. The very next year Ethiopian authorities (the Ministry of Culture) placed a ban on all foreign paleoanthropology expeditions to the region. After this happened, Mary Leakey noted that this was one of the factors that influenced the Ministry of Culture's decision to ban future expeditions.[17] The ban would not be lifted until 1989. Regardless, Johanson got what he wanted and was able to garner further funding and bring the fossil to Cleveland on loan for further analysis.

Lovejoy had already published comparative studies of modern human knees with those of South African *Australopithecus* fossils. Johanson was confident he would be able to confirm the human-looking anatomy seen in the fossil. When Johanson showed him the knee joint, Lovejoy said that he *"knew instantly that was a human knee."*[18] He was convinced it belonged to a biped.[19] Next he compared the knee joint to human and chimpanzee skeletons housed at the Cleveland Museum of Natural History. His evaluation didn't change. A number of features stood out to Lovejoy as undeniably human: *"Owen pointed out a lip of bone on the outer edge of the femur that helps hold the kneecap in place. A human's knee has this same feature; a chimpanzee's does not."*[20] Other features could be identified as human, such as the shape of the knee joint:

> Although the fossil was about the same size as the chimpanzee knees we examined, it had a distinctly different shape. … the two bony bumps, or condyles, on the end of the femur had a long, fairly flat edge where they rested on top of the shinbone. That is a human trait, but in a quadruped like the chimpanzee the condyles are shorter and rounder.[21]

To be extra certain, Lovejoy brought the knee joint to an orthopedic surgeon that he knew. The surgeon's conclusion was the same, *"The only difference between this fossil combination and a human knee was the fossil's small size."*[22] Johanson's suspicions were confirmed, but a human knee joint dating nearly three-and-a-half million years old really puzzled him. Johnson shares his thoughts at the time of discovery:

> I felt sure we were onto something completely new. Yet the knee poised troubling questions. What sort of ancient creature would have a modern knee? I kept turning

17. Leakey M., *Disclosing the Past: An Autobiography*, Rainbird Publishing Group Limited, New York, p. 184, 1984.
18. Johanson D., (Lovejoy speaking), *Nova, In Search of Human Origins* (Part 1). PBS Airdate: June 3, 1997. Transcript at: http://www.pbs.org/wgbh/nova/transcripts/2106hum1.html
19. Johanson D. and Johanson L., *Ancestors: In Search of Human Origins*, Villard Books, New York, p. 54, 1994.
20. Johanson D. and Johanson L., *Ancestors: In Search of Human Origins*, Villard Books, New York, p. 56, 1994.
21. Johanson D. and Johanson L., *Ancestors: In Search of Human Origins*, Villard Books, New York, p. 56, 1994.
22. Johanson D. and Johanson L., *Ancestors: In Search of Human Origins*, Villard Books, New York, p. 54, 1994.

it over and over in my mind, what did it mean? ... The mysterious fossil really perplexed us. What was a modern looking human knee doing among fossils that were millions of years old?[23]

If all parties agreed the knee joint looked strikingly similar to modern humans, why couldn't they simply conclude it looked human because it was human? After all, the only significant difference was its small size. But the size wasn't what ruled out the possibility that it was human—because even today there are small-bodied humans, such as the pygmies of central Africa. The average adult male pygmy grows no taller than 4 feet 9 inches in height, females are even shorter. Surely, they have small skeletons and small knee joints. The real reason why they felt they couldn't classify the fossil as a human knee joint, despite it being described as looking *"virtually identical"* to modern humans, was because of its presumed age and certain critical evolutionary preconceptions. The model of human origins that Johanson had embraced demanded that man had not yet existed at the time of Lucy, 3–4 million years ago. This is the view that is still widely taught today. According to the ape-to-man story, *H. sapiens* and *H. erectus*, both of which display a modern human postcranial anatomy, had not yet evolved. And so, there was no way they could claim that the knee joint belonged to an ape-like hominin ancestor if anatomically modern-looking humans had already inhabited the region. Johanson understood this, and that's precisely why the human-looking anatomy was so troubling to him. Such a finding would effectively falsify his favored evolutionary model. Therefore, the remarkably human-looking knee joint had to be attributed to Lucy's kind, *Australopithecus afarensis*—and so it was, but not until additional fossils were found during the field seasons that followed.

At first, Johanson felt he couldn't make any certain determinations about the owner of the isolated knee joint. He was committed to the human-looking, bipedal interpretation of its anatomy, but he refrained from assigning it to a specific hominin species. To verify his finding, Johanson felt he needed to find a more complete skeleton. In particular, he needed to find a skeleton that preserved enough of the cranium to make a more confident evaluation. Johanson pondered:

> What sort of hominid I had found was anybody's guess. It was impossible to declare an isolated knee joint *Homo*, *Australopithecus*, or anything else. All I could say for sure was that the creature had been bipedal and surprisingly small. Most of the features on a skeleton that can pin down its identify are found from the neck up.[24]

Later during the 1973 field season, two other fossils gave them more to think about. They were fragments that made up an upper end of a thigh bone—the part that forms the neck and ball that fits into the hip socket. The specimen lacked the head but because of how the fossil had broken, a cross section of the femur neck was

23. Johanson D., *Nova, In Search of Human Origins* (Part 1). PBS Airdate: June 3, 1997. Transcript at: http://www.pbs.org/wgbh/nova/transcripts/2106hum1.html
24. Johanson D.C. and Shreeve J., Early Man Publishing, Inc., New York, *Lucy's Child: The Discovery of a Human Ancestor*, p. 83, 1989.

exposed for analysis. X-rays revealed what Johanson and Lovejoy have described as *"dramatic differences"* when compared to the femur neck of a chimpanzee. They insisted that *"The Hadar fossils are almost identical to the human pattern."*[25] Is it possible that the isolated knee joint and partial femur bone looked human simply because they belonged to humans? If they looked essentially identical to those of modern humans, why did Johanson later decide to attribute them to Afarensis?

Second Field Season (1974)—Some *Homo* Jawbones

The second field season of the IARE began in early October of 1974. Within a week of setting up camp, an Ethiopian who had joined their team from the Ministry of Culture, Alemayehu Asfaw, discovered three upper jawbones, one of which preserved a complete set of 16 teeth. A fourth specimen, half of a lower jawbone, was discovered by a local Afar worker. All were found within a span of three days. Because of their presumed age of over 3 million years, they signified a breakthrough in the study of human origins. The valley where the jawbones were found was named "Hominid Valley". The specimens were described as aligning best with the human genus *Homo*, but like the knee joint and partial femur bone, they would later be reassigned to *Australopithecus afarensis*, the species Lucy is said to represent. However, this was not what Johanson and his team had originally reported.

In the October 28 issue of the Paris *Herald Tribune*, the IARE team made a public statement claiming that they had found the earliest members of the genus *Homo*. The headline of the newspaper article was deliberately titled, *"3-Million-Year-Old Human Fossils Found."*[26] The Hadar jawbones were described by Johanson as looking similar to modern humans, and distinct from australopith jawbones of equivalent age. The article reads:

> At the press conference, Mr. Johanson pulled out of a cigar box the three specimens plus another jawbone believed to belong to a creature called *Australopithecus*, contemporary in time with the genus *Homo* from which modern man descended. By far the most remarkable of the four fossils is the complete upper jaw whose size and teeth appeared to be very similar to those of humans today. The find is likely to shift the center for the search for the cradle of *Homo sapiens* from the southern portions of the Great East African Rift in Kenya and Tanzania to the northern Ethiopian Afar region of the same valley. Previously the oldest human fossils found in Tanzania and Lake Rudolf by the late Louis Leakey and his son Richard were no more than 2 million to 2.8 million years and the latter dating is seriously contested. … The fossils, still in excellent condition for their age, are the strongest evidence to date that man's origins date to a far more distant past than anyone had previously suspected: four million years and perhaps more. … Furthermore, Mr. Johanson and his colleague believe the genus *Homo* or "true man" almost certainly coexisted with the "near man"

25. Johanson D. and Johanson L., *Ancestors: In Search of Human Origins*, Villard Books, New York, p. 58, 1994.
26. Ottoway D.B., 3-million-year-old human fossils found, *Herald Tribune*, Paris, 28 October, 1974. Open source: https://archive.org/details/InternationalHeraldTribune1974FranceEnglish

Australopithecus in the Afar region.

Johanson, Taieb, and Asfaw explain further in their prepared statement:

> We have in a matter of merely two days extended our knowledge of the genus *Homo* by nearly 1.5 million years. All previous theories of the origin of the lineage which leads to modern man must now be totally revised.

In a 1976 issue of *National Geographic* magazine, Johanson affirmed his attribution of the human-looking jawbones to the genus *Homo*.[27] There can be no doubt that Johanson and his team of researchers were convinced that their findings proved conclusively that *Homo* had lived in the Hadar region at the time of Lucy, 3–4 million years ago. Johanson was confident that his findings had demonstrated the coexistence of two parallel lineages, *Australopithecus* and *Homo*. Johanson wrote:

> Characteristics of the teeth were gathered suggested affinities with known fossils from a later period. Such fossils—the jaws more rounded in front, and the front and back teeth more evenly proportioned than the parallel group of australopithecines, or near men—have been assigned to the genus *Homo*, which includes modern man. This could make our specimens, more than three million years old, among the oldest evidence for the *Homo* lineage in the world.

Those same jawbones and teeth closely resembled Mary Leakey's sets of jawbones and teeth found by her team in Laetoli during their 1974 and 1975 field seasons (see section below). In 1974 when Mary and her son Richard had come to meet Johanson in Hadar to compare their jawbones, they had agreed that the jawbones belonged to *Homo*.[28] Johanson writes:

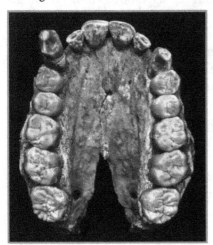

> Richard and his wife, Meave, flew in from Nairobi on November 28, together with Mary and paleontologist John Harris. To my delight, the Leakey's agreed with my suspicions that the jaws might be *Homo*. Richard and Mary were not only my friends, they were also the most famous investigators working in East Africa. Their opinion carried a lot of weight with me. If the jaws were indeed *Homo*, then I had found in the Afar no less than the oldest trace of man's tenure on earth. That is a seductive idea for any physical anthropologist. For someone as young and ambitious as I was, it was almost irresistible.[29]

Figure 5. An isolated upper jawbone (AL 200-1) recovered during the 1974 field season from Hadar, Ethiopia.

Johanson and his colleagues were thrilled that they had found evidence of what they

27. Johanson D.C., Ethiopia Yields First "Family" of Early Man, *National Geographic*, pp. 790-811, 1976.

28. Reader J., *Missing Links*, Oxford University Press, New York, p. 382, 2011.

29. Johanson D.C. and Shreeve J., *Lucy's Child: The Discovery of a Human Ancestor*, Early Man Publishing, Inc., New York, p. 85, 1989.

thought was the oldest human fossils. Ironically, Johanson would soon decide to reassign all of his *Homo* jawbones, to his reputed new species, *Au. afarensis*—as well as many other human fossils that would be found in the field seasons that followed. However, in this particular case, Johanson's decision to reassign *most* (but not all) of the jawbones to *Australopithecus* seem warranted. For instance, the most complete jawbone that was found in October (AL 200-1), does appear to belong to an australopith (Figure 5). The specimen is distinctly ape-like in morphology; it bears a U-shaped dental arcade characteristic of apes, spatulate incisors, conical canines, diastema (i.e., a gap between canine and second incisor), shallow palate, alveolar prognathism, and canine wear typical of apes.[30,31,32]

Second Field Season Continued (1974)—Discovery of "Lucy"

The day after Mary and Richard left, Johanson found his famous Lucy skeleton. On November 30, 1974, Johanson and his grad student Tom Gray were on a plateau searching for hominin fossils. It started out as a typical uneventful day. All that they had found was more of the usual—fragments of a pig skull, antelope and horse teeth, and piece of a monkey jaw. Johanson and Gray had had enough. It was close to noon when fossils are harder to spot because of the lack of cast shadows that reveal the shape of fossils, and so they decided to head back to camp.

As Johanson was walking back to his Land Rover *"through a little gully on the other side of a rise,"*[33] a glint of a 2-inch long protruding fossil caught his eye. It was an ulna, the larger bone of the forearm that makes up the elbow. Johanson thought it might be from a monkey but it lacked a diagnostic feature, suggesting to him it belonged to something else entirely. He concluded the ulna was *"unquestionably hominid."*[34] Higher up the slope he found more bones—some rib fragments, part of a hip, segments of the vertebrae, part of a skullcap, and a piece of thigh bone. All of these bones were found in Johanson's *"immediate surroundings."*[35] Johanson believed that what he had found belonged to a single skeleton. The thought occurred to him even as he was picking up the individual bone fragments, *"perhaps all these bones might belong to a single individual."*[36] As he picked up the scattered bones, Johanson

30. Johanson D.C. and Edey M.A., *Lucy: The Beginnings of Humankind*, Simon & Schuster, New York, p. 267, 1981.
31. Johanson D.C., *ed.* Lars-Konig Konigsson, Pergamon Press, Early African Hominid Phylogenesis: A Re-Evaluation, *Current Argument on Early Man: Report from a Nobel Symposium*, 1978.
32. Whitehead P.F., Sacco W.K., and Hochgraf S.B., *A Photographic Atlas for Physical Anthropology*, Peabody Museum of Natural History, Yale Universty, Morton Publishing Company, p. 286, 2005.
33. Johanson D.C. and Shreeve J., *Lucy's Child: The Discovery of a Human Ancestor*, Early Man Publishing, Inc., New York, p. 85, 1989.
34. Johanson D.C. and Shreeve J., *Lucy's Child: The Discovery of a Human Ancestor*, Early Man Publishing, Inc., New York, p. 86, 1989.
35. Johanson D.C. and Wong K., *Lucy's Legacy: The Quest for Human Origins*, Crown Publishing Group, New York, p. 5, 2009.
36. Johanson D.C. and Shreeve J., *Lucy's Child: The Discovery of a Human Ancestor*, Early Man Publishing, Inc., New York, p. 86, 1989.

yelled to Tom Gray *"Hominin! It's all hominin!"*[37] Then they both went bonkers, hugging, dancing and weeping for joy. Johanson marked the location of the ulna and jawbone, wrapped them up in his handkerchief and took them back to camp to show his team. He would leave the other bones at the site until he could mark and excavate them the next day. That night was perhaps the loudest celebration the team would ever have during their expedition. The hit Beetles song, *Lucy in the Sky with Diamonds*, that played over and over again inspired them to name the 3.2 million-year-old partial skeleton "Lucy". Additional bones that were thought to belong to the skeleton were found as excavations continued in the weeks that followed—raising questions about whether all of the bones truly belonged to a single skeleton.

The disconnected bones attributed to Lucy were scattered as loose, fragmentary bones that were eroding out of the hillside. Most of the bones were exposed on the surface. Additional recovered bones that were presumed to belong to the Lucy skeleton were found only after sifting mass amounts of sediment over a period of a few weeks. Workmen sifted a total of 20 tons of sediment, covering an area of roughly 50 square meters. This was done *"so as not to miss any bit of Lucy."*[38] Johanson recalls that a number of the recovered bones were found lying on the surface in his general vicinity. These bones could possibly belong to a single individual just as Johanson claimed, but due to its fragmentary nature this may be impossible to verify apart from DNA analysis (which has never been performed). It is also unclear as to which other bones were later added to the skeleton as more sediment was sifted. Johanson's description of the excavation process reveals this uncertainty, *"During two fall seasons, expedition members screened more than twenty tons by hand and discovered hundreds of other fragments that may fit into Lucy's skeleton."*[39] Elsewhere Johanson writes, *"Following weeks of painstaking excavation we recovered hundreds of fragments, allowing us to piece together approximately forty percent of an individual skeleton."*[40] Johanson claimed he was confident that all of these loose bones belonged to a single individual skeleton. He was "sure" of this because they showed the same fossil coloration, which is questionable, and there were no duplicate parts (e.g., he found one right thigh bone, not two). However, the lack of duplicate parts may not be a statistical improbability when we realize that only 20% of the skeleton was actually preserved—and most of these bones were fragmentary.

Could the Lucy skeleton contain bones that do not belong to the same individual, or more importantly, the same species? This is not unreasonable. Lucy's skeleton was found in a mixed bone bed consisting of all types of African fauna, including

37. Johanson D.C. and Wong K., *Lucy's Legacy: The Quest for Human Origins*, Crown Publishing Group, New York, p. 6, 2009.
38. Johanson D.C., Ethiopia Yields First "Family" of Early Man, *National Geographic*, pp. 790-811, 1976.
39. Johanson D.C., Ethiopia Yields First "Family" of Early Man, *National Geographic*, pp. 790-811, 1976.
40. Johanson D.C. and O'Farrel K., *Journey from the Dawn: Life with the World's First Family*, Villard Books, New York, pp. xii, 1990.

primates such as monkeys and baboons. In fact, paleo-experts reported in the *Journal of Human Evolution* (2015) that one Lucy's vertebrae segments belonged to a baboon.[41] It was mistakenly included as part of Lucy's skeletal reconstructions in textbooks, publications, and in museums around the world for forty years before paleo-experts noticed it belonged to a baboon. Could there be other bones that do not belong? What did the real Lucy look like?

Johanson's *Nature* Report (1976)—*Homo* and *Australopithecus* in Hadar

---

Plio–Pleistocene hominid discoveries in Hadar, Ethiopia

D. C. Johanson
Cleveland Museum of Natural History, Department of Anthropology, Case Western Reserve University, Cleveland, Ohio 44106

M. Taieb
Laboratoire de Géologie du Quaternaire, CNRS, Meudon-Bellevue, France

The International Afar Research Expedition has now recovered remains of twelve hominid individuals from geological deposits estimated to be ~ 3.0 Myr in Hadar, Ethiopia. A partial skeleton represents the most complete hominid known from this period. The collection suggests that Homo and Australopithecus coexisted as early as 3.0 Myr ago.

FOLLOWING a short reconnaissance expedition in 1972 (ref. 1) to the central Afar, one of us (M.T.) organised the International Afar Research Expedition. We have now codirected two field campaigns (September–December, 1973 and 1974 (refs 2 and 3)) in the area known as Hadar (see Fig. 1).

adjacent, previously unexplored regions will substantially increase the area.

Preliminary palaeontological investigations, particularly of the suids and the elephants, have suggested a biostratigraphic correlation of the Hadar Formation with the Usno and the lower portion of the Shungura Formations[3,4]. Two radiometric K–Ar age determinations for a basalt support this with an age estimate of 3.0 ± 0.2 Myr (ref. 5).

All hominid fossils (Table 1), and most of the vertebrate material, were surface finds, although some small scale excavation and sieving operations were undertaken. A painted marker was placed at each palaeontological locality, each located on a map and the geological section carefully examined to determine the horizon yielding fossil material (see Fig. 2). At each hominid locality, a topographical map

Figure 6. The abstract of Johanson and Taieb's *Nature* report published in 1976. Johanson was originally convinced that *Homo* and *Australopithecus* were represented in his Hadar sample.

Johanson and Taieb published a technical summary of their findings from the first two field seasons of the IARE in *Nature* in 1976 (Figure 6). Included in their report were descriptions of the isolated knee joint, jawbones, teeth, human-looking femur elements, and the bones attributed to the partial Lucy skeleton. Johanson and Taieb were both convinced that their Hadar collection consisted of bones from multiple species, belonging in two morphologically distinct genera—*Homo* and *Australopithecus*. They plainly stated this in their abstract:

> The International Afar Research Expedition has now recovered the remains of twelve hominid individuals from geological deposits estimated to be ~3.0 Myr in Hadar, Ethiopia. A partial skeleton represents the most complete hominid known from this period. The collection suggests that *Homo* and *Australopithecus* coexisted as early as 3.0 Myr ago.[42]

---

41. Meyer M.R. *et al.*, Lucy's back: Reassessment of fossils associated with A.L. 288-1 vertebral column, *J Hum Evol* 85:174-180, 2015.
42. Johanson D.C. and Taieb M., Plio-Pleistocene hominid discoveries in Hadar, Ethiopia, *Nature* 260(5549):293-297, 1976.

Johanson and Taieb noted that the isolated knee joint and femur fragments found during their first field season looked *"strikingly similar"* to the comparable parts preserved in the Lucy bones. They concluded that they belonged to the same species. The human-looking bones were believed to represent *"at least two individuals of a very small hominid in Hadar"*[43] that could walk upright like modern humans. Interestingly, at one-point Johanson actually questioned if Lucy might be a dwarfed human. He wondered this when he first laid the skeleton before his colleague, Owen Lovejoy, anatomist from Kent State University. Johanson asked him, *"You don't think it's a dwarf, do you?"*[44] Lovejoy reassured him saying:

> "Nah, the skeleton doesn't show any pathology. And what's more," Owen pointed to the leg bones, "these are about the same size as the knee joint from last year. I'll bet you the females were small and the males were large."

Lovejoy's response was interesting. He claimed that Lucy could not be a dwarf because the bones do not show any signs of pathology. Yet as we mentioned earlier, even today there is a population of small-bodied modern humans living in central Africa, called pygmies. The average adult male pygmy grows no taller than 4 feet 9 inches in height, females are even shorter. They obviously have very small skeletons and yet they show no evidence of pathology in their bones. Furthermore, a small-bodied modern human was found on the Indonesian island of Flores in 2003. The fossil species was named *Homo floresiensis* (nicknamed "Hobbit"). However, many experts in the field, including members of the discovery team, insisted it was a modern human and should be reclassified *H. sapiens* (others suggested *H. erectus*). The best-preserved *H. floresiensis* specimen is LB1 which preserves a partial skeleton. LB1 shares many similarities with the Lucy skeleton, particularly its small stature, limb proportions, inferred brain size, hip anatomy, and more. The striking similarities in their postcranial anatomy has been noted by paleo-experts William Kimbel and Lucus Delezene in the *Yearbook of Physical Anthropology*.[45]

In addition to the small-bodied individuals represented, Johanson and Taieb reported the presence of two other species in their Hadar collection. For example, some of the jawbones were described as closely aligning with *H. erectus* specimens from East Turkana, Kenya. Meanwhile, other bones were thought to belong to an already-existing species from South Africa known as *Australopithecus africanus*. Still other bones were described as sharing affinities with the robust australopithecines, which are very gorilla-like and markedly different from the *Homo* bones. Johanson and Taieb stated:

> On the basis of the present hominid collection from Hadar it is tentatively suggested that some specimens show affinities with *A. robustus*, some with *A. africanus* (sensu

---

43. Johanson D.C. and Taieb M., Plio-Pleistocene hominid discoveries in Hadar, Ethiopia, *Nature* 260(5549):293-297, 1976.
44. Johanson D. and Johanson L., *Ancestors: In Search of Human Origins*, Villard Books, New York, p. 62, 1994.
45. Kimbel W.H. and Delezene L.K., "Lucy" Redux: A Review of Research on *Australopithecus afarensis*, Yearbook of Phys Anthropol 52:2-48, 2009.

stricto), and others with fossils previously referred to *Homo*.[46]

In their 1976 paper, there was no hint at all that Lucy and her kind belonged to a new species—nor did they claim that she was ancestral to all later hominins. They had just completed arguing for the coexistence of *Homo* and *Australopithecus* in the Hadar region dating from 3–4 million years ago. Their own findings did not allow Johanson to claim that his hominin findings (including Lucy) were ancestral to the genus *Homo*. But that didn't matter to Johanson at that time. He was totally convinced that there were multiple species represented in his Hadar sample. So, what changed Johanson's mind? Why did he later decide to reassign all of his *Homo* bones to his reputed new species, *Au. afarensis*?

To answer those questions, we have to look to Laetoli, Tanzania. This was where Mary Leakey (assisted by Tim White) found her own collection of bones, including a trail of fossilized footprints that would play a central role in Johanson's bold new story about Lucy and her kind. But first, Johanson was about to make another remarkable discovery in his next field season—a load of fossils that seemed to further confirm the presence of *Homo* in Hadar.

Third Field Season (1975)—"First Family" Haul of *Homo* Bones

During the third field season of the IARE, Johanson found a *"vast jumble"*[47] of hominin fossils that Johanson recalled *"seemed to be cascading, almost as from a fountain, down the hillside."*[48] Nineteen specimens were excavated from the hillside *in situ*—the rest were screened from the *"bone-strewn slope"* (Figure 7).[49] A total of 216 loose bone were recovered that seemed to arise from 13 to 17 individuals of all different ages—infant, children, and adults.[50,51] Due to the presence of duplicate bones it was possible to tell that there were multiple individuals present. Among the recovered remains were fragmentary cranial and facial remains, a partial foot and hand, other loose foot bones, isolated limb bones, individual teeth, mandibles, and other bits and pieces of broken bone. None could be put together as an intact skeleton. Most were found as small bits of broken bone that were randomly scattered down the hillside as a loose jumble. The fossil site was labeled AL 333, but it is more popularly known as the "First Family" site.

Johanson's co-leader, Maurice Taieb speculated that the hominins were suddenly

---

46. Johanson D.C. and Taieb M., Plio-Pleistocene hominid discoveries in Hadar, Ethiopia, *Nature* 260(5549):293-297, 1976.

47. Johanson D.C. and Edey M.A., *Lucy: The Beginnings of Humankind*, Simon & Schuster, New York, p. 217, 1981.

48. Johanson D.C. and Edey M.A., *Lucy: The Beginnings of Humankind*, Simon & Schuster, New York, p. 213, 1981.

49. Johanson D.C. and Edey M.A., *Lucy: The Beginnings of Humankind*, Simon & Schuster, New York, p. 213, 1981.

50. Johanson D.C., Lucy, Thirty Years Later: An Expanded View of *Australopithecus afarensis*, *J Anthropol Res*, 60(4):465-486, 2004. http://www.jstor.org/stable/3631138

51. Johanson *et al.*, *American Journal of Physical Anthropology*, 57(4):373-719, 1982. The First Family and the entire Hadar collection is described in a series of papers that occupy the full volume.

drowned in a flash flood that buried an entire "family" that was trapped or perhaps sleeping in a narrow ravine—a theory that Johanson had fully supported. Taieb stated, *"They could have only been buried together... some natural catastrophe, I think maybe a flash flood, perhaps while they were resting or sleeping."*[52] Several other theories have been proposed, including a "surplus killing" by a saber-toothed cat or some other large predator, and even food poisoning.[53] But it's hard to imagine 13 or more individuals being killed and dismembered by a carnivore all at once. What these theories have in common is the assumption that they all died at once as a group, which was necessary to support Johanson's one-species hypothesis. If they were not killed together as a single group, it would be much harder for Johanson to defend his claim that all 200-plus bones belonged to a single hominin species (given the extensive variation seen in the bones).

"First Family" site (AL 333)

Figure 7. The "First Family" site where over 200 bone and bone fragments were found eroding out of the hillside. Johanson originally claimed they belonged to *Homo*, but later he reclassified the entire collection as *Australopithecus*. The collection displays a substantial range of variation in size and anatomy, suggesting the presence of two or more taxa, as numerous paleo-experts have argued.

The most credible of these theories was Taieb *et al.*'s flash flood hypothesis.[54] But a subsequent study would later challenge this theory. The latest stratigraphic and taphonomic study (all that happens to the bone after death) has overturned the death and burial by flash flood hypothesis. It turns out, there is no evidence to suggest a group of hominins that were supposedly foraging or sleeping together were all drowned and buried in a single catastrophic flood. It was pure speculation, as Taieb himself admitted.[55] Anna K. Behrensmeyer, a taphonomist from Harvard reported in *The Geological Society of America*, *"The burial of hominin remains involved fine-grained deposition indicating low-energy, seasonal flood events, and there is no sedimentological evidence for a high energy, catastrophic flood that could*

52. Johanson D.C., Ethiopia Yields First "Family" of Early Man, *National Geographic*, pp. 790-811, 1976.
53. Kruuk, H. Surplus killing by carnivores, *Journal of Zoology*, 166(2):233-244, 1972. DOI: 10.1111/j.1469-7998.1972.tb04087.x
54. Radosevich S., Retallack G., and Taieb, M., Reassessment of the paleoenvironment and preservation of hominid fossils from Hadar, Ethiopia, *Am J of Phys Anthropol*, 87(1):15-27, 1992. DOI: 10.1002/ajpa.1330870103
55. Johanson D.C. and Edey M.A., *Lucy: The Beginnings of Humankind*, Simon & Schuster, New York, p. 216, 1981.

have caused the demise of the hominins."[56]

Behrensmeyer concluded that the individuals did not die all at once and that they were washed in *"by a very gentle flow of water,"*[57] perhaps within weeks to no more than a few years after death. They still could have died from a predator of some sort, a few bones do show questionable traces of carnivore damage, but there was no reason to assume that they were *"struck down all at one time"*[58] as a single group. Behrensmeyer suggested that they could have been transported *"from a wider scatter on the adjacent floodplain."*[59] Summarizing the significance of her findings, Brian Switek writes:

> The initial hypothesis—that they were a family drowned and buried by a flash flood—was simple and neat, but Behrensmeyer's reanalysis of AL 333 forces us to throw out this narrative. Nor does the predation or surplus killing scenario presently have much direct evidence to support it. We may never know the exact circumstances of what killed these humans. If the AL 333 deposit represents an accumulation of bones washed off the nearby plain and mixed together—a good possibility, given the scrappy nature of other fossils found in association—then the circumstances by which each individual australopithecine died are almost entirely obscured.[60]

The implications of these findings are clear. If the individuals had died over an unknown period of time, at separate unknown locations prior to their deposition at the family site—then the claim that all 216 isolated bone and bone fragments belonged to a single species is highly unlikely.

Despite the controversy, Johanson has remained committed to the sudden group death hypothesis, apparently for strategic regions.[61] The argument that all of the bones belonged to a single family or group that was suddenly killed and buried would become crucial to Johanson's claim that all of those bones belonged to his reputed new species, Afarensis. But this is not what Johanson had originally claimed. Prior to the influence of Tim White (who would later join Johanson in his study of the Hadar bones), Johanson had offered a very different explanation for the First Family site. His initial interpretation was that the bones all belonged to *Homo*.[62] Several bones were described as looking indistinguishable from modern *H. sapiens*, and not at all like the australopiths. In a 1976 *National Geographic* article describing the First Family findings, Johanson writes:

56. Behrensmeyer A.K., Paleoenvironmental context of the Pliocene A.L. 333 "First Family" hominin locality, Hadar Formation, Ethiopia, *GSA Special Papers*, 446:203-214, 2008.

57. Johanson D.C. and Wong K., *Lucy's Legacy: The Quest for Human Origins*, Crown Publishing Group, New York, p. 96, 2009.

58. Johanson D.C., Ethiopia Yields First "Family" of Early Man, *National Geographic*, pp. 790-811, 1976.

59. Behrensmeyer A.K., Paleoenvironmental context of the Pliocene A.L. 333 "First Family" hominin locality, Hadar Formation, Ethiopia, GSA Special Papers, 446:203-214, 2008.

60. Switek B., What Killed the Hominins of AL 333?, *WIRED*. Accessed 06-07-18. https://www.wired.com/2011/01/what-killed-the-hominins-of-al-333/

61. Johanson no longer accepts the flash flood hypothesis but still tries to argue for a sudden group death by some other means. More recently he has suggested that *"maybe cats had chased some of the First Family into this area of mud or quicksand, where they became mired."* From: *Lucy's Legacy: The Quest for Human Origins*, p. 96.

62. Johanson D.C., Ethiopia Yields First "Family" of Early Man, *National Geographic*, pp. 790-811, 1976.

Reaching across the millenniums, hand bones from 333, arranged as a composite pair (above), bear an uncanny resemblance to our own—in size, shape, and function. The backs of the metacarpal heads have no ridges, so these individuals did not walk on their knuckles as African apes do. The thumb rotates, making it possible to manipulate tools with finesse. Prehistoric foot bones also appear. A fossil fifth metatarsal (upper left) corresponds closely to that of modern man.[63]

A paper published in *Journal of Human Evolution,* years after Johanson renamed his First Family bones to Afarensis, affirmed Johanson's original interpretation of the *"uncanny resemblance"* of the AL 333 hand to modern humans. Unfortunately, and despite the unmistakable human anatomy seen in the bones, they refused to attribute the hand to *H. sapiens* because of its presumed age and the absence of stone tools found in Hadar dating to that time period. However, recent findings have now confirmed the presence of stone tool use in Ethiopia, dating to the time of Lucy and the First Family site (see chapter 11). At any rate, these paleo-experts clearly describe the modern human configuration of the AL 333 hand. The only thing that prevented them from classifying it as a human hand was their commitment to the ape-to-man story. Paleo-experts David Alba *et al.* report:

> Our results indicate that *A. afarensis* possessed overall manual proportions, including an increased thumb/hand relationship that, contrary to previous reports, is fully human and would have permitted pad-to-pad human-like precision grip capability. We show that these human-like proportions in *A. afarensis* mainly result from hand shortening, as in modern humans, and that these conclusions are robust enough as to be non-dependent on whether the bones belong to a single individual or not. Since *A. afarensis* predates the appearance of stone tools in the archeological record, the above-mentioned conclusions permit a confident refutation of the null hypothesis that human-like manual proportions are an adaptation to stone tool-making, and thus alternative explanations must be therefore sought.[64]

Johanson also described a modern human-looking mandible that was recovered from the family site:

> In size and shape the jaw could fit a *Homo* skull discovered in Kenya by Richard Leakey... The Mandible is U-shaped, like those of humans today, not V-shaped like those of australopithecines. One evening, for a lark, members of the research expedition made clay casts of their own teeth; one woman's jaw bore a startling resemblance to a three-million-year-old specimen.[65]

In addition to these and a number of other bones that were described as resembling modern humans, distinctly ape-looking bones were recovered from the family site as well. For example, cranial and facial remains from adult and juvenile individuals (AL 333-1 and AL 333-105) revealed a distinctly ape-looking morphology. These were later more appropriately classified as *Australopithecus.* They were described

---

63. Johanson D.C., Ethiopia Yields First "Family" of Early Man, *National Geographic,* pp. 790-811, 1976.
64. Alba D.M. *et al.,* Morphological affinities of the *Australopithecus afarensis* hand on the basis of manual proportions and relative thumb length, *J Hum Evol,* 44(2):225-254, 2003.
65. Johanson D.C., Ethiopia Yields First "Family" of Early Man, *National Geographic,* pp. 790-811, 1976.

by Johanson in a later publication as displaying a number of features that are seen in other australopith species such as *Au. boisei*, *Au. africanus*, as well as pongids (apes). Johanson further noted the *"frequent lack of association between cranial and post-cranial elements."*[66] This observation is important because it shows that there was no way he could prove his assertion that the ape-looking cranial and facial remains belong to the owners of the modern human-looking postcranial bones described above. The coexistence of *Homo* and *Australopithecus* seen at other Hadar sites, was now being confirmed at the First Family site. But initially, Johanson attributed all of his first family bones to the human genus, *Homo*.

The remaining field seasons of the International Afar Research Expedition (1975–1977) were devoted to excavating all of the scattered hominin bones from the First Family hillside. There is little doubt that the First Family site contained numerous anatomically modern human-looking bones (as well as australopith bones) that Johanson later reassigned to his reputed new species, *Australopithecus afarensis*.

Mary Leakey and the Laetoli Expeditions (1974–1979)

Mary Leakey was the wife of paleo-expert Louis Leakey, and mother of Richard Leakey. In the 1960's the Leakey family had conducted breakthrough research in Olduvai Gorge, Tanzania. It was there that they found the hominin species named *Homo habilis*. It's association with stone tools and a presumed human-like hand earned its name "Handy Man"—the oldest toolmaker. Johanson himself was inspired by the Leakey's as he read about their exciting findings as a young man. By the 1970's Louis Leakey had passed away and Mary moved her camp 30 miles south of Olduvai to Laetoli to continue her investigations in geologically older strata. Richard would go on to head his own expeditions at Lake Turkana in northern Kenya, under the auspice of the Koobi Fora Research Project. His success there made him as famous as his father and mother.

Mary was convinced (along with her husband and her son Richard), that the origin of the genus *Homo* was already established sometime around 4–6 million years ago, or perhaps even earlier. This view meant that *Australopithecus* was not ancestral to the genus *Homo*—they were parallel lineages with a much older undiscovered common ancestor. The Leakey model postulated that *Homo* and *Australopithecus* coexisted extensively in the fossil record, hence australopiths did not give rise to *Homo*. Other paleo-experts would argue *Homo* first appeared much later, around the time of *Homo habilis* from Olduvai that dated no older than 2 million years. This was supposedly supported by the correlation of pig teeth fossils from Omo that were potassium-argon dated to 1.8 million years old. Those who embraced the younger date for the origin of *Homo* would not expect to find human bones dating much older than this. According to the "Johanson model", humans did not exist during the time of Lucy's species, Afarensis. Johanson believed that the

---

66. Johanson D.C., *ed.* Lars-Konig Konigsson, Pergamon Press, Early African Hominid Phylogenesis: A Re-Evaluation, *Current Argument on Early Man: Report from a Nobel Symposium*, 1978.

australopiths were ancestral to *Homo*, so finding human bones as old as Lucy would be impossible (and certainly unwelcome). Johanson's model conflicted with the Leakey model which asserted just the opposite—that human fossils should be found dating to the time of Afarensis, 3–4 million years ago (they were not convinced by the pig teeth).

Additional support for the Leakey model turned up in the early 70s in Koobi Fora, Kenya. Stone tools and a human-looking skull (KNM-ER 1470) were found by Richard and his team in an ash deposit called the KBS Tuff that dated nearly 3 million years old. Those findings sparked a heated controversy among the paleo-community. Did early man evolve 1.8 million years ago as seen at Olduvai, or 3 or more million years ago suggested by the findings in Koobi Fora? The dispute over when *Homo* first emerged became known as the "KBS Tuff Controversy" (discussed further in chapter 12).

Johanson seemed to originally embrace the Leakey model, but he would later change his mind—especially after the Bishop Conference in London in 1975, when the proponents of these two opposing models went toe-to-toe. Tim White found himself in the middle of the controversy. He had done well working under Richard Leakey in East Turkana, but during the 1977 field season, they engaged in a bitter dispute over the age of the KBS Tuff, which still had not been settled. At that time, White published a study on pig teeth from Turkana that correlated with the pig teeth from Omo.[67] His findings supported the earlier date for origin of *Homo* at 1.8 million years old. Richard was not happy about this. It meant that the older potassium-argon dates for the KBS Tuff (2.9 mya) were wrong, and so his fossils could no longer be seen as the earliest evidence for *Homo*. Their friendship came to an abrupt end. White left Turkana after that field season to join Richard's mother in Laetoli. Unfortunately, he didn't get along with her either. As White's relations with the Leakey's unraveled, his association with Johanson grew into a collaboration.

Johanson described White as a *"blunt and prickly man,"*[68] perhaps that's why he didn't get along too well with others—but Johanson liked him and they seemed to agree on certain key issues. Johanson had also come to accept the younger age for the timing of *Homo* based on the pig teeth, which was essential to support his (and White's) later claims that Afarensis was the early australopithecine ancestor that gave rise to *Homo*. In short, Johanson and White were both opposed to the Leakey model.

This historical context is helpful to keep in mind as we discuss the findings of Mary in Laetoli, Tanzania. Johanson's later reassessment—that Afarensis was an ancestral lineage leading to man—could only work if there were no *Homo* bones

---

67. White T.D., and Harris J.M., Suid evolution and correlation of African hominid localities, *Science* 198:13-21, 1997.
68. Johanson D.C. and Edey M.A., *Lucy: The Beginnings of Humankind*, Simon & Schuster, New York, p. 238, 1981.

contemporary with the 3–4-million-year-old Hadar deposits. The problem for Johanson was that the evidence for the presence of anatomically modern humans during that time period was continuing to grow—not only in Hadar (as he had initially reported on numerous occasions) and possibly Kenya, but also in Laetoli, Tanzania.

Mary Leakey's Findings—Some *Homo* Jawbones (1974–1975)

Field work was carried out by a multidisciplinary team of researchers in Laetoli between 1974 and 1979, headed by Mary Leakey.[69] During the first field season a member of Mary Leakey's African staff, Mwongela Mwoka, found a hominin premolar tooth. More fossils were recovered by Richard Leakey's highly trained "Hominid Gang" of fossil hunters who came to visit later that year. They found two lower jawbones, an upper jawbone, and several teeth. They were dated to between 3.59 and 3.77 million years old. This was older but within the same general time frame as Johanson's findings from Hadar. These were the same jawbones that the Leakey's compared with Johanson's when they met with him in Hadar, just before he found Lucy. During the second field season in 1975, additional jawbone fragments and isolated teeth were found.

Mary Leakey, Tim White, and colleagues reported their findings of 13 specimens of jawbones and teeth in the journal *Nature* in 1976.[70] White, who was working alongside Mary at that time, was responsible for writing the technical descriptions of her fossils (published in a separate paper). All of the hominin material discovered was assigned to *Homo*, representing the earliest members of the genus (3.6–3.7 mya). In their *Nature* paper it was noted that the jawbones and teeth resembled those found in Hadar that Johanson attributed to *Homo*—also published in *Nature* earlier that year.[71] The similarities seen in the jawbones and teeth would soon play a central role in Johanson's unilateral decision to reclassify all of the Hadar-Laetoli findings to his new species, Afarensis. One of the Laetoli fossils found by Mary's team was a weathered jawbone with teeth in place, designated LH-4. Interestingly, the poorly preserved jawbone would soon become the type specimen of Johanson's new species—a taxonomic maneuver that Mary would vehemently oppose—both ethically and scientifically. White, who had not been getting along well with Mary during the excavation of the Laetoli footprints would soon take sides with Johanson and rejoin with him to study his findings from Hadar. White parted ways with Mary after the 1978 field season, never to return.[72] He would

---

69. Leakey M., *Disclosing the Past: An Autobiography*, Rainbird Publishing Group Limited, New York, p. 179, 1984.

70. Leakey M.D., Hay R. L., Curtis G. H., Drake R.E., Jackes M. K., White T. D., Fossil hominids from the Laetolil beds, *Nature* 262:460-466, 1976.

71. Johanson D.C. and Taieb M., Plio-Pleistocene hominid discoveries in Hadar, Ethiopia, *Nature* 260(5549):293-297, 1976.

72. Leakey M., *Disclosing the Past: An Autobiography*, Rainbird Publishing Group Limited, New York, p. 178, 1984. *"Tim White was not there: he and I had ended the previous season on rather bad terms, for reasons that will become clear later."*

later withdraw the permission he had granted Mary, to reprint his descriptions of her Laetoli hominin jawbones and teeth.[73]

The fallout between Mary and White can be traced back to 1975, when Johanson brought his First Family haul of bones to Nairobi, Kenya—to show Mary and her son Richard. White also happened to be in Nairobi studying jawbones and teeth for his doctoral research alongside Mary. It was there that White first met Johanson. It was the beginning of a collaboration that has been described as *"one that was to have a tremendous impact on the science of paleoanthropology and on the community itself."*[74] Because of the heated controversy that would later transpire, Mary, would describe their meeting as *"a rather fateful event."* She writes in her autobiography:

> This was the occasion on which he and Don Johanson first met—a rather fateful event, as it turned out, because Tim White became deeply involved in the study of the Hadar hominid material for publication and was co-author of two reports on it which appeared in 1978 and 1979. At that time Tim White impressed me as a good scientist and a hard worker, if sometimes a little naïve. The purely descriptive reports he produced for me on the Laetoli hominid finds were clear and admirable, making no attribution of any hominid type. However, his interpretation of the Hadar material was to prove very controversial.[75]

Although the taxonomic assignment of the Hadar-Laetoli jawbones proved to be *"very controversial"*, a trail of fossilized footprints found in close proximity to the jawbones provided unequivocal evidence for the presence of *Homo* in Laetoli. However, this too would be challenged by Johanson and White. Like all of the other hominin fossils discussed so far, they would be reassigned to his new species, Afarensis—and in the process, throw the whole paleo-community into turmoil.

Mary Leakey's Findings—The Laetoli Footprints (1976–1979)

By far the most significant discovery from the Laetoli expeditions happened in 1976 when a few visiting scientists decided to throw dried lumps of elephant dung at each other. During the smelly debacle, paleontologist Andrew Hill fell onto what appeared to be a resistant layer preserving an extraordinary variety of animal footprints that were fossilized in ash. The exposure was marked Site A and contained tens of thousands of tracks from diverse African fauna—including trackways of insects, birds, apes, monkeys, rhinoceros, elephants, and much more. A total of 18 exposures were located and described in detail. The most exciting exposure was labeled site G, excavated during the 1978–1979 field seasons. White

---

73. *"M D. Leakey explains, not without a trace of annoyance, that T. D. White first granted and then withdrew his permission to reprint his descriptions from 1977 and 1980 (Am. J. Phys. Anthrop.)."* See: https://onlinelibrary. wiley.com/doi/abs/10.1002/jqs.3390030113; White T.D., New fossil hominids from Laetolil, Tanzania, *Amer. J. Phys. Anthro.*, 46:197-230, 1977.

74. Lewin R., *Bones of Contention*, University of Chicago Press, Chicago, p. 275, 1987.

75. Leakey M., *Disclosing the Past: An Autobiography*, Rainbird Publishing Group Limited, New York, p. 180, 1984.

was placed in charge of the excavation but parted ways with Mary after the 1978 field season. He had left on bad terms with Mary for reasons that will become clear later.[76] At site G, a worker spotted what appeared to be a human heel impression. As the covering soil was removed, more prints were exposed revealing an entire bipedal footprint trail cemented in the Laetoli ash. A parallel trail of larger footprints was found soon after, which were later found to be superimposed by the footprints of a smaller, third individual (Figure 8).

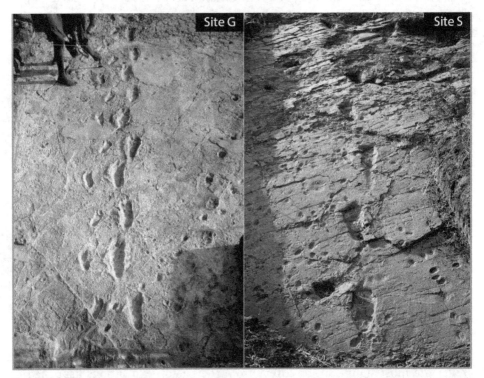

Figure 8. (Left) In 1976 British paleontologist Mary Leakey discovered footprints fossilized in volcanic ash in Laetoli, Tanzania. The track way (designated "site G") covers a distance of some 88 feet (27 m). Three individuals left the footprints—a child (G1) walked along the left side of an adult (G2) and a second intermediate-sized individual (G3) followed behind, occasionally stepping in the tracks of the adult. The footprints clearly show they walked upright on two feet. A number of anatomists who have examined the footprints have noted that they look identical to those of modern humans. Despite this, Johanson and colleagues have attributed the Laetoli footprints to Lucy's kind. (Right) In 2015, a dozen additional footprints were found less than 500 feet (150 m) south of site G (designated site S). The footprints belonged to two individuals who walked on the same surface and in the same direction as the G footprints discovered years earlier. The average foot length of the larger individual (S1) was 10.28 inches (261 mm). Had the individual lived today he could have worn a size 11 shoe size and would stand over 6 feet tall. Paleo-experts have nicknamed the larger individual after the *Star Wars* character "Chewie." Chewie's footprints are human in shape, size, and gait. These findings confirm the coexistence of *Homo* and *Australopithecus* during the time of Afarensis, therefore, Lucy's kind could not have been ancestral to *Homo* as Johanson claimed.

---

76. Reader J., *Missing Links*, Oxford University Press, New York, p. 410, 2011.

Mary described the fossil impressions as a well-preserved trail of *"undoubted human footprints"*[77] and *"remarkably similar to those of modern man."*[78] The trail of 77 footprints extended for a combined distance of 80 feet. They were left by three individuals of different stature, walking together in the same direction. Mary writes, *"It is tempting to see them as a man, a woman and a child. Whether or not this is so, the middle-sized individual was stepping deliberately in the prints left by the largest."*[79] The Laetoli G footprints were human in size, shape, and gait. They preserved a large heel impression, a well-developed arch, and a big toe in line with the other four toes (as opposed to a splayed out grasping toe like chimps)—totally consistent with the feet of modern humans. As Mary commented, *"The essentially human nature and modern appearance of the footprints were quite extraordinary."*[80] Bruce Latimer, evolutionary paleo-expert and expert on hominin foot anatomy, agreed saying, *"when I saw those footprints being excavated, I thought, gosh, you'd lose these on a modern-day beach, they have an arch and a totally human gait."*[81] White, who had begun the excavations with Mary, also acknowledged its striking similarities to modern human footprints:

> Make no mistake about it … They are like modern human footprints. If one were left in the sand of a Californian beach today, and a four-year old were asked what it was, he would instantly say that somebody had walked there. He wouldn't be able to tell it from a hundred other prints on the beach, nor would you. The external morphology is the same. There is a well-shaped modern heel with a strong arch and a good ball of the foot in front it. The big toe is straight in line. It doesn't stick out to the side like an ape toe, or like the big toe in so many drawings you see of australopithecines in books.[82]

Distinguished primate morphologist and paleo-expert from University of Chicago, Russell Tuttle, was called on to carefully analyze the Laetoli footprint trail. Tuttle concluded in the *American Journal of Physical Anthropology*, *"In discernible features, the Laetoli G prints are indistinguishable from those of habitually barefoot Homo sapiens."*[83] Paleo-expert Michael Day and colleague performed a detailed comparison of the Laetoli footprints with modern humans.[84] Day summarizes their findings that were reported in *Nature*, stating:

77. Leakey M., *Disclosing the Past: An Autobiography*, Rainbird Publishing Group Limited, New York, p. 176, 1984.
78. Lewin R., *Bones of Contention*, University of Chicago Press, Chicago, p. 279, 1987.
79. Leakey M., *Disclosing the Past: An Autobiography*, Rainbird Publishing Group Limited, New York, p. 178, 1984.
80. Leakey M., *Disclosing the Past: An Autobiography*, Rainbird Publishing Group Limited, New York, p. 177, 1984.
81. Kaplan M., These bones were made for walking, *Nature News*, February 10, 2011. DOI:10.1038/news.2011.85
82. Johanson D.C. and Edey M.A., *Lucy: The Beginnings of Humankind*, Simon & Schuster, New York, p. 250, 1981.
83. Tuttle R.H. and Webb D.M., The Pattern of Little Feet, *Am J Phys Anthropol* 78(2):316, 1989.
84. Day M.H. and Wickens E.H., Laetoli Pliocene hominid footprints and bipedalism, *Nature* 286, 385-387, 1980.

Details of the footprints, analysed by photogrammetry, have been given and comparisons drawn with modern human experimental footprints (Day and Wickens, 1980; Day, 1985). These studies conclude that the form of the foot during bipedal walking, are remarkably similar to those of modern human habitually unshod [bare-footed].[85]

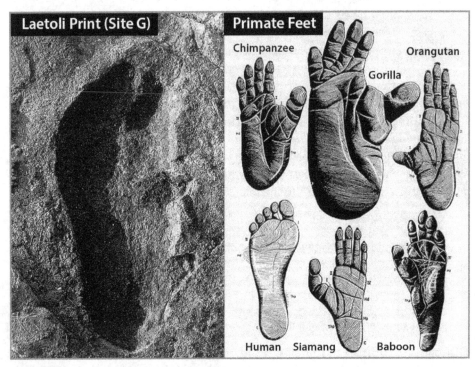

Figure 9. In a side-by-side comparison with the human and ape soles, it is clear that the fossilized Laetoli footprints are anatomically human. Leading evolutionary paleo-experts (such as Mary Leakey and Russell Tuttle, among others) directly involved with in-depth analyses of the footprints, have acknowledged that they are indistinguishable from modern human footprints.

Figure 9 shows a close view of a fossilized Laetoli footprint found in the volcanic ash tuff, contrasted with the feet of human and anthropoid apes. An opposable, thumb-like great toe used for arboreal locomotion (called an abducted hallux) is a fundamental characteristic of all apes. The presence of a limb-grasping free great toe is such a distinct trait that evolutionary anatomists regard it as the *"sine qua non* [the essential condition] *of primate arboreality."*[86] It is clear that the fossilized footprints from Laetoli lack a divergent grasping toe. They are totally discordant with the feet of any type of ape. As Owen Lovejoy, functional anatomist from Kent State University explains:

When we compare the Laetoli prints to that of a chimpanzee the difference is immediately obvious. The chimpanzee which is a quadruped... still has a free great

---

85. Day M.H., *Guide to Fossil Man*, 4th Edition, University of Chicago Press, Chicago, p.189, 1985.
86. Latimer B. and Lovejoy C.O., Hallucal tarsometatarsal joint in *Australopithecus afarensis, Am J Phys Anthropol*, 82:125-133, 1990.

toe and that great toe extends out away from the foot and leaves a very distinct mark. On the other hand, when we compare the Laetoli print to that of a crime scene human print, they're virtually indistinguishable. The great toe is in line with the rest of the toes and what this has done in the human and the Laetoli print is to create an arch, and that's a hallmark of typical modern upright locomotion.[87]

If there is such widespread agreement amongst the paleo-community that the Laetoli footprints are *"indistinguishable from those of modern humans"*, why didn't they conclude that they were formed by *H. sapiens* or *H. erectus*? The reason has everything to do with scientific politics and deeply entrenched evolutionary preconceptions. The Laetoli footprints were potassium-argon dated to be nearly 3.7 million years old—according to Johanson, this was far too old be attributed to any member of the genus *Homo*. The model of human origins that was favored by the paleo-community at that time (and is still widely taught today), insisted that anatomically modern *H. sapiens/H. erectus* had not lived during the time of Lucy's kind, Afarensis. If that were the case, it would be untenable for Johanson to claim that his reputed new species gave rise to the genus *Homo*. And so, for the next few years the Laetoli footprints would not be assigned to any hominin species.[88] Yet Johanson would argue that the Laetoli footprints were made by his reputed new species, Afarensis. But in order for his claim to sound credible, he would have to prove two crucial points: 1) that Afarensis is a sound taxon, and 2) that Afarensis had remarkably modern-looking human feet.[89] Neither of these points have ever been conclusively established, leading to ongoing debates in the paleo-community.

Implications of Mary Leakey's Findings—Presence of *Homo* at Laetoli

The Laetoli footprint trail dated 3.6–3.7 million years old using potassium-argon dating, the same age assigned to the jawbones and teeth that were found nearby. Mary's description of the Laetoli footprints were published in the journal *Nature* in 1979.[90] It was (or should have been) clear evidence that *Homo* had existed during the time of Afarensis in Tanzania. Not only was there evidence of *Homo* in Laetoli from a well-preserved footprint trail, Richard Leakey had also found a human-looking skull and stone tools in Kenya. They were found in and below a volcanic ash bed that was originally dated 2.6–3.0 million years old. But the findings from Kenya were soon re-dated to a younger age to agree with the then favored evolutionary model, which placed the origin of the genus *Homo* at 1.8 million years old (see chapter 12, "KBS Tuff Controversy"). Not surprisingly, the re-dating of the KBS Tuff was supported by both Johanson and White. The younger dates

---

87. WGBH Educational Foundation. Laetoli Footprints. PBS Video, Evolution: Library: Laetoli Footprints, 2001. Accessed 08/08/14: http://www.pbs.org/wgbh/nova/transcripts/2106hum1.html
88. Day M.H., *Guide to Fossil Man*, 4th Edition, University of Chicago Press, Chicago, p.191, 1985.
89. Anatomically modern human foot bones have been found at Hadar (such as a fourth metatarsal bone), however, these are typically isolated finds. They are not associated with a more complete Afarensis skeleton. Such bones may look strikingly human simply because they are human.
90. Leakey M.D. and Hay R.L., Pliocene footprints in the Laetolil Beds at Laetoli, northern Tanzania, *Nature* 278:317-323, 1979.

assigned to Richard's *Homo* bones and stone tools would no longer be an obstacle for Johanson's reassessment. But Mary's Laetoli jawbones and footprints—as well as Johanson's own fossils from Hadar, which he had also assigned to *Homo*—still stood in his way. As long as the Hadar-Laetoli findings were attributed to the genus *Homo*, it would be a hard sell for Johanson and White to claim Lucy and her kind had given rise to early man. Their new claim to fame would not allow a single bone dating to the time of Afarensis (3–4 mya), to be assigned to the genus *Homo*. To establish their reputed new species as the ancestor to all later hominins, all of the *Homo* bones would have to be reclassified. What Johanson did next is almost as shocking as his gravesite raid.

Johanson Reassessment (1978, 1979)—"They All Belong to Lucy's Kind!"

Let's summarize all of the evidence supporting the presence of *Homo* in Hadar and Laetoli that led up to their major reassessment in 1978. Prior to 1978, Johanson and co-leaders of the IARE had reported on numerous occasions that their Hadar collection contained a commixture of at least two distinct hominin species, belonging in separate genera—*Homo* and *Australopithecus* (see sections above). As discussed, this was widely publicized in several popular press releases, including major news sources and popular magazines like *National Geographic*. Their findings were also published in the primary scientific literature. In the journal *Nature* (1976), Johanson and Taieb reported the presence of gracile and robust australopiths, as well as small and large *Homo* bones. They noted that some of their Hadar specimens closely resembled two known taxa, *Au. africanus* and *Au. robustus*, and others resembled *H. erectus* specimens from East Turkana, Kenya. As Johanson writes, *"I was convinced that there were two species at Hadar."*[91]

The bones that they had described in their *Nature* report were found in the first two field seasons (1973-1974). To their credit, they cautioned that their report was a preliminary assessment and subject to later revision as more fossils were examined.[92] Just as they had hoped, more fossils were found in the following field season in 1975. The First Family site contained over 200 bones. At that time, Johanson had attributed them to the genus *Homo*, which further supported their preliminary assessment. The fossil evidence revealing the presence of *Homo* in Hadar was very strong. In fact, many of those bones were described by Johanson as looking remarkably similar to modern *H. sapiens*, as researchers still acknowledge today. Yet it would become clear as the collection was further studied that the First Family displayed a substantial range of anatomical variation, some bones looked distinctly human-like (*Homo*) and others looked distinctly like ape-like (australopith). All parties, including the Leakey's, seemed to agree that the Hadar

---

91. Johanson D.C. and Edey M.A., *Lucy: The Beginnings of Humankind*, Simon & Schuster, New York, p. 257, 1981.
92. Johanson D.C., *ed.* Lars-Konig Konigsson, Pergamon Press, Early African Hominid Phylogenesis: A Re-Evaluation, *Current Argument on Early Man: Report from a Nobel Symposium*, 1978. Johanson cautioned, *"identifications and phylogenetic interpretations of the Hadar material should be considered very preliminary."*

collection belonged to two or more species from separate genera. At the end of the 1975 IARE field season, Johanson brought his First Family collection of bones to Nairobi to show the Leakey's (when White was present) and other accompanying scientists. Mary comments on what seemed to be apparent to them:

> To me and Richard, it seemed that they included a considerable range of variation, such that there must be at least two hominid types present. Lucy herself was a very small creature and seemed to us distinctive in several morphological details. The jaw and teeth, for example, had many primitive features, although the leg bones seemed to show that she had been fully bipedal. In contrast, several of the other Hadar hominins were much larger and seemed to us far more *Homo*-like than australopithecine. There was nothing unusual in the idea that two different kinds of hominids should be contemporary in one region... At East Turkana, Richard has an early *Homo erectus* which is demonstrably contemporary with a late robust australopithecine.[93]

It seemed clear to everyone who had looked at the fossils that the Hadar-Laetoli sample revealed the coexistence of two distinct genera, *Homo* and *Australopithecus*, just as the Leakey's had observed in both Olduvai Gorge, Tanzania and in East Turkana, Kenya. As one of *Nature's* anonymous paleoanthropology correspondents wrote:

> The Lake Turkana and Hadar discoveries have provided virtually unquestionable evidence that at least two forms of hominid had coexisted.... The second implication of the new fossil material is that the genus *Homo* may be far older than previously thought.[94]

If all parties agreed that the Hadar-Laetoli collection consisted of a commixture of human and australopith bones, how did Johanson and White justify reclassifying all of the human bones to an entirely different genus?

Johanson and White's rationale was primarily based on the jawbones and dentition (this was Johanson and White's area of expertise). The similar-looking jawbones was the broom that they used to sweep all of the Hadar-Laetoli bones into their new species, *Au. afarensis*.

Things became muddied because some of the Laetoli jawbones Mary had attributed to *Homo* appeared to have been misclassified, and those misclassified jawbones closely resembled Johanson's jawbones from Hadar, which he had also attributed to *Homo*. White noticed this when he examined Johanson's Hadar fossils in Nairobi, and he made sure to share his opinion with Johanson. Johnson tells of the impact White's observation had on him, saying, *"Tim discussed some of the fossils Mary Leakey was beginning to find at Laetoli. Finally, he stepped forward to examine the Hadar specimens. After looking at them, he said something that I will never forget: "I think your fossils from Hadar and Mary's fossils from Laetoli are the same." He*

---

93. Leakey M., *Disclosing the Past: An Autobiography*, Rainbird Publishing Group Limited, New York, p. 177, 1984.
94. Lewin R., *Bones of Contention*, University of Chicago Press, Chicago, 2nd edition, p. 273, 1997.

showed me a couple of them. They seemed nearly identical."[95]

Mary's jawbones from Laetoli really did appear to belong to *Australopithecus* (not *Homo*).[96] And they also happened to look a lot like Johanson's jawbones from Hadar, just as Mary had pointed out in her 1976 *Nature* paper (compare AL-400 with LH-4). This was an observation that Johanson would later use as a basis for his claim that they all belonged to his new species, *Afarensis*. Conveniently, White was responsible for the descriptions of the Laetoli jawbones (on behalf of Mary)[97] and now he would be working with Johanson as he prepared the descriptions of the Hadar jawbones. White's study of the Hadar and Laetoli jawbones made him a sort of "middle man", which was an ideal circumstance for them to build a case for their new story. From that point on, Johanson and White had met on and off, working together to devise a radical new hypothesis for the Hadar-Laetoli findings; one that would change the course of paleoanthropology.

During the summer of 1977, Johanson and White met together in the basement of the Cleveland Museum of Natural history where they lined up the jawbones from Laetoli and Hadar. White had noticed that the jawbones from Laetoli closely resembled the ones he was studying from Hadar. It was during this time of collaboration that Johanson and White decided (behind Mary's back) that the Hadar and Laetoli material needed to be treated together as a single species. But now the jawbones from Laetoli and Hadar, which were both originally classified as *Homo*, would be reclassified as *Australopithecus*. This is the part of the story that seems reasonable. Many of the features seen in the Hadar and Laetoli jawbones suggested a far more ape-like anatomy, as seen in australopiths.[98]

However, not all of the Hadar-Laetoli jawbones looked similar. For example, some of the Hadar jawbones were V-shaped (including Lucy's) and significantly smaller. They looked distinct from the others in both size and morphology, as Johanson and the Leakey's had observed. Johanson wondered, *"It had an odd lower jaw that came together in a V-shape at the front. Alemayehu's jaws were not V-shaped. Did they represent a different species?"*[99] Elsewhere, Johanson writes:

> And then there was Lucy. Her jaw was very different. First of all it was clearly smaller, Second, the dental arcade was V-shaped. …Halfway through the analysis I was more convinced than ever that she was a different species from the bigger jaws at Hadar,

---

95. Johanson D.C. and Edey M.A., *Lucy: The Beginnings of Humankind*, Simon & Schuster, New York, p. 218, 1981.

96. Mary's rationale for attributing them to *Homo* was questionable. Mary actually acknowledged that *"They have many characteristics that are very similar to those of Australopithecus."* However, she classified her Laetoli bones as *Homo* because she saw them as the only *"possible candidate for an ancestral form of Homo at this particular date."* In other words, her taxonomic assignment of the jawbones and teeth was based more on speculation than anatomy. See Leakey R.E., *The Making of Mankind*, Rainbird Publishing Group Limited, p. 67, 1981.

97. White T.D., New fossil hominids from Laetolil, Tanzania, *Am J Phys Anthropol.*, 46:197-230, 1977.

98. Johanson D.C. and Edey M.A., *Lucy: The Beginnings of Humankind*, Simon & Schuster, New York, p. 276, 1981.

99. Johanson D.C. and Edey M.A., *Lucy: The Beginnings of Humankind*, Simon & Schuster, New York, p. 217, 1981.

including some from the First Family site. On the other hand, some of the First Family jaws were small and Lucy-like.[100]

At least one other jawbone seemed out of place—one that Johanson had described in *National Geographic* as looking virtually identical to modern humans. At first, Johanson was convinced that these "out-of-place" jawbones belonged to a different taxon. He argued vigorously with White about it during several visits before finally caving in and agreeing with him that they too could be subsumed into a single highly variable *Australopithecus* species. Having finally agreed, they were now ready to present their "new species" to the world.

Largely on the basis of the few similar-looking jawbones and cranial material, Johanson and White claimed that the entire Hadar-Laetoli collection of around 300-plus bone and bone fragments, all belonged to a single hominin species, *Australopithecus afarensis*—the ancestral stock from which all later hominins arose, including the genus *Homo*. All of the *Homo* and ape-like australopith bones that Johanson *et al.* had reported as belonging to separate genera were now all reassigned to one species, Afarensis. Included among them were the bones that Johanson and others had described as looking virtually identical to *H. sapiens*, such as the human-looking knee joints (large and small), human-looking distal femurs, human-looking hands, human-looking foot bones, and more. The entire First Family collection of 216 isolated bones, and also all of the bones nicknamed "Lucy", were reclassified. And not only did Johanson reclassify his own *Homo*-designated specimens from Hadar as Afarensis—he attributed Mary's *Homo* bones and human-looking Laetoli footprints to Afarensis as well.

White was involved with the excavation of the Laetoli footprints during the 1978 field season. Both White and Johanson were convinced that the footprints looked virtually identical to those of modern humans. Johanson insisted that Lucy's kind must have formed the Laetoli footprints even though the feet of Lucy were missing, and the other foot bones from Hadar were isolated finds that could not unambiguously be assigned to the same species. More importantly, the Laetoli footprints dated half a million years older than the Hadar bones, and they were found 1,000 miles away. Richard considered this to be *"an audacious move that raised many eyebrows among evolutionary biologists."*[101]

Johanson and White *et al.* first announced the naming of their reputed new species, *Au. afarensis* in the house journal of the Cleveland Museum of Natural History, *Kirtlandia* in 1978.[102] A more in-depth reassessment was published in their 1979

---

100. Johanson D.C. and Shreeve J., *Lucy's Child: The Discovery of a Human Ancestor*, Early Man Publishing, Inc., New York, p. 107, 1989.
101. Leakey R.E. and Lewin R., *Origins Reconsidered: In Search of What Makes Us Human*, Anchor Books (Doubleday), New York, p. 114-116, 1992.
102. Johanson D.C., White T.D., Coppens Y., A New Species of the Genus *Australopithecus* (Primates: Hominidae) From the Pliocene of Eastern Africa, *Kirtlandia*, 28:1-14, 1978.

Science paper, A Systematic Assessment of Early African Hominids.[103] Johanson's famous Y-shaped diagram with the Laetoli-Hadar hominins (representing Afarensis) positioned at the base of the tree as the ancestor to all later hominins was first shown in this paper.

Nobel Symposium (1978)—Johanson's "Surprise Attack"

Johanson was invited to speak at the Royal Swedish Academy of Sciences, for a Nobel Symposium on the Early Argument for Man, held in late May 1978, in honor of the 200th anniversary of the death of Carolus Linnaeus. His presentation was entitled *Early African Hominid Phylogenesis: A Re-evaluation.*[104] As the son of immigrants from Sweden, Johanson saw it as the perfect opportunity to announce his new species to *"some of paleoanthropology's most accomplished scholars"*[105] who would be attending. Unfortunately, his one-species proposal didn't go nearly as well as he had hoped.

Johanson was unaware that Mary was present in the meeting when he made his bold new claims. Mary was supposed to be the co-author of their upcoming joint paper on the Hadar-Laetoli findings, but she had no idea that Johanson and White had decided to reclassify her Laetoli findings to their new species, Afarensis.[106] Johanson even elected one of Mary's jawbones (LH-4) as the type specimen for his species, when he could have used any of his better-preserved specimens from Hadar. To Mary, this was like adding insult to injury. As Reader recounts:

> White knew Johanson who was then busy preparing his formal description of the Afar material. Because of the similarities that had been noted between the two collections, it was obviously sensible that White and Johanson should compare and discuss the finer points of the fossils, but certainly not inevitable, or even to be expected, that they would publish a joint paper grouping the material together— the Laetoli and Afar fossils—as the remains of an entirely new australopithecine species, with the mandible Mary Leakey had said was *Homo* formally described as the type specimen of the new taxon. When she invited White to describe the Laetoli material, Mary Leakey was confident there were two species to be named. The Laetoli specimens were all *Homo* in her view, and even her critics seemed to agree that the large and small specimens from Afar must represent two distinct species.[107]

Mary was furious! She demanded that her name be removed from their upcoming publication. This was not the reaction Johanson had hoped for. Their dispute over the taxonomic assignment of the Hadar-Laetoli fossils created a rift between them

---

103. Johanson D., White T. D., A Systematic Assessment of Early African Hominids, *Science* 203(4378):321-330, 1979.

104. Johanson D.C., *ed.* Lars-Konig Konigsson, Pergamon Press, Early African Hominid Phylogenesis: A Re-Evaluation, *Current Argument on Early Man: Report from a Nobel Symposium*, 1978.

105. Johanson D.C. and Wong K., Crown Publishing Group, New York, *Lucy's Legacy: The Quest for Human Origins*, p. 19, 2009.

106. Reader J., *Missing Links*, Oxford University Press, New York, p. 386, 2011. Reader notes, *"There would be no pre-announcement. The new species would remain a secret until Johanson gave his talk at the Symposium."*

107. Reader J., *Missing Links*, Oxford University Press, New York, p. 383, 2011.

as deep as the Great Rift Valley itself (Johanson's controversial reassessment of the Hadar-Laetoli fossils is discussed further in chapter 11). Other members of the paleo-community were equally unimpressed by Johanson's paper. As Reader says, *"The reaction was decidedly low."*[108] Johanson writes that his presentation was met with *"dead silence"* and *"immediate skepticism… most of the guests were unconvinced. How could I be sure that all of the Hadar hominids were of a single species?".*[109] A number of prominent members of the paleo-community who were in attendance, including Philip Tobias, Alan Walker, Andrew Hill, and Richard Leakey (all members of the East Turkana Research Project) expressed strong scientific opposition. They argued that the range of variation seen in the Hadar-Laetoli sample was far too extensive to be from a single species.

While the whole field was convinced that the Hadar-Laetoli collection of bones was a taxonomic mix of *Australopithecus* (ape) and *Homo* (human), Johanson and White were suddenly insisting that all those mixed and diverse bones from diverse parts of East Africa constituted a single hypodigm (i.e., all those bones constituted the complete representation of a single species). How did Johanson and White explain the great range of variation in size and morphology seen in the Hadar-Laetoli collection of bones? In his Nobel Symposium proceedings paper, Johanson provides his best explanation:

> It is best to interpret the new material as representing a distinctive early hominid taxon, *A. afarensis*, which is typified by considerable sexual dimorphism. Previously, provisional suggestions have been offered to imply two hominid taxa at Hadar, but at the present time the available evidence cannot be used convincingly to support such a hypothesis. *Australopithecus afarensis* possesses a complex of primitive, cranial, dental and perhaps post-cranial traits which, when taken together, characterize a new taxon which has important implications for early hominid phylogeny.[110]

To explain the substantial range of variation in the Afarensis hypodigm, Johanson and White proposed that it was due to sexual dimorphism, a phenomenon observed in living apes, such as gorillas, where males are significantly larger than females. Sexual dimorphism was used to explain the significant range of variation in the jawbones, as well as the impressive range of variation seen in the postcranial bones. However, the variation seen in the Hadar sample was not merely about size, it was variation in postcranial morphology suggesting to paleo-expert two fundamentally different forms of locomotion—a level of sexual dimorphism that has never been observed among any living primate species (discussed below). Not surprisingly, Johanson's sexual dimorphism hypothesis raised many suspicions in the paleo-community. Some rejected his one-species claim and others tried to make sense out of the wide range of variation in both size and functional anatomy,

108. Reader J., *Missing Links*, Oxford University Press, New York, p. 386, 2011.
109. Johanson D.C. and Wong K., *Lucy's Legacy: The Quest for Human Origins*, Crown Publishing Group, New York, p. 20-21, 2009.
110. Johanson D.C., *ed.* Lars-Konig Konigsson, Pergamon Press, Early African Hominid Phylogenesis: A Re-Evaluation, *Current Argument on Early Man: Report from a Nobel Symposium*, 1978.

resulting in competing views in the paleo-community with regard to how Afarensis locomoted. This led to bizarre and even humorous stories suggesting that the Afarensis males looked and acted like humans, while the females looked and acted like apes. Paleo-experts, Fred Smith and Matt Cartmill acknowledge that to this day, *"the dispute continues unresolved in the scientific literature."*[111]

Two Competing Views—Arborealists vs Terrestrialists (1979–Present)

In the classic work, *Guide to Fossil Man*, paleo-expert Michael Day outlines how Johanson and colleagues have depicted Afarensis:

> In general terms the remains are those of primitive hominids of australopithecine type with small brains, evidence of the ability to stand upright, some primitive dental and cranial features and (if the sample from Hadar is drawn from one species, a matter of current debate) a very wide range of sexual dimorphism.[112]

At the core of this ongoing debate is the widely-recognized observation that some of the postcranial bones in the Afarensis hypodigm look distinctly like apes, whereas other postcranial bones look distinctly like modern humans. Paleo-experts in the *Proceedings of the National Academy of Sciences* describe this observation as a *"persistent arboreal-terrestrial dichotomy."*[113] This dichotomy has sparked contentious debates about the validity of the sexual dimorphism hypothesis and how the reputed species locomoted. Did Afarensis walk habitually upright in a manner that is *"virtually identical to that of modern humans"*[114] as Johanson, White, and others have argued? Or did Afarensis live among the trees and move about more like apes? There are two major competing views within the paleo-community. Johanson refers to these two groups as the "arborealists" and the "terrestrialists" (others refer to the latter group as "bipedalists"). Johanson explains:

> The former group, led by Jack Stern at Stony Brook University, sees *A. afarensis* as having spent lots of time climbing, whereas the terrestrials' view, championed by Owen Lovejoy, holds that *A. afarensis* was essentially a ground-walking biped.[115]

Arborealists tend to emphasize certain distinctly ape-like specimens from Hadar, in order to support their claim that Afarensis was predominantly a tree-dwelling species, like living apes.

Terrestrialists do just the reverse—they emphasize specific postcranial bones in the Afarensis hypodigm that look distinctly like those of modern humans to support

111. Cartmill M. and Smith F.H., *The Human Lineage*, Wiley-Blackwell, Hoboken, NJ, p. 176, 2009.

112. Day, M.H. and Wickens, E.H. Laetoli Plicocene hominid footprints and bipedalism, *Nature* 286, 385-387, 1980.

113. Venkataraman V.V. *et al.*, Tree climbing and human evolution, *Proc Natl Acad Sci*, USA 110(4):1237-1242, 2013. https://doi.org/10.1073/pnas.1208717110

114. Johanson D.C., ed. Lars-Konig Konigsson, Pergamon Press, Early African Hominid Phylogenesis: A Re-Evaluation, *Current Argument on Early Man: Report from a Nobel Symposium*, 1978.

115. Johanson D.C. and Wong K., *Lucy's Legacy: The Quest for Human Origins*, Crown Publishing Group, New York, p. 145, 2009.

their claim that Afarensis walked habitually upright, just like us. Terrestrialists will emphasize many of the same Hadar bones described earlier in this chapter that Johanson described as looking virtually indistinguishable from *H. sapiens*, such as the human-looking knee joints and the human-looking femoral heads in the Hadar collection. Or they will point to more recent discoveries such as a partial skeleton (KSD VP-1/1) that was found in Woranso-Mille in the Afar region of Ethiopia.[116] This skeleton was much taller than Lucy, and was nicknamed "Kadanuumuu" which means, "Big Man". It was dated to 3.6 million years old and was included in the Afarensis hypodigm. According to paleo-expert Haile Selassie, *"It had long legs and a torso and a pelvis more like a modern human than an African ape, showing that fully upright walking was in place at this early date."*[117] The anatomy seen in the knee joint, pelvis, ribcage, shoulder blade, neck vertebra, and the overall body proportions neatly align with *H. sapiens/H. erectus*.

In fact, paleo-expert Carol Ward from the University of Missouri compares Big Man to the nearly complete "Turkana Boy" (*H. erectus*) skeleton which displays a modern human body skeleton (Figure 10). She concludes that Afarensis and Turkana Boy, *"weren't really different, especially from the neck down… the picture is that there is not a dramatic change here in the origin of Homo that has anything to do with the postcranial skeleton."*[118] Ward also points to additional bones in the Afarensis hypodigm that she describes as looking just like modern *H. sapiens*, such as an isolated fourth metatarsal bone. There can be no doubt that Ward (a committed terrestrialist) aims to portray Afarensis as a habitual biped with a modern human postcranial skeleton, much like ours. Of course, this is expected because she is specifically emphasizing the human-looking specimens in the Afarensis hypodigm.

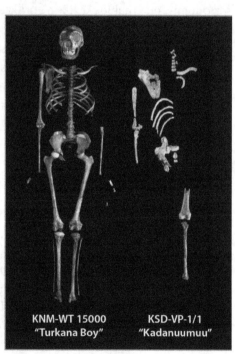

KNM-WT 15000   KSD-VP-1/1
"Turkana Boy"   "Kadanuumuu"

Figure 10. The resemblance of the Kadanuumuu skeleton (Afarensis) to the modern human body plan seen in Turkana Boy (Erectus) is striking.

116. Haile-Selassie Y. *et al.*, An early *Australopithecus afarensis* postcranium from Woranso-Mille, Ethiopia, *Proc Natl Acad Sci.*, USA 107(27):12121-12126, 2010. https://doi.org/10.1073/pnas.1004527107

117. Gibbons A., Oldest Skeleton of Lucy's Species Unveiled, June 22, 2010. http://www.sciencemag.org/news/2010/06/oldest-skeleton-lucys-species-unveiled

118. Ward C., Origins of Genus *Homo*. Recorded on 02/05/2016. Series: CARTA–Center for Academic Research and Training in Anthropogeny [4/2016] [Science] [Show ID: 30632]. Timecode 37:00. https://www.youtube.com/watch?v=9W005V6OV_E

The human-looking Afarensis specimens like Big Man and the fourth metatarsal bone (discussed below) further confirm the dichotomous nature of the Afarensis hypodigm. The human-looking bones directly conflict with the comparable ape-looking bones. For example, paleo-experts describe the shoulder blade (scapula) of the juvenile partial skeleton nicknamed "Salem" (DIK 1-1) as having a "cranial oriented" shoulder that looks virtually identical to that of a young gorilla.[119,120] However, other experts in the field provide *"an alternative interpretation"* because the human-looking Big Man skeleton preserves a *"scapula that lacks the similarity to Gorilla that is reported for DIK 1-1 [Salem],"* and *"differs from that of African apes in having a less cranial orientation of the spine, which is a feature that best differentiates human scapulas (2-4). It is further similar to human scapulars in features associated with a primary manipulatory function of the upper limb..."*[121] Put simply, it appears that there are two distinct shoulder morphs in the Afarensis hypodigm—one that looks like a gorilla and one that looks like a modern human.

The partial foot and isolated foot bones from the First Family site in Hadar is another example of conflicting or dichotomous anatomies seen in the Afarensis hypodigm. An evolutionary anatomists from Stony Brook University, Randall Susman describes the partial foot (AL 333-115) in the journal *Foot & Ankle* as *"strikingly similar to chimpanzees."* He states further, *"The proximal phalanges of AL 333- 115 are, in overall morphological pattern, like those of African apes."*[122] Like true arborealists, Susman and his colleague Jack Stern conclude in a separate study that Afarensis must have been a tree-dwelling species and could not have been a fully committed biped that walked upright like modern humans.[123] They also cited evidence for the presence of a grasping big toe, as has been suggested in at least two other studies by Tuttle (1981) and Deloison (1991).[124,125]

As expected, the terrestrialists dispute the Stony Brook team's interpretation of the Hadar foot and offer the exact opposite interpretation. Paleo-expert Bruce Latimer of Case Western Reserve University, who Johanson had put in charge of analyzing the Hadar foot, insisted it is essentially a modern human foot with an adducted hallux (i.e., big toe in line with the other four). Johanson writes that Afarensis had, *"feet that were functionally the same as those of modern humans. ... But structurally they are a little different. The Afarensis phalanges are arched, and proportionally a*

119. Alemseged Z. et al., A juvenile early hominin skeleton from Dikika, Ethiopia, *Nature* 443:296-301, 2006.

120. Young NM et al., Fossil hominin shoulders support an African ape-like last common ancestor of humans and chimpanzees. *Proc Natl Acad Sci* 112(38):11829–11834, 2015.

121. Melillo S.M., An alternative interpretation of the *Australopithecus* scapula, *Proc Natl Acad Sci* 112(52):2015. DOI: 10.1073/pnas.1520902112

122. Susman R.L., Evolution of the human foot: evidence from Plio Pleistocene hominids, *Foot and Ankle* 3(6):365-376, 1983.

123. Stern J.T. and Susman R.L., The Locomotor Anatomy of *Australopithecus afarensis*, *Am J Phys Anthro* 60:279-317, 1983.

124. Tuttle R.H., Evolution of hominid bipedalism and prehensile capabilities, *Phil Trans Royal Soc London Series B.*, 1981.

125. Deloison Y., Les australopitheques marchaient—ils comme nous? In *Origine(s) de la Bipédie chez les Hominidés*, 1991.

good deal longer than those of modern feet. They might also be mistaken for finger bones."[126] Suspiciously, Latimer and Lovejoy reconstructed the Hadar foot using an anatomically modern human foot fossil recovered from Olduvai Gorge (OH 8) as a template.[127] As committed terrestrialists, they saw no problem with this. Other paleo-experts view this as unacceptable bias, especially the arborealists.[128,129] To explain the especially long toes, Latimer speculated they *"may have been of service to it in moving over rough stony ground, or in mud, where some slight gripping ability might have been useful."*[130] Clearly, the debate is far from settled. But a new discovery of a fourth metatarsal bone (AL 333-160) gave the terrestrialists confidence that their locomotor model of Afarensis is correct. The fourth metatarsal is a long bone of the mid foot which has a diagnostic "articular configuration"—which simply means it is possible to tell whether the foot functioned like the flexible midfoot of an ape (called a midtarsal break) or the ridged midfoot of a human that bears a strong longitudinal arch.

In 2011, Ward, Kimbel, and Johanson (all proponents of the terrestrial model) published an article in *Science* describing the foot bone recovered by sieving eroded surface sediments at the First Family site.[131] Ward *et al.* claimed that the isolated foot bone belonged to Afarensis. In their paper they described it as looking indistinguishable from modern humans, clearly displaying a longitudinal arch. The anatomy suggested to these researchers that Afarensis walked upright and was not flat-footed like apes. Ironically, the morphology seen in the fourth metatarsal bone directly conflicted with the descriptions of the partial Hadar foot found from the same dig site in the 70s (First Family site). For example, paleo-experts Russel Tuttle *et al.* in the journal *Human Evolution* described the Hadar foot as lacking a longitudinal arch.[132] In a separate study, William Harcourt-Smith in *American Journal of Physical Anthropology* agreed with Tuttle's observation that the Hadar foot displayed a flexible midfoot just like African apes.[133,134] Again, we

126. Johanson D.C. and Edey M.A., *Lucy: The Beginnings of Humankind*, Simon & Schuster, New York, p. 344-345, 1981.

127. White T.D. and Suwa G., Hominid Footprints at Laetoli: Facts and Interpretations, *Am J Phys Anthropol* 72:485-514, 1987.

128. Cartmill M. and Smith F.H., *The Human Lineage*, Wiley-Blackwell, Hoboken, NJ, p. 181, 2009.

129. DeSilva J., Bipedalism and Human Origins—Foot and Ankle Diversity in Australopithecus, [2/2013] [Show ID: 23664] CARTA–Center for Academic Research and Training in Anthropogeny, Timecode: 5:00, *"What is preserved in the Hadar foot is not preserved in the OH foot and visa versa. And so one cannot infer the remaining anatomy of one foot from the other. Unfortunately, these bones as well are from different species and from things that lived over a million years apart in time."* https://www.youtube.com/watch?v=AvOh9OKTq8g&t=305s

130. Johanson D.C. and Edey M.A., *Lucy: The Beginnings of Humankind*, Simon & Schuster, New York, p. 344-346, 1981.

131. Ward C. V., Kimbel W. H., Johanson D. C., Complete Fourth Metatarsal and Arches in the Foot of *Australopithecus afarensis*, *Science* 331(6018):750-750, 2011.

132. Tuttle R.H. *et al.*, Laetoli toes and *Australopithecus afarensis*, *Hum Evol* 6:193-100, 1991. https://link.springer.com/article/10.1007%2FBF02438142

133. Harcourt-Smith W. E. and Hilton C, Did Australopithecus afarensis make the Laetoli footprint trail? New insights into an old problem, *Am J Phys Anthropol* 126, 112, 2005.

134. Wong K., Footprints to Fill: Flat feet and doubts about makers of the Laetoli tracks, *Sci Am* 293(2):18-19, Aug 2005. https://www.scienti americam.com/article/footprints-to- ll/

are seeing two distinct morpho-types within the Afarensis hypodigm. So which bones from the First Family site reveal the correct anatomy of the Afarensis foot? Is it the Hadar foot with an ape morphology—or the fourth metatarsal bone with a modern human morphology recovered from the same site?

In response to Ward's 2011 publication of the fourth metatarsal bone, the popular press exploded with news articles proclaiming to the world the latest "proof" that Afarensis walked upright. The mainstream media was full of headlines like the one in *Nature News* that said, *"These bones were made for walking—human-like foot arches strengthen argument that Australopithecus 'Lucy' was not a climber."*[135] Similarly, *National Geographic News* reported, *"An unprecedented fossil foot bone appears to confirm that Australopithecus afarensis—the early human ancestors made by the "Lucy" skeleton—walked like modern humans, a new study says."*[136] The researchers involved in the study accepted the finding as undisputed evidence that Afarensis was a habitual biped. To these paleo-experts, the arboreal-terrestrial debate was now totally settled. As Bruce Latimer, a well-known proponent of the terrestrial model confidently asserted, *"This work certainly puts a nail in the coffin of that argument."* But how could these researchers be so sure that the isolated foot bone belonged to Afarensis? Keep in mind, the fourth metatarsal bone was found at the same site as the Hadar hand and foot bone (fifth metatarsal) that Johanson had originally described as bearing an uncanny resemblance to *H. sapiens*. And now they have found the fourth metatarsal bone that also happens to look identical to *H. sapiens*. But today we are told the isolated foot bone (and hand) must belong to Afarensis because Johanson had already decided that all of the First Family bones belong to one species, *Au. afarensis*.

More dichotomous anatomies have been observed in the Afarensis hypodigm. For example, the larger femur bones have been described as looking just like modern humans, whereas the smaller femur bones closely resemble those of the australopiths: *"The femur of the larger morph, they claimed, resembled ours ... the small morph's femur looked more like those of South African Australopithecus."*[137] Similarly, the same pattern is seen in the small and large distal tibiae (i.e., large lower limb bone) of Afarensis: *"In the small morph, the distal articular surface of the tibia faced downward and backward, as it does in apes; in the large morph, it faced downward and forward, like a human's..."*[138]

In light of the larger human-looking bones, how do terrestrials explain the smaller ape-looking bones the Afarensis hypodigm? Interestingly, leading proponents of the terrestrial view, such as Johanson, White, Lovejoy, and Latimer do not deny

---

135. Kaplan M., These bones were made for walking: Human-like arches strengthen argument that *Australopithe- cus* 'Lucy' was not a climber, *Nature News*, 2011.

136. Handwerk B., An unprecedented fossil foot bone appears to con rm that *Australopithecus afarensis*—the early human ancestors made famous by the "Lucy" skeleton—walked like modern humans, a new study says, *National Geographic News*, 2011.

137. Cartmill M. and Smith F.H., *The Human Lineage*, Wiley-Blackwell, Hoboken, NJ, p. 175, 2009.

138. Cartmill M. and Smith F.H., *The Human Lineage*, Wiley-Blackwell, Hoboken, NJ, p. 175, 2009.

the ape anatomy seen in many of these bones. Instead, they downplay them as *"evolutionary baggage"*—left over traits handed down from an ape ancestor that lived in the trees. Johanson expresses this view writing:

> Stern has seized on the baby's [Salem fossil] curved finger bones and upward-facing glenoid as confirmation of his theory that *A. afarensis* spent a lot of time in the trees. But Lovejoy continues to view these features in a way that we might interpret our appendix: as remnants of our past, evolutionary baggage left over from a time when our ancestors were accomplished arborealists. I tend to agree with Owen on this.[139]

This is pure speculation (incidentally the appendix is not evolutionary baggage, it is known to support the immune system). The "evolutionary baggage" claim is assumed out of necessity in order for the terrestrialists to maintain their position that Afarensis was a habitual bipedal human ancestor. However, arborealists like Stern and Susman see so many ape-looking bones in the Afarensis hypodigm that they feel strongly that they cannot merely dismiss them as "evolutionary baggage." They write:

> The notion that "... afarensis was an exceptionally strong walker, and that its elongated toes may have been service to it moving over rough stony ground, or in mud, where some slight gripping ability would have been useful" (Johanson and Edey, 1981, pp. 345-346) is untenable. There is no evidence that any extant primate has long, curved, heavily muscled hand and feet for any purpose other than to meet the demands of full or part-time arboreal life.[140]

To these paleo-experts, the *"remarkably chimpanzee-like"* anatomy seen in the postcranial bones of Afarensis, such as the Hadar foot, *"can only be understood as adaptations for grasping such as occurs in arboreal locomotion."*[141] Yet because they see so many other modern human-looking bones in the Afarensis hypodigm that they can't ignore (and because they wish to maintain the one-species hypothesis), they are left in the awkward position of assuming that the Afarensis males locomoted differently than the females. Stern and Susman noticed that the larger postcranial bones look like modern humans, whereas the comparable bones of the smaller individuals closely resembled tree-dwelling apes. Stern and Susman took these dichotomous morphologies to mean that the larger human-looking bones belonged to males that walked habitually upright like modern humans, whereas the smaller ape-looking bones belonged to females that swung from trees like apes (which is actually quite humorous). In *American Journal of Physical Anthropology*, Stern and Susman state their position while dismissing the most obvious solution:

> There are several different ways to interpret the disparity between the morphology of the small and large Hadar specimens. One is that they represent different taxa,

---

139. Johanson D.C. and Wong K., *Lucy's Legacy: The Quest for Human Origins*, Crown Publishing Group, New York, p. 146, 2009.

140. Stern J.T. and Susman R.L., The Locomotor Anatomy of *Australopithecus afarensis*, Am J Phys Anthropol 60:279-317, 1983.

141. Stern J.T. and Susman R.L., The Locomotor Anatomy of *Australopithecus afarensis*, Am J Phys Anthropol 60:279-317, 1983.

the larger of which is more human-like in posture and gait (Tardieu, 1979, 1981). A second is that they represent the same taxon (presumably of different sexes thereof) which is characterized by very large morphological variability compatible with a single overall pattern of locomotor behavior. ... Finally, a third alternative, which we favor, is that although only one taxon is represented at Hadar, the locomotor behavior of the larger individuals showed a greater component of terrestriality than did that of the smaller ones. If the different sizes are different sexes, this last alternative implies a marked degree of sexual differences in locomotor behavior. ... It is possible that the more pongid-like [ape-like] morphology of the smaller, female Hadar hominid reflect an increased arboreal component in its locomotor profile over the larger males.[142]

This is such a strange theory that even Stern and Susman admit it is unlike anything they have ever seen among the living apes. They admit it is a problem for the one-species model that they are proposing:

... our own preliminary studies on this problem have not revealed sexual dimorphism in the locomotor skeleton comparable to what is suggested for A. afarensis. Therefore, we must conclude that the degree of sexual difference in locomotor behavior in A. afarensis was greater than in any living ape.[143]

The sexual dimorphism hypothesis (not just in size but in locomotor anatomy) does not seem credible. How then do we explain these arboreal-terrestrial dichotomies? We believe the answer is staring everyone in the face.

Third Competing View—Afarensis is a "Jumble of Species" (1979–Present)

The field of paleoanthropology largely rejected what was obvious to the founders of the field—which was that human beings coexisted with all the australopith types. The Leakey team and the Johanson team were consistently finding australopith bones in the same strata as human bones, along with human tools, human shelters, and human footprints. These findings were obvious to all, but were disturbing because the pattern did not reveal an ape-to-man progression. The australopith bones that were being found obviously did not pre-exist man, (as so many experts in the field had hoped for).

Johanson resolved this dilemma by asserting that all bones older than 3 million years must always be designated australopith, even when they are indistinguishable from human bones, and even if they were corroborated by human footprints. In order to explain why there were human-looking bones found in the same strata as australopiths, Johanson claimed that his Afarensis species was sexually dimorphic in the extreme. This hypothesis is not even remotely credible. It was a forced-fit ever since Johanson and White first proposed it. This forced fit is the cause of the on-going conflict between the "arborealists" (who focus on the ape bones), and

---

142. Stern J.T. and Susman R.L., The Locomotor Anatomy of *Australopithecus afarensis*, Am J Phys Anthropol 60:279-317, 1983.
143. Stern J.T. and Susman R.L., The Locomotor Anatomy of *Australopithecus afarensis*, Am J Phys Anthropol 60:279-317, 1983.

the "terrestrialists" (who focus on the human bones). The solution is surprisingly simple—the Afarensis hypodigm is a false taxon—it is a mixture of ape and human bones. From the beginning, both the Leakey team and the Johanson team understood this very clearly. This is what we are calling the Third Competing View (or two-taxon view), which is really just taking us back to where this all started.

In *The Human Lineage*, paleo-experts Cartmill and Smith describe the two-taxon view:

> Stern and Susman's third claim, that the two sexes of *A. afarensis* had different locomotor patterns, drew upon earlier work by Tardieu. ... Tardieu concluded that these groups represented two different species. The smaller morph, she suggested, was a persistently primitive hominin that had retained more arboreal locomotor behavior, while the larger morph was a more advanced terrestrial biped with closer affinities to humans.[144]

Michael Day discusses Tardieu's two-species hypothesis further, saying:

> This conclusion is supported in part by the work of Senut and Tardieu (1985) who see two forms of locomotor anatomy present from the examination of knees and elbows. One is more arboreally adapted and the other more bipedally adapted. This they do not accept as possible in a widely sexually dimorphic single species, thus they favor specific or even generic separation of the Hadar remains into two groups.[145]

Numerous observations like these have been consistently made, clearly showing that *Au. afarensis* is a mixed hypodigm. Indeed, since the naming of the species, numerous paleo-experts have insisted that Afarensis is an invalid taxon consisting of a jumble of at least two or more species from separate genera. For example, in the paper titled, *"Australopithecus afarensis: two sexes or two species"* paleo-expert Adrienne Zihlman observes:

> The Hadar postcranial fossils support the proposal that the extreme size variation is better interpreted as more than one species. This possibility takes on added significance in light of accumulating evidence that demonstrates two morphological patterns in postcranial and cranial anatomy. Features which show two different patterns cannot easily be accommodated within one species. ... The upper limb material shows that, in addition to size variation between, as well as within, localities, two morphological patterns exist (Senut 1981; Senut, Tardieu 1985). Similarly, for the lower limb, there are two morphological patterns in the distal femur (Tardieu 1983; Senut, Tardieu 1985).[146]

Primate evolutionist Walter Ferguson of Tel Aviv University came to the same conclusion as Zihlman, Tardieu, and Senut cited above. In agreement with their analysis of the postcranial bones, Ferguson noted that there were two distinct

---

144. Cartmill M. and Smith F.H., *The Human Lineage*, Wiley-Blackwell, Hoboken, NJ, p. 176, 2009.
145. Day M.H., *Guide to Fossil Man*, 4th Edition, University of Chicago Press, Chicago, p.256, 1985.
146. Zihlman A., *Australopithecus afarensis*: two sexes or two species? In: P.V. Tobias (ed.) *Hominid Evolution: Past, Present and Future*, pp. 213–220. New York: Alan R. Liss, Inc., 1985.

morphologies seen in the crania, jawbones, and dentition—undermining the very basis for Johanson's reassessment. Ferguson insisted that the Hadar-Laetoli sample was a commixture of two distinct taxa, *Homo* and an extinct ape species. He reported his findings in the journal *Primates* stating:

> The anatomical characters that distinguish hominids from pongids are almost entirely differences in proportions, the relations of parts and the type of dental attrition. According to these criteria, and the lack of evidence associating the apelike fossils with the hominid fossils, it was determined that *"Australopithecus afarensis"* is not a single species of hominid, but a synthesis of two taxa, a relatively unspecialized hominid and a generalized pongid [ape].[147]

Respected paleo-experts, Peter Schmid of the University of Witwatersrand and Martin Häusler of the University of Zurich, have also rejected the one-species hypothesis proposed by Johanson and White. They have done so based on yet another independent line of evidence—a reconstruction of the "Lucy" pelvis. Measurements of the pelvic inlet (the birth canal) signaled to these researchers that Lucy was not actually a female like Johanson and Lovejoy had assumed after all. They found *"major constrictions"* in the inlet suggesting to them that *"delivery in AL 288-1 would have been more complicated than in modern humans, if not impossible… It is more plausible that AL 288-1 is simply not built for giving birth."*[148] Instead of the name "Lucy," Schmid and Häusler decided a more appropriate name for a male would be "Lucifer." If the Lucy hip belongs to a male then Johanson's hypothesis of a single sexually dimorphic species (which assumes males were significantly larger than females) can no longer be considered valid. In their published paper in the *Journal of Human Evolution*, Schmid and Häusler conclude:

> Consequently, there is more evidence to suggest that AL 288-1 was male rather than female. A female of the same species as AL 288-1 would have had a pelvis with a larger sagittal diameter and a less protruding promontorium. Difficulties of birth would have been comparable or smaller than in modern humans. Simultaneously, sexual dimorphism in body size in this species would have been quite limited. In this case, the Hadar (and by inference the Sterkfontein) material consists of several distinct species which were previously jumbled together.[149]

To this day, the debate regarding the validity of Afarensis as a sound species has not been resolved. In a fairly recent publication, paleo-expert Zeresenay Alemseged leaves unanswered the lingering question, *"How valid is the suggestion that there are multiple species at Hadar?"*[150] In June of 2018, Richard Leakey was asked by the authors of this book whether he still believed that the Afarensis hypodigm

147. Ferguson W.W., An Alternative Interpretation of *Australopithecus afarensis* Fossil Material, *Primates* 24(3):397-409, 1983.
148. Häusler M. and Schmid P., Comparison of the pelves of Sts 14 and AL 288-1: implications for birth and sexual dimorphism in australopithecines, *J Hum Evol* 29:363-383, 1995.
149. Häusler M. and Schmid P., Comparison of the pelves of Sts 14 and AL 288-1: implications for birth and sexual dimorphism in australopithecines, *J Hum Evol* 29:363-383, 1995.
150. Alemseged Z., *Australopithecus* in Ethiopia, in Reed K., Fleagle J.G. and Leakey R.E. (eds.), The Paleobiology of *Australopithecus*, Springer, New York USA, pp. 63-71, 2013.

represented a jumble of *Homo* and *Australopithecus* bones (just as he concluded years ago when he first examined the Hadar fossils in Nairobi in 1975). Richard graciously wrote back, saying:

> I have seen no new evidence to review my original comments about *A. afarensis* and the claims put forward by Johanson, White (and Coppens). Of course, since then the story has become less simple and *Kenyanthropus* and *A. anamensis* from the Turkana basin contemporary or older sediments than Hadar have to be taken into consideration.[151]

Conclusion

The bones that are now known as *Australopithecus afarensis* include bones that appear to be ape, and other bones that appear to be human. These bones have been highly contested ever since Afarensis was named. That controversy continues even now. There is very straightforward evidence that it is a "mixed hypodigm" (more than one species).

There is no better way to make an ape-man than to combine ape bones with human bones. This was true with the Piltdown man fraud, and appears to also apply to Afarensis. As we will see in the following chapters, *Homo habilis* and *Australopithecus sediba* also appear to be mixtures of ape and human bones.

The primary discoverers of those bones that are now called Afarensis, could easily see that the bones were a mixture of ape bones and human bones. This view was overthrown by Johanson *et al.*, who claimed all the bones were a single species—with the human-like bones being male and the ape-like bones being female. We agree with numerous paleo-experts who report in the scientific literature that Johanson's sexual dimorphism theory is not credible. On this point many paleo-experts agree with us including Coppens,[152,153] Falk,[154] Hartwig-Scherer,[155] Olsen,[156,157] Senut,[158] and Schmid.[159] This also includes Deloison, Ferguson, Häusler,

151. Personal communication, June 2018.
152. Coppens Y., Le cerveau des hommes fossiles, *Comptes Rendues de l'Academie des Sciences*, Paris: Supplément à la vie académique 3–24, 1981.
153. Coppens Y., Systematics, phylogeny, environment and culture of the *Australopithecines*, hypothesis and synthesis, *Bulletin et Mémoires de la Société d'Anthropologie de Paris* 13:273–284, 1983.
154. Falk D., Evolution of cranial blood drainage in hominids: enlarged occipital/marginal sinuses and emissary foramina, *Am J Phys Anthropol* 70:311–324, 1986.
155. Hartwig-Scherer S., Body weight prediction in early fossil hominids: towards a Taxon-"Independent" approach, *Am J Phys Anthropol* 92:17–36, 1993.
156. Olson T.R., Basicranial morphology of the extant hominoids and Pliocene hominids: the new material from the Hadar Formation, Ethiopia, and its significance in early human evolution and taxonomy. In: C.B. Stringer (ed.) *Aspects of Human Evolution*, pp. 99–128. London: Taylor and Francis, 1981.
157. Olson T.R., Cranial morphology and systematics of the Hadar formation hominids and *"Australopithecus" africanus* In E. Delson (ed.) *Ancestors: The Hard Evidence*, pp. 102–119. New York: Alan R.Liss, Inc. (1985)
158. Senut B. and Tardieu C., Functional aspects of Plio-Pleistocene hominoid limb bones: implications for taxonomy and phylogeny, In: E. Delson (ed.) *Ancestors: The Hard Evidence*, pp. 193–201. New York: Alan R.Liss, Inc., 1985.
159. Schmid P., Eine Rekonstruktion des skelettes von A.L. 288–1(Hadar) und deren Konsequenzen, *Folia Primatologica* 40:283–306, 1983.

M. Leakey, R. Leakey, Tardieu, Walker, and Zihlman.

Since that time, two groups of paleo-experts have been arguing back and forth, arguing whether Afarensis is more ape-like or more human-like (depending on whether they are focusing on the ape bones or the human bones). That ongoing controversy would instantly go away if those paleo-experts simply agreed with the assessment of the primary discovers. We firmly hold the Third Competing View, which is consistent with the original assessments of the primary discoverers—that the Afarensis bones are a commixture of ape and human bones.

The extensive coexistence of *Homo* and *Australopithecus* in Eastern Africa is described in more detail in chapter 11. Such coexistence calls into serious question the popularized ape-to-man story. Outside of the paleoanthropological community, people have not been told the full story about Afarensis. The vast majority of students and the general public have never been exposed to the competing views. Textbooks and the popular press give the misleading impression that there is only one view in the paleo-community. This is the view promoted by Johanson that depicts Lucy and her kind as *"the ape that stood up"*[160,161]—a habitual bipedal hominin ancestor with an ape head and a human-looking body. To preserve the integrity of science it is essential that the alternative views regarding Afarensis be made known.

160. Johanson D. and Johanson L., *Ancestors: In Search of Human Origins*, Villard Books, New York, p. 50-51, 1994.
161. PBS, *Your Inner Monkey*, PBS video aired on 4/22/14, quote of Neal Shubin, http://pbs/org/video/2365206925/

Section III—Bones of the "Middle" Type

Introduction to Chapters 8–10

In this section we will examine the bones that paleo-experts regard as key transitional species—the latest and greatest "missing links." These reputed transitional species are essential to the ape-to-man story. In order to validate the theory, they must fill the gap in the human lineage, as required in order to link the australopiths to early humans.

It is widely recognized in the paleo-community that there is a "vast gulf" separating the australopiths (the ape type) and the genus *Homo* (the human type). The bones of the ape type are quite obviously ape, and the bones of the human type are quite obviously human. The challenge for paleoanthropologists has always been to find what lies between these two very different looking groups. It is true that there are a few disputed bones that are held up as possible transitional forms that might help bridge this vast gulf between australopith and man. However, those bones are so fragmentary and poorly defined that they have been described as "the muddle in the middle" or the "murky period." The bulk of those sparse assemblages of bones have been assigned to *Homo habilis* (or *Homo rudolfensis*, a further sub-division according to some paleo-experts). As we will see, Habilis has been largely dismissed as an undefined taxon that should be "scrapped." The most recent discoveries have added to the muddle in the middle. These include *Australopithecus sediba* ("Sediba"), and *Homo naledi* ("Naledi"). Sediba and Naledi are the most sensationalized hominin bones found in recent times, but as we will see, they have already fallen into disrepute and have been dismissed by the paleo-community. The bones in the middle fail to fill the gap—they do not reveal any clear progression from australopith to man. We still do not see any true "ape-man" intermediates or "missing links." World-renowned evolutionary paleoanthropologists acknowledge that the origin of the genus *Homo* remains "elusive."

This third section describes: *Homo habilis* (chapter 8); *Australopithecus sediba* (chapter 9); and *Homo naledi* (chapter 10).

CHAPTER 8

Homo habilis
Crucial "Missing Link" or Invented Species?

Homo habilis [is] *an all-embracing "wastebasket" species into which a whole heterogeneous variety of fossils could be conveniently swept.*[1]

Paleoanthropologists Ian Tattersall, Curator Emeritus with the American Museum of Natural History in New York City, and Jeffery Schwartz, University of Pittsburgh

Background and Discovery of "Handy Man"

Figure 1. Olduvai Gorge (pictured above) is a famous hominin-bearing site in Tanzania. It is a steep-sided ravine spanning 30 miles across East Africa and in places, 300 feet deep. The remains of several key hominin species were found here by the Leakey's in the 1960s, including *Australopithecus boisei*, Erectus, and the taxon *Homo habilis*. A rich collection of stone tools and butchered bones (called living sites) have also been found, indicating the presence of nomadic hunter-gatherer groups.

In the early 1960s, Louis and Mary Leakey found bones in the Olduvai Gorge of Tanzania (Figure 1), which they claimed were the remains of the earliest humans. They named these bones *Homo habilis* (Habilis). These bones were thought to bridge the gap between australopiths and man. Most of the bones looked very

---

1. Tattersall I. and Schwartz J., *Extinct Humans*, Westview Press, New York, p. 111, 2001.

ape-like, being similar to the australopithecines. However, some looked distinctly human-like, and in addition there were many stone tools present. This seemed to show that these "ape-like" creatures were on their way to becoming human, and were already making and using stone tools. From their discovery until 2008 (more than four decades) these bones and bone fragments were the only candidate bones that might bridge the gap between the ape-like australopiths and man. This was the reason the Leakeys' discovery was considered so important (it also made the Leakeys world-famous celebrities). Habilis was prominently displayed in textbooks, museums, and popular media broadcasts. Without Habilis, the ape-to-man story did not hold together. However the Habilis taxon was in trouble from the start, and for the last decade, it has largely been dismissed as a "poorly defined" or invalid taxon by most of the paleoanthropology community. So why is Habilis still featured in all the textbooks and museums? It seems that it is for the simple reason that Habilis is crucial to the ape-to-man story. Therefore, all those who are committed to promoting that story must hold onto Habilis until they have something better that can take its place. Ever since the naming of Habilis, there has been disquiet within the paleoanthropology community regarding whether or not Habilis was a sound species, and belonged in the genus *Homo*. The strikingly ape-like qualities of Habilis led many to conclude that Habilis bones are of the ape-type, not of the human-type, justifying reclassification as an australopith that looked even more ape-ish than Ardi and Lucy.

Is Habilis a real species? Many contend it is a mixture of ape and human bones. If there were australopith and human bones mixed together at the same site, this would result in chimeric skeletons that would literally be "ape-men" skeletons. This would also explain why stone tools were found at these locations. So although Habilis is still in all the textbooks, within the paleoanthropology community, Habilis has consistently been questioned ever since its announcement in 1964. Paleo-expert Richard Leakey and son of the discoverers of Habilis notes, *"Habilis has always been controversial in anthropology."*[2]

"Nutcracker Man"—An Extinct Ape Mistaken to be a Human Ancestor

There is no better way to discuss the historical controversy surrounding Habilis than by starting with the discovery of *Zinjanthropus*—an extinct ape which the Leakey family claimed was a human ancestor because its skull was found in close proximity to stone tools.

During an expedition in 1959, Mary Leakey found a skull (OH 5) belonging to a young adult that they named *Zinjanthropus boisei* (Figure 2). "Zinj" was described as having a small brain, large face, and small canines—but its massive jaws and chewing teeth earned it the nickname "Nutcracker Man."[3] At that time it was

---

2. Leakey R. and Lewin R., *Origins Reconsidered: In Search of What Makes Us Human*, Anchor Books (Double-day), New York, p. 110, 1992.
3. Wood B., Human evolution: Fifty years after *Homo habilis*, Nature 508(7494):31-33, 2014.

believed to be our oldest human ancestor, and it became widely known to the general public.[4] Zinj was presented to the world as a new species that looked more human than australopithecine—an interpretation that, according to experts on human evolution, was quite a stretch. John Reader discusses this in his acclaimed Oxford University publication *Missing Links*:

> When Louis Leakey squeezed *Zinjanthropus boisei* into his scheme of human evolution, he subjected both the interpretation of the evidence and his own preconceptions to some distortion. He claimed the specimen resembled modern humans more closely than it resembled the South African australopithecines— which even the most casual observer might have disputed; and he accepted the unseemly creature as a direct ancestor...[5]

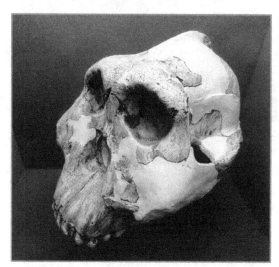

Figure 2. "Nutcracker Man" aka "Zinj" (originally *Zinjanthropus boisei* now classified as *Australopithecus boisei* or *Paranthropus boisei*) is a partial skull (designated OH 5) discovered by paleo-expert Mary Leakey in 1959 at Olduvai Gorge, Tanzania. At the time, the fossil was widely promoted to the public as the oldest human ancestor. It was thought that the stone tools found nearby were made by Zinj. This interpretation was retracted shortly thereafter with the discovery of *Homo habilis* (aka "Handy Man"). According to the announcement paper in *Nature* (1964), the "real" toolmaker at Olduvai was Habilis, not Zinj. Since then Habilis has also fallen into disrepute.

Zinj is now universally recognized by the paleoanthropological community to be a robust australopithecine. As the genus name suggests, it most closely resembles a large-bodied ape. Leading paleo-expert Bernard Wood affirms, *"Its small brain, large face, tiny canines and massive, thumbnail-sized chewing teeth are not at all like those of H. erectus."*[6] Moreover the cranium displayed a distinct sagittal crest that lined the top of the skull, as is typical of adult male gorillas. Zinj has since been appropriately reclassified as *Paranthropus boisei* (alternatively *Au. boisei*), an extinct ape far removed from the lineage of man.[7] Louis Leakey's misconstrued interpretation was influenced by his strong desire to find an early human ancestor, and the loose assumption that the large collection of stone tools found nearby were manufactured and used by Zinj.

Within a year of finding Zinj, the Leakeys discovered additional bones about

4. Meredith M., *Born in Africa: the quest for the origins of human life*, Public Affairs, New York, p. 63, 2011.
5. Reader J., *Missing Links*, Oxford University Press, New York, p. 317, 2011.
6. Wood B., Human evolution: Fifty years after *Homo habilis*, *Nature* 508(7494):31-33, 2014.
7. Wood B., Human evolution: Fifty years after *Homo habilis*, *Nature* 508(7494):31-33, 2014.

650 feet north of the FLK-Zinj site, in strata of equivalent age.[8] The bones were of a lighter build, and did not seem to fit with the robust morphology of *Zinjanthropus*. More Habilis bones were found in the years following, but these were embarrassingly incomplete. Among these were the partial remains of a hand with inferred precision grasping abilities typical of modern man (an interpretation that is still debated today).[9] The new collection of bones appeared more human-like than Zinj. In 1964, Louis Leakey, Philip Tobias, and John Napier announced the discovery of *Homo habilis*—nicknamed "Handy Man" for its inferred tool-making abilities. Habilis was declared the "real" toolmaker at Olduvai and presented to the world as an early ancestor to man—a precursor species to Erectus. Louis Leakey and colleagues discussed this reassessment in the announcement paper published in *Nature* (1964):

> When the skull of *Australopithecus* (*Zinjanthropus*) *boisei* was found on a living floor at F.L.K. I, no remains of any other type of hominid were known from the early part of the Olduvai sequence. It seemed reasonable, therefore, to assume that this skull represented the makers of the Oldowan culture. The subsequent discovery of remains of *Homo habilis* in association with the Oldowan culture at three other sites has considerably altered the position. While it is possible that *Zinjanthropus* and *Homo habilis* both made stone tools, it is probable that the latter was the more advanced tool maker and that the *Zinjanthropus* skull represents an intruder (or a victim) on a *Homo habilis* living site.[10]

Why didn't the Leakey's consider the obvious possibility that the stone tools were manufactured and used by *Homo sapiens* or Erectus (as opposed to Habilis)? As we will see, the Leakeys had collected plenty of evidence supporting this conclusion in the years leading up to the *Nature* publication. Modern human-looking bones had been found in both Beds I and II—in the same beds where Habilis bones were excavated. This evidence included a complete modern human skeleton (OH 1) discovered years earlier in Bed II, as well as an Erectus skull from Bed II found in December 1960 (just one month after the Habilis type specimen, OH 7, was found).[11] In 1960 an anatomically modern human foot (OH 8) was recovered from Bed I (which was assumed to belong to Habilis). And also in 1960 an *"essentially human leg"* was found in Bed I (FLK-Zinj site) that was incorrectly assigned to *Zinjanthropus*. In addition, the Leakeys discovered what they called "living floors"—archaeological layers displaying clear evidence of modern human habitation, including shelter, a wide variety of sophisticated stone tools, and thousands of butchered bones (see chapter 11).

---

8. The bones of Zinj were found at the FLK site in level 22 of Bed I. The holotype OH 7 assigned to Habilis were also found in Bed I, 200 meters north at the FLK NN site. For a cross section of the Olduvai Gorge outcrop and corresponding ages, see M. Dominguez-Rodrigo M *et al.*, *Deconstructing Olduvai: A Taphonomic Study of the Bed I site*, 33-38, Springer 2007.

9. Susman R.L., Brief communication: evidence bearing on the status of *Homo habilis* at Olduvai Gorge, *Am J Phys Anthropol* 137:356-361, 2008.

10. Leakey L.S.B. *et al.*, A new species of the genus *Homo* from Olduvai Gorge, *Nature* 202:7-9, 1964.

11. Rightmire G.P., *The Evolution of Homo erectus*, Cambridge University Press, p. 59, 1990. See also: Reader J., *Missing Links*, Oxford University Press, New York, p. 322, 2011.

In light of this wealth of evidence that humans coexisted with the bones called Habilis, why didn't the Leakeys attribute the stone tools and living sites to *Homo sapiens*/Erectus? This would be the most reasonable interpretation except that Erectus (and especially *Homo sapiens*) were not supposed to have existed in the earliest deposits at Olduvai Gorge (Bed I was dated 1.7–2.0 million years).[12] Because the human bones at these sites did not fit the ape-to-man narrative, the Leakeys felt they had no choice but to assign them to Zinj (initially), and then to Habilis. Likewise, even though the stone tools and "living floors" provided further evidence for the presence of true humans at Olduvai, these too had to be attributed to Habilis. Other bones included in the Habilis collection were very ape-like, but were fragmentary and incomplete.

The Bones of "Handy Man"—Isolated and Fragmentary

Figure 3. The defining specimen (designated OH 7 nicknamed "Johnny's child") of the reputed species *Homo habilis*. Mary Leakey and son Jonathan Leakey recovered it from Bed I at Olduvai Gorge, Tanzania in 1960. As can be seen, Habilis was proclaimed to the world as a human ancestor on the basis of a very limited sample of bones. The defining specimen consists of a broken and deformed lower jawbone that holds 13 teeth, an isolated molar, a couple of skull fragments, and 21 finger, hand, and wrist bones. Six of the 21 finger bones were mistakenly assumed to be Habilis but later found to be non-hominin. One "finger bone" was a vertebral fragment and two others belonged to an arboreal monkey. The original interpretation of the OH 7 partial hand was described as looking anatomically human. Its inferred precision grasping abilities led to the assumption that Habilis was the toolmaker at Olduvai, hence the name "Handy Man." This interpretation has been challenged. Paleo-experts have argued the OH 7 hand belonged to *Au. boisei* (a robust australopithecine ape).

The first bones attributed to Habilis are catalogued as specimen OH 7 (Figure 3). It is the "defining specimen" of the species, and is shown on the cover of this book. Mary Leakey and her son Jonathan found the bones in 1960. The OH 7 specimen consists of a broken and deformed lower jawbone with 13 teeth in place, an isolated molar, 2 small skull fragments, and 21 finger, hand, and wrist bones.[13] Other bones originally assigned to Zinj were later reassigned to Habilis. This included the human-looking tibia and fibula (OH 35) as well as the anatomically modern partial foot (OH 8). The Leakeys found those specimens in Bed I in 1960. Additional fragmentary remains were recovered from Bed I and II at Olduvai

---

12. Hay R.L., Lithofacies and environments of Bed I, Olduvai Gorge, Tanzania, *Quaternary Research* 3(4):541-560, 1973. https://doi.org/10.1016/0033-5894(73)90030-6

13. Lieberman D.E. *et al.*, Homoplasy and early *Homo*: an analysis of the evolutionary relationships of *H. habilis* sensu stricto and *H. rudolfensis*, *J Hum Evol* 30: 4–6, 1996.

Gorge and locations in Kenya and South Africa.

Virtually all of the bones attributed to Habilis were found as isolated bones or bone fragments. None of the bones were found physically connected to other bones. This means that paleo-experts cannot reliably reconstruct even a partial Habilis skeleton; even skull reconstructions are highly questionable. These bones were found in mixed bone beds (containing many animal species), opening the door to accidentally combining ape and human bones into a chimeric "species" (a false taxon). Under such conditions it is arguably impossible to know for certain which bones belonged to which individual or species.[14]

Pitifully Few Bones, Pitifully Mangled

The ongoing controversy surrounding Habilis is in part because of the fragmented and incomplete nature of the bones. Habilis was established as a species based on its holotype (the "defining specimen" or "type specimen"). It is the standard from which all, subsequent discoveries are compared to in order to identify whether or not they belong to the same species. In other words, the defining specimen is critical to establishing the legitimacy of any hominin species. Paleo-experts understand this.[15] Yet Habilis was established as a taxon with almost no evidence—as one paleo-expert put it, it was established "on the basis of material so scanty and incomplete."[16] The defining specimen of Habilis is OH 7, which consists of stray finger bones (making up a partial hand), a deformed jawbone, and a few small skull fragments. The bones of OH 7 were scattered broadly across the excavated area and there was no way of knowing if the bones even belonged together. In fact, two of the finger bones turned out to be from a monkey that were mistakenly included. What was thought to be a third finger bone was actually a vertebra fragment.[17] The OH 7 partial hand was originally described as looking anatomically human. Its inferred precision grasping abilities led to the assumption that Habilis was the toolmaker at Olduvai, hence the name "Handy Man." This interpretation has been challenged. In the *Journal of Anatomy* paleoanthropologists have argued that the OH 7 hand belonged to *Zinjanthropus* (the robust australopithecine that was found nearby).[18] In a separate publication, paleo-experts Sergio Almécija *et al.* note that the OH 7 hand "*displays a monkey-like pattern*" and "*most likely belongs to a robust australopith* [an extinct ape]"[19] Perhaps Habilis was not very "handy" with tools after all?

The very poorly defined holotype, and consequently the murky definition of what

---

14. Wood B. *et al.*, A technique for establishing the identity of 'isolated' fossil hominin limb bones, *J Anat* 193: 61–72, 1998.

15. Tattersall I. and Schwartz J., *Extinct Humans*, Westview Press, New York, p. 111, 2001. Habilis is *"a species whose identity depends on the OH 7 fragments."*

16. Bielicki T. and Tobias P.V., On *Homo habilis*, *Curr Anthropol* 7(5):576-578, 1966.

17. Reader J., *Missing Links*, Oxford University Press, New York, p. 320, 2011.

18. Tocheri M.W. *et al.*, The evolutionary history of the hominin hand since the last common ancestor of *Pan* and *Homo*, *J Anat* 212:544-562, 2008.

19. Almécija S. *et al.*, OH 7, The Curious Case of the Original Handy Man? *Paleolusitana*, número 1, 2009.

Habilis is, has led to the uncritical inclusion of any unknown bones into the Habilis group. It is no wonder leading experts like Tattersall and Schwartz describe Habilis as *"an all-embracing "wastebasket" species into which a whole heterogeneous variety of fossils could be conveniently swept."*[20] Schwartz and Tattersall emphasize the same problem in a 2015 *Science* article:

> The inclusion in *Homo* of the *H. habilis* fossils so broadened the morphology of the genus that further hominids from other sites could be shoehorned into it almost without regard to their physical appearance. As a result, the largely unexamined definition of *Homo* became even murkier.[21]

The bones used to first identify Habilis (and later most of the other recovered bones) were found in a mixed bone bed containing thousands of unarticulated, broken, and loose bones belonging to a wide variety of creatures including catfish, pigs, tortoises, apes, monkeys, and humans. The isolated bones were found randomly scattered across the excavated area and were jumbled together. Not even a partially complete Habilis skeleton has ever been found. Habilis bones are often described as distorted, poorly preserved, scrappy, crushed, flattened, and broken into little pieces. Almost all of the skulls presumed to belong to Habilis have been reconstructed more than once, with each new reconstruction calling into question earlier reconstructions. Many of the skull and facial remains were found severely crushed and flattened. Two of the skulls were washed into a gully and trampled by cattle. Rightmire describes the challenges associated with trying to assess such fossils in the *American Journal of Physical Anthropology*:

> Unfortunately, the Olduvai remains are very fragmentary. OH 7 (the type) consists of a broken mandible with teeth, parts of two parietals, and hand bones. Other individuals described in the 1964 report are just as incomplete, and several have been removed from the hypodigm at least temporarily, as noted before. The cranium of OH 24, which was badly crushed when found, is still distorted. The affinities of this hominid also have been questioned. Given this state of the material and continuing uncertainty over which of the specimens are *Homo habilis*, the Olduvai assemblage cannot readily serve as a basis for identifying fossils from other localities.[22]

Many other experts in the field have raised similar criticisms. Habilis is simply too fragmentary to accurately define—a *"morass of specimens"* that unrealistically broadened the *Homo* genus.[23] The credibility of the ape-to-man story depends upon these bones, yet after 50 years, nobody knows for sure whether Habilis is a real taxonomic entity or just a collection of random bone fragments. Paleo-expert Tim White of UC Berkeley admits, *"we still don't understand Habilis."*[24]

20. Tattersall I. and Schwartz J., *Extinct Humans*, Westview Press, New York, p. 111, 2001.
21. Schwartz J.H. and Tattersall I., Defining the Genus *Homo*, *Science* 349 (6251):931-932, 2015.
22. Rightmire G.P., Variation among early *Homo* crania from Olduvai Gorge and the Koobi Fora Region, *Am J Phys Anthropol* 90:1-33, 1993.
23. Schwartz J.H. and Tattersall I., Defining the Genus *Homo*, *Science,* 349 (6251):931-932, 2015.
24. Gibbons A., New Fossils Put Face on Mysterious Human Ancestor, *Science*, August 8, 2012. http://www.sciencemag.org/news/2012/08/new-fossils-put-face-mysterious-human-ancestor

World Authority on Habilis Rejects "Species" as a Human Ancestor

Bernard Wood of George Washington University is a world-renowned evolutionary paleoanthropologist, and one of the foremost authorities on Habilis. After having extensively studied the skeletal remains attributed to Habilis for almost all of the 50 years since its naming,[25] Wood is more than qualified to make the following assessment in the journal *Nature* (2014). He confesses, *"In my view, the species is too unlike H. erectus to be its immediate ancestor, so a simple, linear model explaining this stage of human evolution is looking less and less likely."*[26] In the article, Wood summarizes some of the key reasons *"the announcement of 'handy man' in April 1964 threw the field of hominin evolution into a turmoil that continues to this day."*[27] Wood himself has come to the firm conclusion that Habilis is not our ancestor and he offers no substitute in its place. He writes, *"Even with all the fossil evidence and analytical techniques from the past 50 years, a convincing hypothesis for the origin of Homo remains elusive."*[28] Much earlier in *Nature*, Wood made a similar confession, and since then the situation has not improved:

> It is remarkable that the taxonomy and phylogenetic relationships of the earliest known representatives of our own genus, *Homo*, remain obscure. … reassessments of the fossils themselves have rendered untenable a simple unilineal model of human evolution, in which *Homo habilis* succeeded the australopithecines and then evolved via *H. erectus* into *H. sapiens*—but no clear alternative consensus has yet emerged.[29]

What he is saying is that the human fossil record does not reveal a discernable evolutionary transition from the australopithecine apes into the early members of the genus *Homo*, and unfortunately Habilis has only made things "murkier."[30] Wood blames the confusion on the *"luxuriant diversity"* of hominin species that make up the messy bush of human origins.[31] He claims the complexity has muddled our ability to discover the path leading to man. And so he confesses that the vast gulf between australopith and *Homo* remains unfilled. The theoretical model of australopith-to-man rests upon ever-elusive transitional fossils, and leading experts like Bernard Wood are saying that after half-a-century the crucial evidence is still missing.

Habilis Shrouded in Controversy and Confusion for 50 Years

Habilis is perhaps the most fiercely contested hominin finding in the history of paleoanthropology. At one point the disagreement over Habilis had more to do

25. *"I have been involved with H. habilis for all but two of its 50 years, starting in 1966…"* Wood B., Fifty years after *Homo habilis*, *Nature News* 508:31-33, 2014.

26. Wood B., Human evolution: Fifty years after *Homo habilis*, *Nature* 508(7494):31-33, 2014.

27. Wood B., Human evolution: Fifty years after *Homo habilis*, *Nature* 508(7494):31-33, 2014.

28. Wood B., Human evolution: Fifty years after *Homo habilis*, *Nature* 508(7494):31-33, 2014.

29. Wood B., Origins and evolution of the genus *Homo*, *Nature* 355(6363):783-790, 1992. http://www.ncbi.nlm.nih.gov/pubmed/1538759

30. Schwartz J.H. and Tattersall I., Defining the Genus *Homo*, *Science* 349(6251):931-932, 2015.

31. Wood B., Human evolution: Fifty years after *Homo habilis*, *Nature* 508(7494):31-33, 2014.

with naming the species, rather than its validity as a species.[32] However, the focus of the debate among paleo-experts has generally been over whether or not it is a real species. Paleo-experts Cartmill and Smith affirm this stating, *"Researchers have been debating the reality of this species ever since it was first discovered in 1964."*[33] They then list three central problems that have plagued this taxon, summarized as follows: 1) Do all of the bones belong to a single species? 2) If not, how many species are really there? 3) Do any of these bones really belong to *Homo*?[34] Brian Villmoare and colleagues more recently reiterate this uncertainty in *Science* (2015): *"Fifty years after the recognition of the species Homo habilis as the earliest known representative of our genus, the origin of Homo remains clouded."*[35]

The reason this taxon has been so controversial for so long is because the actual fossil evidence is not only poor, but actually has internal contradictions. Yet the huge gap separating australopith and man has for 50 years, as Tattersall admits, *"begged to be filled."*[36] Paleoanthropologist Milford Wolpoff from the University of Michigan affirms the magnitude of this problem, stating:

> Ironically, after all the years of unresolved phenetic debate about the validity of *Homo habilis*, the phylogenetic outlook suggests that if there weren't a *Homo habilis* we would have to invent one.[37]

Habilis Primarily Consists of *Australopithecus* Bones

To properly identify Habilis, more complete skeletons were required. Without this, paleo-experts could not even guess what Habilis looked like. A few specimens were eventually recovered (OH 62 and KNM-ER 3735) where the bones of the face and cranium were found in clear association with other parts of the body (Figure 4).[38] Unfortunately, those "partial skeletons" were described as scrappy and disappointingly incomplete.[39] Nevertheless, because of the scarcity of postcranial skeletons, the remains still had some value. Donald Johanson and Tim White found these bones in 1986. They reported their discovery of hominin fossil OH 62 in the journal *Nature*.[40] The specimen consisted of upper and lower limb bones, and on the basis of associated teeth, jaw, and facial fragments, Johanson

---

32. Reader J., *Missing Links*, Oxford University Press, Oxford, p. 324, 2011.
33. Cartmill M. and Smith F.H., *The Human Lineage*, Wiley-Blackwell, Hoboken, NJ, p. 217, 2009.
34. Cartmill M. and Smith F.H., *The Human Lineage*, Wiley-Blackwell, Hoboken, NJ, p. 222, 2009.
35. Villmoare B. *et al.*, Early *Homo* at 2.8 Ma from Ledi-Geraru, Afar, Ethiopia, *Science* 347:1352-1355, 2015; http://science.sciencemag.org/content/347/6228/1352
36. Tattersall I. and Schwartz J., *Extinct Humans*, Westview Press, New York, p. 106, 2001.
37. Wolpoff M.H., Book review: *Olduvai Gorge, Volume 4: The Skulls, Endocasts, and Teeth of Homo habilis*, by Phillip V. Tobias, *Am J Phys Anthropol* 89(3):402, Nov 1992.
38. Johanson D.C. *et al.*, New partial skeleton of *Homo habilis* from Olduvai Gorge, Tanzania, *Nature* 327:205-209, 1987. Johanson notes OH 62 *"represents the first time that limb elements have been securely assigned to Homo habilis."*
39. Johanson D. and Edgar B., *From Lucy to Language*, Simon & Schuster, NY, p.176, 1996.
40. Johanson D.C. *et al.*, New partial skeleton of *Homo habilis* from Olduvai Gorge, Tanzania, *Nature* 327:205-209, 1987.

identified it as Habilis.[41] The specimen preserved enough of the limb bones to measure its length proportions (humeral-femoral index). Thus OH 62 provided a clearer picture of what Habilis might have looked like. What they found was a body that was distinctly ape-like (*Australopithecus*). Apparently, Habilis had the limb proportions of an ordinary ape with hands that hung down to its knees. Henry McHenry, paleo-expert at the University of California laughed when he saw how small the partial skeleton was, *"It is so tiny... Now we have to go back to the fossil collections and fish out the hominid limb bones that have been misclassified as monkeys."*[42] In other words, OH 62 looked so ape-like that it would be easy to confuse it with the bones of an arboreal monkey.

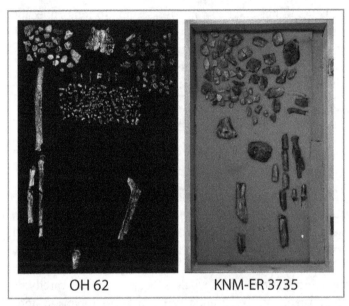

OH 62   KNM-ER 3735

Figure 4. From an article published in *Science* (1987) describing the limb proportions of Habilis based on a partial skeleton found at Olduvai Gorge, Tanzania (left). Another partial skeleton attributed to Habilis recovered from Koobi Fora, Kenya (right). What did the "real" Habilis look like?

OH 62 has been described as more ape-like than Lucy. Christopher Ruff reports this observation in the *American Journal of Physical Anthropology*. He notes that the humero-femoral length index of OH 62 is *"more like that of modern chimpanzees"* and *"more primitive"* than that of Lucy.[43] He then concludes that Habilis must have been an arboreal species and not a habitual biped. Wood also discussed the significance of these findings:

Only 1 well-attested associated skeleton from Olduvai, OH 62, samples the upper

41. Cartmill M. and Smith F.H., *The Human Lineage*, Wiley-Blackwell, Hoboken, NJ, 2009. *"The teeth and facial anatomy of OH 62 resembled those of H. habilis from Olduvai, and so D. Johanson and his colleagues assigned it to that species (Johanson, 1987)."*
42. Lewin R., The Earliest "Humans" Were More Like Apes, *Science* 236:1061-1063, May 1987.
43. Ruff C., Relative limb strength and locomotion in *Homo habilis*, Am J Phys Anthropol 138:90-100, 2009.

and lower limbs…. The specimen itself is fragmentary and poorly-preserved but, because it includes elements of both the upper and lower limbs, it is possible to estimate the limb proportions and these have been assessed as being remarkably ape-like (Hartwig-Schrerer & Martin, 1991).[44]

Not long after this, in the *Journal of Anatomy* (2000), Wood and Richmond list Habilis in the *Australopithecus* genus. The discovery of OH 62 *"muddied the concept of Homo habilis even further."*[45] Paleoanthropologists were working hard to find a transitional species to connect the ape-ish australopiths (*Au. afarensis*) with the first anatomically modern humans (Erectus). In order for Habilis to occupy this evolutionary position in the human lineage it had to look a certain way; it couldn't be too ape-ish or too human. And so, without ever having sufficient skeletal evidence to determine what it looked like, paleo-experts had already assumed Habilis would display the sought-after combination of traits. They put the cart before the horse and prematurely envisioned Habilis as walking in a distinctly human manner with body proportions similar to modern humans. Yet the discovery of OH 62 shattered this hope.

Many experts in the field who have carefully considered the OH 62 specimen have reassigned *Homo habilis* to the extinct ape genus *Australopithecus*. This view is being embraced by a growing number of paleoanthropologists. Lee Berger is one of them, and notes, *"the post-cranial remains of H. habilis appear to reflect an australopith-like body plan."*[46] The fossil evidence seems to clearly show that most of the Habilis bones should be assigned to the genus *Australopithecus*. If Habilis is an australopithecine ape, it would mean there is no rational basis to position it as the immediate precursor of Erectus, so the vast gulf between the australopithecines and man would remain unfilled. However, this is not the whole story because some of the Habilis bones appear to be human—which is why Habilis was assigned to the genus *Homo* in the first place.

Is Habilis a Mixture of Ape and Human Bones?

Numerous lines of evidence suggest that Habilis is an invalid species, the product of active imaginations and fossil beds with both ape and human bones. Many have suspected this over the years, including renowned paleoanthropologist Loring Brace, who insisted, *"Homo habilis is an empty taxon inadequately proposed and should be formally sunk."*[47] An "empty taxon" implies a category with no specimens—i.e., a taxonomic mistake. It is widely acknowledged by leaders in the field that many of the bones attributed to Habilis should never have been assigned

---

44. Wood B., *et al.*, A technique for establishing the identity of 'isolated' fossil limb bones, *J Anat* 193:61–72, 1998.

45. Cartmill M. and Smith F.H., *The Human Lineage*, Wiley-Blackwell, Hoboken, NJ., 2009.

46. Berger L.R. *et al.*, *Homo naledi*, a new species of the genus *Homo* from the Dinaledi Chamber, South Africa, *eLife* 4:e09560, p. 23, 2015.

47. Brace C.L., Biological parameters and Pleistocene hominid life-ways, in: Bernstein I.S. and Smith E.O. (eds.) *Primate Ecology and Human Origins: ecological influences on social organization*, Garland STPM Press, NY, 1979.

to "the species" to begin with. Numerous paleo-experts have argued that the loose collection of bones attributed to Habilis contain a mixture of bones from both *Homo* and *Australopithecus*. The problem is, they can't seem to agree on which bones belong where. Given so much uncertainty for so long—it is unreasonable to continue to treat this loose collection of bones as a real taxonomic group. This is why prominent experts in the field are saying Habilis should simply be *"scrapped."*[48] For instance, Tattersall and Schwartz refer to this mixed assemblage of bones called Habilis as a *"mess"* and emphasize *"we make no apologies for the term."* They state:

> The mystery of *H. habilis* thus persists. The ancestry of later hominids is presumably represented somewhere within the large and miscellaneous aggregation of fossils that have at one time or another been called *H. habilis*. But for the time being there is no agreement on exactly how many hominid species are included in this assemblage.[49]

Richard Leakey is a paleoanthropologist who has followed in the footsteps of his famous parents, Louis and Mary Leakey (the primary discoverers of the Habilis bones). As a distinguished paleo-expert in his own right, Richard expresses his frustration over the same problem noted by so many other experts. In his book *Origins Reconsidered* he writes:

> Of the several dozen specimens that have been said at one time or another to belong to this species, at least half probably don't. But there is no consensus as to which 50 percent should be excluded. No one anthropologist's 50 percent is quite the same as another's.[50]

Do the bones belong to *Zinjanthropus*, Habilis, *Australopithecus*, Erectus, *Homo rudolfensis*, or *Kenyanthropus rudolfensis*? It depends on which paleo-expert you ask. Richard explains that when it comes to deciding which bones belong to Habilis, it is largely dependent on whatever the particular paleo-expert "feels" like including.

There is at least one observation that seems to be widely agreed upon among paleo-experts; that the variation in the assemblage of bones called Habilis is far too

---

48. Schwartz J. and Tattersall I. write in Defining the Genus *Homo*, Science 349(6251):931-932, 2015. *"If we want to be objective, we shall almost certainly have to scrap the iconic list of names in which hominin fossil specimens have historically been trapped and start from the beginning..."* Here they are referring to Habilis among other problematic taxonomic designations.
49. Tattersall I. and Schwartz J., *Extinct Humans*, Westview Press, New York, p. 123, 2001.
50. Leakey R.E. and Lewin R., *Origins Reconsidered: In Search of What Makes Us Human*, Anchor Books (Doubleday), New York, p. 112, 1992.

extensive to be from a single species.[51,52,53,54,55,56,57] Two decades after the discovery of Habilis, Wood raised this concern in *Nature*:

> Despite the enlarged hypodigm [the discovery of new Habilis bones], the main present-day doubts about *H. habilis* (does it represent more than one taxon and, if so, is the second taxon *Homo* or 'gracile' australopithecine?) are the same ones that paleoanthropologists debated in *Nature* more than 20 years ago. Robinson considers that the original *H. habilis* hypodigm was a conflation of *Australopithecus africanus* and *Homo erectus*, whereas Louis Leakey saw Habilis as possibly embracing two species of *Homo* from separate lineages... More recent contributions have suggested different splits of the *H. habilis* hypodigm but all these commentators are in agreement that, as is presently understood, *H. habilis* is too variable to be a 'sound' species.[58]

Rightmire, in the *American Journal of Physical Anthropology*, agreed with Wood's evaluation. In his paper published 30 years after the discovery of Habilis, he observes, *"It is clear that there is much variation within the hypodigm of Homo habilis, and the status of this taxon remains unsettled."*[59] Rightmire explains that the variation found in Habilis exceeds what is expected of sexually dimorphic species (which display differences between male and females of the same species).[60] The unrealistic degree of anatomical variation further confirms that Habilis consists of bones from multiple species. Paleoanthropologists Cartmill and Smith point this out in *The Human Lineage*:

> As specimens assigned to *Homo habilis* accumulated, it became increasingly clear that there was a lot of variation in individual features within the Habiline sample. In 1986, Stringer concluded there was evidence for as many as three African species of early *Homo*: *Homo habilis* (including ER 1470, ER 1590, OH 7, and OH 24), *Homo* cf. *erectus* (including OH 13, OH 16, and ER 1805), and another species

---

51. Leakey R.E. and Lewin R., *Origins Reconsidered: In Search of What Makes Us Human*, Anchor Books (Doubleday, New York, p.112, 1992. Leakey notes, *"the issue of extreme anatomical variability in the species sample persisted, and debate on this remains as vigorous as ever..."*
52. Donnelly S.M., How different are KNM-ER 1470 and KNM-ER 1813? A multivariate comparison using randomization methods, *Am J Phys Anthropol Suppl* 22:99, 1996.
53. Grine F.E. *et al.*, Phenetic affinities among early *Homo* crania from East and South Africa, *J Hum Evol* 30:189-225, 1996.
54. Lieberman D.E. *et al.*, A probabilistic approach to the problem of sexual dimorphism in *Homo habilis*: A comparison of KNM-ER 1470 and KNM-ER 1813, *J Hum Evol* 17:503-511, 1988.
55. Stringer C.B., The credibility of *Homo habilis*, In: Wood B. *et al.* (eds) *Major topics in primate and human evolution*. Cambridge Univ. Press, Cambridge, UK, 1986.
56. Wood B., Early *Homo* in Kenya, and its systematic relationships. In: Delson E. (ed), *Ancestors: The hard evidence*, Alan R. Liss, New York, 1985.
57. Cartmill M. and Smith F.H., *The Human Lineage*, Wiley-Blackwell, Hoboken, NJ, pp. 229-230, 2009. *"As specimens assigned to Homo habilis accumulated, it became increasingly clear that there was a lot of variation in individual features within the Habiline sample."*
58. Wood B., Who is the 'real' *Homo habilis?*, *Nature* 327:187-188, 1987.
59. Rightmire G.P., Variation among early *Homo* crania from Olduvai Gorge and the Koobi Fora Region, *Am J Phys Anthropol* 90:1-33, 1993.
60. Rightmire GP., *Am J Phys Anthro* 90:1-33, 1993. *"There is now substantial support for the view that in the Turkana and perhaps also in the Olduvai assemblages, there is more variation than would be expected among male and female conspecifics."*

(possibly *H. ergaster*) represented by ER 992 and ER 1813.[61]

Paleo-experts observe some of the bones assigned to Habilis align neatly with the genus *Homo* (such as a partial foot designated OH 8), and may actually belong to Erectus (Figure 5). Yet other bones align better with *Australopithecus* (such as OH 62). This supports the contention offered by Brace and others that Habilis is an "empty taxon" and should be sunk into existing species designations.

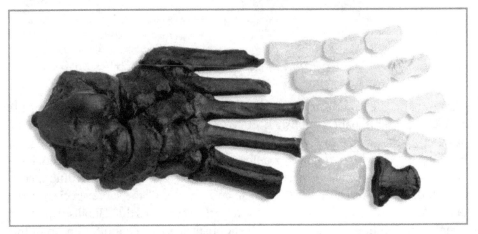

Figure 5. Olduvai Hominid 8 (OH 8) preserves a partial left foot recovered in 1960 from middle Bed I at Olduvai Gorge, Tanzania. The specimen is shown together with a great toe bone found a year later in upper Bed I. The isolated foot was presumed to belong to Habilis despite the lack of any evidence to confirm its association. Not surprisingly, many paleo-expert reject this claim and note that the partial foot is *"remarkably like those of modern humans"*— it does not match the arboreal locomotory behavior suggested by the australopith body plan of Habilis.

The invention of a "new species" by combining bones from different species has occurred several times in the field of paleoanthropology. Paleo-experts acknowledge that it is not uncommon for hominin-bearing sites to contain a commixture of *Homo* and *Australopithecus* bones. Making an "ape-man" out of human and ape bones is an easy mistake to make, especially when disconnected bones from multiple species are randomly jumbled together in the same bone bed, precisely the manner in which the remains of Habilis were found. The same situation appears to have occurred with Lucy's kind, Afarensis. Like Habilis, the bones now attributed to Afarensis display extensive morphological variation. Since the naming of the species, paleo-experts have argued the degree of variation is too extensive to be explained by sexual dimorphism, and that Afarensis consists of bones from multiple species. Lucy herself has at least one baboon bone, and the total collection of bones attributed to the species was originally described by Johanson, Mary Leakey, and others as containing at least three separate species, including Erectus and *Australopithecus* bones (see chapters 7 and 11). In the next chapter we will show that Sediba also appears to be a mixture of ape and human bones.

61. Cartmill M. and Smith F.H., *The Human Lineage*, Wiley-Blackwell, Hoboken, NJ, p. 229, 2009.

The Extensive Coexistence of Erectus and Habilis

Habilis is not a real species. Even if it were, many paleo-experts would reject Habilis as a human ancestor due to the extensive temporal overlap with its generally accepted descendant species, Erectus. The two species have been found in rock strata of equivalent ages, indicating they coexisted extensively—not what would be expected in an ancestor-descendant relationship.

Until recently, the fossil evidence indicated that Habilis and Erectus were separated in time by 200,000 years and never lived together. However, in 2007 an upper jawbone assigned to Habilis, and a skull assigned to Erectus were reported in the journal *Nature*. The findings revealed that Habilis lived more recently than previously thought and that Erectus lived much earlier than previously thought. Paleo-expert Fred Spoor and colleagues wrote in *Nature*: "*With the discovery of the new, well dated specimens from Ileret, H. habilis and H. erectus can now be shown to have co-occurred in eastern Africa for nearly half a million years.*"[62] This has challenged the classical interpretation that places Habilis as the direct ancestor to Erectus. Lee Berger is one of a number of paleo-experts who prefers the *Australopithecus* designation of the species. He affirms the growing doubt about Habilis as an ancestral species in the journal *Science*:

> *H. habilis* is generally thought to be the ancestor of *H. erectus*, although this might be questioned on the basis of the considerable temporal overlap that existed between them. The identity of the direct ancestor of the genus *Homo*, and thus its link to earlier *Australopithecus*, remains controversial.[63]

The problem of extensive coexistence among what are thought to be ancestor/descendant species is discussed further in chapter 11.

Conclusion—Habilis is a Jumble of *Homo* and *Australopithecus* Bones

Habilis is widely recognized by paleo-experts as an invalid taxon, or at best an incoherent assemblage of fragmentary bones. Habilis is a "wastebasket taxon"—a commixture of *Australopithecus* and *Homo* bones. Habilis has failed to fill the "vast gulf" that separates australopith and man. Habilis can now be added to the growing list of falsely claimed "ape-men." John Reader is a distinguished human evolution researcher in the department of Anthropology at University College, London. In his book *Missing Links*, Reader effectively summarizes the current status of Habilis:

> Nearly half a century of accumulating evidence and discussion has left *Homo habilis* more open to question, more insecure than it ever was… *Homo habilis* remains more of an evolutionary idea than an example of anatomical fact linking one species to another.[64]

---

62. Spoor F., Leakey M.G. *et al.*, Implication of new early *Homo* fossils from Ileret, east of Lake Turkana, Kenya, *Nature* 448:688-691, 2007.

63. Berger L.R. *et al.*, *Australopithecus sediba*: a new species of *Homo*-like Australopith from South Africa, *Science* 328:195, 2010.

64. Reader J., *Missing Links*, Oxford University Press, New York, p. 332, 2011.

CHAPTER 9

Australopithecus sediba
A "Mosaic" Species?

It's not everything the rumor mill said it was going to be. It's not a missing link.[1]

Paleoanthropologist and Discovery Team Leader, John Hawks,
University of Wisconsin–Madison

The "Muddle in the Middle"

Until recently, the only evidence supporting the evolutionary transition from the genus *Australopithecus* to the genus *Homo*, consisted of very limited fragmentary remains that have been hotly contested within the field of paleoanthropology.[2] Evolutionary paleo-experts have openly acknowledged this. In an article published in *Science* (2015), researchers wrote:

> Our understanding of the origin of the genus *Homo* has been hampered by a limited fossil record in eastern Africa [the region where humans allegedly evolved from] between 2.0 and 3.0 million years ago (Ma) ... This leaves a thin scatter of isolated, variably informative specimens dated to 2.4 to 2.3 Ma as the only credible fossil evidence bearing on the earliest known populations of the genus *Homo*.[3]

A *National Geographic* author similarly writes, "*The birth of our genus has long been a conundrum for paleoanthropologists, to say the least. Only a few scattered and fragmentary fossils older than two million years have been argued to belong to the genus.*"[4] And evolutionary paleoanthropologist and director of the Institute of Human Origins at Arizona State University, William Kimbel said, "*There are only a handful of specimens. You could put them into a small shoe box and still have room for a good pair of shoes.*"[5] Experts in the field freely confess that after a century and a half of collecting hominin fossils, the origin of *Homo* remains clouded. This critical

---

1. John Hawks quoted in Choi C.Q., Fossil skeletons may be human ancestor, https://www.livescience.com/6313-fossil-skeletons-human ancestor.html.
2. Villmoare B. *et al.*, Early *Homo* at 2.8 Ma from Ledi-Geraru, Afar, Ehtiopia, *Science* 347:1352-1355, 2015.
3. Villmoare B. *et al.*, Early *Homo* at 2.8 Ma from Ledi-Geraru, Afar, Ehtiopia, *Science* 347:1352-1355, 2015.
4. Fischman J., Malapa Fossils Part Ape, Part Human. *National Geographic*, August 2011.
5. Kimbel quoted in Fischman, *National Geographic*, 2011

transitional period during which humans are said to have evolved from an ape-like australopith, is described as the "muddle in the middle"[6] or the "murky period".[7] It is out of those few broken bones that paleoanthropologists have endeavored to assemble credible transitional species that link apes to man.

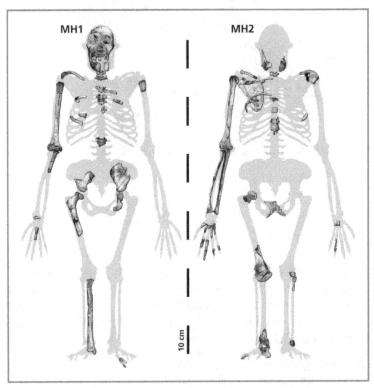

Figure 1. The remains of the adolescent male dubbed Malapa Hominin 1 (MH-1) on the left and an adult female dubbed Malapa Hominin 2 (MH-2). Both are claimed to represent a single new species, *Australopithecus sediba.*

The absence of credible fossil evidence in this crucial part of the ape-to-man-story seemed to come to an end with the recent discovery of the bones dubbed *Australopithecus sediba* ("Sediba"). Sediba is by far the most complete skeleton recovered from this critical time period. While only 40%–60% of two skeletons have been recovered, there are also bone fragments from four other individuals. This entire set of bones has been boldly promoted as representing a new species that bridges apes (*Australopithecus*) and men (*Homo*).

Sediba is considered unprecedented in terms of completeness.[8] Scott Simpson, anatomist from Case Western Reserve University, who was involved with analyzing

6. University of the Witwatersrand public release: Sept. 8, 2011. New evidence suggests that *Au. sediba* is the best candidate for the genus *Homo*; https://www.eurekalert.org/pub_releases/2011-09/uotw-nes090111.php
7. Gibbons A., Skeletons present an exquisite Paleo-puzzle, *Science* 333:1370-1372, 2011.
8. Gibbons A., Skeletons present an exquisite Paleo-puzzle, *Science* 333:1370-1372, 2011.

Sediba's remains, comments in *Science Daily*, "*Paleoanthropologists are used to being fed scraps of fossils*," but with Sediba "[i]*t's like a feast getting a skeleton of this magnitude. After a lifetime of crumbs, it's a welcome meal.*"[9] To paleoanthropologists, a skeleton that is nearly 50% complete is considered "a feast." There's still not much there, yet huge claims have been made about Sediba. Some suggest it may be the biggest discovery in paleoanthropology in recent history.

Background and Discovery of "Sediba"

Figure 2. The first specimen attributed to Sediba preserves a collarbone, catalogued Malapa Hominin 1 (MH-1). In August of 2008, 9-year-old Mathew Berger stumbled upon a bone protruding from a clump of sediment lying on the ground next to an open pit on the Malapa Nature Reserve in South Africa. Paleo-expert and father of Mathew, Lee Berger, identified the bone as a juvenile australopithecine. Additional skeletal parts presumed to belong to the same individual (MH-1) were found soon after.

The Cradle of Humankind World Heritage Site of Gauteng Province, South Africa is well known for its wealth of early hominin fossil remains, including those belonging to *Australopithecus africanus*, *Homo ergaster* (aka the African *Homo erectus*) as well as Sediba. On the 15th of August in 2008, nine-year-old Matthew Berger was chasing his dog along an open pit (Figure 3) referred to as the Malapa site (on the Malapa Nature Reserve) when he stumbled upon a bone protruding from a clump of sediment (Figure 2). It was a collarbone!

To the amazement of his father, paleo-expert Lee Berger, the bone belonged to a partial skeleton of a child who was about 12–13 years old.[10] Excavated remains of what was later found to be an adolescent male dubbed Malapa Hominin 1 (MH-1) included a skull, mandible, portions of the upper and lower limbs, ribs, vertebrae, hip fragments, and elements of the hands and feet.[11] Nearly a month later, on September 4th, Lee Berger discovered a second specimen believed to belong to the same species. The remains were of an adult female dubbed Malapa Hominin 2 (MH-2).[12] Bones recovered included the mandible and teeth, much of the right upper

9. Nuwer R. and Richards S., The mosaic pre-man, *The Scientist Magazine*, September 8, 2011; http://the-scientist.com/?articles.view/articleNo/31147/title/The-Mosaic-Pre-Man/

10. Berger L.R., *Australopithecus sediba* and the earliest origins of the genus *Homo*, J Anthropol Sci 90:1-16, 2012.

11. Berger L.R., *Australopithecus sediba*: A New Species of *Homo*-Like *Australopithecus* from South Africa, *Science*, 328:195-204, 2010. DOI:10.1126/science.1184944

12. Berger L.R., *Australopithecus sediba* and the earliest origins of the genus *Homo*, J Anthropol Sci 90:1-16, 2012.

limb, portions of the lower limbs, ribs, vertebrae, hip fragments, a nearly complete right hand, a complete right ankle and one metatarsal bone.[13] Since then, at least 4 other specimens (MH-3–6) have been found—two infants and two adults— though not nearly as complete as MH-1 and MH-2 (e.g., MH-4 consists of a single tibia).[14] Twenty-six additional putative hominin bones have been recovered but do not seem to fit with any of the skeletons just mentioned.[15] To date only MH-1 and MH-2 have been fully analyzed and described (Figure 1). A limestone deposit that underlies the fossil-bearing strata where the specimens were found was radioactively dated to 1.97 million years old using the uranium-thorium-lead method (see chapter 12 for details on dating methods).[16,17]

Figure 3. The Malapa site is located in the center of the Cradle of Humankind World Heritage Site, near Johannesburg, South Africa. Limestone miners exploited the shallow pit in the 1920s. The bulk of the remains were found *in situ* within the pit. The broken, fragmentary bones were found in loose-to-close anatomical association—some physically joined together. The bones were buried together in a mixed bed containing thousands of bones from at least 18 different species (including *Homo*, *Australopithecus*, and primates). The remains were embedded in water-laid classic sediments *"buried together in a single debris flow"* (indicative of a sudden flow of mud and water). Paleo-experts have since called Berger's findings into question and cite evidence indicating Sediba consists of bones from two separate genera (just like Habilis)—*Australopithecus* and *Homo*.

13. Berger L.R., *Australopithecus sediba*: A New Species of *Homo*-Like *Australopithecus* from South Africa, *Science*, 328:195-204, 2010. DOI:10.1126/science.1184944

14. Berger L.R., The mosaic nature of *Australopithecus sediba*, *Science* 340:163, 2013.

15. Val A.M.S., A 3D approach to understand the taphonomy of the early hominins from the Plio-Pleistocene cave site of Malapa. PhD Thesis Univ of the Witwatersrand, Johannesburg, South Africa, p. 50, July 23, 2013.

16. Pickering R., *et al.*, *Australopithecus sediba* at 1.977 Ma and implications for the origins of the genus *Homo*, *Science* 333:1421-1423, 2011.

17. Gibbons A., Skeletons present an exquisite Paleo-puzzle, *Science* 333:1370-1372, 2011.

These findings were first published in 2010 in *Science*, with later papers being published in 2011 and 2013 describing in detail the remains of MH-1, MH-2, and the tibia (shinbone) of MH4. Berger and colleagues claim that Sediba *"may be the best candidate yet for the immediate ancestor of our genus, Homo."* Sediba would take Habilis's position in the family tree and dethrone Lucy and her kind as our direct ancestor in the process.[18,19,20] *National Geographic* reported on what could be an extensive *"redrawing of the family tree,"* writing:

> Everybody knows "Lucy." For nearly four decades, this famous partial skeleton of *Australopithecus afarensis*, dated to 3.2 million years ago, has been an ambassador for our prehistoric past, and her species has stood as the most likely immediate ancestor of our own genus—*Homo*. But in a spate of new studies, paleoanthropologist Lee Berger, of the University of the Witwatersrand, and a team of collaborators have put forward a controversial claim that another hominin—*Australopithecus sediba*—might be even closer to the origin of our lineage, possibly bumping Lucy from the critical evolutionary junction she has occupied for so long.[21]

The taxonomic classification of Sediba and its proposed status as our direct ancestor is a subject of continued debate amongst paleo-experts. Donald Johanson, discoverer of Lucy and her kind Afarensis, is adamantly opposed to having his species replaced by Sediba. Berger's suggested revision of the hominin ancestral lineage leading to our genus *Homo* is shown below (Figure 4).

Traditional View: *Au. afarensis > H. habilis > H. erectus > H. sapiens*

⬇ ⬇

Berger's Proposal: *Au. africanus > Au. sediba > H. erectus > H. sapiens*

Figure 4. Berger insists that *Homo habilis* does not belong in the direct human lineage and should be replaced by his discovery, *Australopithecus sediba*. With *Au. sediba* in place, *Au. africanus* would have to be reintroduced into the direct human lineage with *Au. afarensis* pushed out as an evolutionary dead end—an offshoot of *Au. africanus*, no longer ancestral to the genus *Homo*. *Au. afarensis* does not fit in Berger's scheme because Lucy's kind is seen as "too advanced" when compared to certain bones belonging to *Au. sediba*.

So what is it about Sediba's fossil remains that would cause some evolutionary paleoanthropologists to abandon the standard story regarding the early ancestry of man? The scientific literature consistently depicts Sediba as a "mosaic" of primitive ape-like bones and more modern human-like bones. *New Scientist* offers a typical description: *"At 2 million years old, they show a mix of features, some similar to the*

---

18. Berger L.R., The mosaic nature of *Australopithecus sediba*, *Science* 340:163, 2013.
19. Balter M., Candidate human ancestor from South Africa sparks praise and debate, *Science* 328:154-155, 2010.
20. AAPA Meeting Briefs, *Science*, 2010.
21. Switek B., New studies shake up human family tree, *National Geographic News*, April 12, 2013; http://news.nationalgeographic.com/news/2013/13/130411-homo-ancestor-hominin-skeleton-lucy-australopithecus-sediba-science/

ape-like australopithecines, others more like our genus, Homo. To its discoverers, this hotchpotch means A. sediba was becoming human."[22] The researchers and authors of papers in *Science* describe Sediba in the same way—exhibiting a suite of "*Australopithecus*-like features" and "*Homo*-like features," representing a *"combination of primitive and derived characters."*[23,24] The researchers routinely make a clear distinction between the "primitive" and "derived" characters—ape-like and human-like, respectively.[25] For instance, the narrow upper ribcage of the female specimen (MH-2) is noted for its obvious resemblance to *"large-bodied apes,"* whereas the lower ribcage is described as *"human-like,"* indicating to them *"a rather unsuspected mosaic anatomy."*[26,27] The explanation for this blend of traits is that some bones evolved to look more like *Homo sapiens*, whereas other bones remained unchanged and ape-like. They refer to this as a *"mosaic acquisition of modern anatomies."*[28] In other words, evolution allegedly operated in such a way that it appears as though Sediba was an assemblage of two different species, belonging in separate genera (*Australopithecus* and *Homo*). A short description of Sediba's remains in *New Scientist* recognizes this, stating:

> A. sediba has a strange mix of human and australopithecine qualities. Some say that if the various bones had been found separately, they would have been assumed to belong to different species.[29]

This was first noted by Steven Churchill, evolutionary paleoanthropologist at Duke University and co-author of a number of the papers published in *Science* describing Sediba's remains. Churchill notes, *"If we found* [the specimens] *as separate parts, we'd probably think they came from different species...."*[30] He writes *"if"* we found them as separate parts. Actually, most of the remains *were* found as separate parts. Only a few of the bones were found in anatomically credible association. The site consisted of a mixed bone bed of many different types of animals; most of the bones were not found physically connected to one another. Thus it is possible that Sediba is not a legitimate species, but may be a mixture of bones from more than one species, as was the case with Habilis (see chapter 8). As we will show, there are multiple lines of evidence supporting this view.

22. Barras C., Human 'missing link' fossils may be jumble of species *New Scientist* 2964: April 09, 2014.
23. Kivell T.L. *et al.*, *Australopithecus sediba* hand demonstrates mosaic evolution of locomotor and manipulative abilities, *Science* 333:1411-1417, 2011.
24. Berger L. *et al.*, *Australopithecus sediba*: a new species of homo-like Austrolpith from South Africa. *Science* 328:195-204, 2010.
25. Berger L.R., *Australopithecus sediba* and the earliest origins of the genus *Homo J Anthropol Sci* 90:1-16, 2012.
26. Berger L.R., The mosaic nature of *Australopithecus sediba*, *Science* 340:163, 2013.
27. Schmid P. *et al.*, Mosaic morphology in the thorax of *Australopithecus sediba*, *Science* 340:1234598-1–1234598-5, 2013. DOI: 10.1126/science.1234598
28. Zipfel B. *et al.*, The foot and ankle of *Australopithecus sediba*, *Science* 333:1417-1420, 2011.
29. Brahic C., 2015 preview: Meet more of your long-lost cousins, *New Scientist*, December 16, 2014.
30. Nuwer R. and Richards S., The Mosaic pre-man, *The Scientist Magazine*, Sept 8, 2011.

New Scientist

 18

THIS WEEK 9 April 2014

Human 'missing link' fossils may be jumble of species

By Colin Barras

Figure 5. Yoel Rak, one of the world's leading paleo-experts of Tel Aviv University, Israel, and colleague Ella Been, also of Tel Aviv and an expert in spinal anatomy, analyzed some of the bones of Sediba. Been was surprised to find that the lumbar vertebrae do not belong to a single species as Berger had claimed. She reported that the lumbar vertebrae of the adolescent male (MH-1) looked strikingly similar to the vertebrae of Turkana Boy (Erectus). On the other hand, the adult female's (MH-2) lumbar vertebrae resembled those of australopithecines. Been discussed her findings in New Scientist (above) stating, *"I think there are two different hominin genera represented at Malapa."* Rak examined the jawbones attributed to the two individuals at Malapa and came to the same conclusion—Sediba is a jumble of species. Rak noted that the male jawbone (MH-1) is morphologically most similar to *Australopithecus* and the jawbone of the female (MH-2) is *Homo*.

Sediba's Spine and Jaw Appear to be Mixed Bones

The two partial vertebral columns assigned to Sediba (23 pre-sacral vertebrae and a partial five-element sacrum) were described by Williams and colleagues in *Science* as having *"evolved in a mosaic fashion."*[31] Many aspects of the vertebrae had distinct features that are present in modern humans (longer lower back, wide curved sacrum, S-shaped spine, etc.). However, other respected evolutionary paleo-experts could not help but notice that some of the vertebral bones appeared to be distinctly ape-like. This led them to believe that Sediba is not evolving in a "mosaic fashion" but is actually a mixture of two different species. This would mean Sediba is not itself a new species but is a mixture of ape and human bones. Evolutionary paleo-experts Ella Been and Yoel Rak, both from the department of anatomy and anthropology at Tel Aviv University, presented their findings at the Paleoanthropology Society in Calgary, Canada in April of 2014. A brief summary of their findings have also been published in *New Scientist*[32] (Figure 5). Been is an expert in spinal anatomy and pathology. After examining photographs taken of the fossil remains assigned to MH-1 and MH-2, Been noticed that the lumbar vertebrae of the adolescent male (MH-1) looked strikingly similar to those of

31. Williams S. *et al.*, The vertebral column of *Australopithecus sediba*, *Science* 340, 2013. DOI: 1126/science.1232996.
32. Barras C., Human 'missing link' fossils may be jumble of species, *New Scientist* 2964, April 09, 2014.

Turkana Boy.[33] Turkana Boy is a *Homo erectus* specimen with lumbar vertebrae which are wider than they are tall, just as in modern man. On the other hand, the adult female's (MH-2) lumbar vertebrae resembled those of apes, being similar to australopithecines, which are taller than they are wide. Been reports:

> According to our analysis, the spinal columns of the two skeletons represent two different hominid genera—*Australopithecus* and *Homo*. …We compared these ratios in the four lumbar vertebrae from Malapa to the ratios that characterize the lumbar elements of 75 modern humans, two *Homo erectus* specimens, and four australopiths. Our measurements indicate that the lumbar vertebrae attributed to the Malapa specimen MH-1 (UW88-92 and UW88-152) fall well within the range of *Homo*, whereas the lumbar vertebrae attributed to the Malapa specimen MH-2 (UW88 127/153 and UW88 126/138) are similar to those found in australopiths.[34]

Been realized the remains discovered by Berger do not represent a single species. Instead, the remains belong to 2 different genera (*Homo* and *Australopithecus*).[35] Been concludes, "*The claim that A. sediba represents a transitional species between Australopithecus africanus and Homo stems from this mixture. The coexistence of Homo and Australopithecus in early South African sites is not unusual, as seen in fossils from the Swartkrans Cave and the nearby Sterkfontein Cave.*"[36] Consistent with these findings, Yoel Rak, found that the unarticulated lower jawbones are also of a different species. The male jawbone (MH-1) appears to be most similar to an australopith's, whereas the jawbone of the adult female (MH-2) resembles that of a human.[37,38,39] In noticing the thinness of the lower jawbone, Johanson notes, "*It's homo.*"[40] In agreement with the human-looking jawbone, the dentition attributed to MH-2 is described as "*remarkably human-like*" lacking pronounced canines characteristic of australopithecines.[41] Paleoanthropologist Darryl de Ruiter, author of a number of the *Science* papers covering Sediba, reports that "*the premolars of Au. sediba plot within the ranges of H. erectus and H. sapiens dentitions.*", with mandibular molars that are "*small, similar to specimens attributed to early Homo.*"[42]

33. Barras C., Human 'missing link' fossils may be jumble of species, *New Scientist*, 2964: April 09, 2014.

34. Been E. and Rak Y., The lumbar spine of *Australopithecus sediba* indicates two hominid taxa. *PaleoAnthropology*, A2, 2014.

35. Barras C., Human 'missing link' fossils may be jumble of species, *New Scientist*, 2964: April 09, 2014.

36. Been E. and Rak Y., The lumbar spine of *Australopithecus sediba* indicates two hominid taxa, *PaleoAnthropology*, A2, 2014.

37. Been E. and Rak Y., The lumbar spine of *Australopithecus sediba* indicates two hominid taxa, *PaleoAnthropology*, A2, 2014.

38. Barras C., Human 'missing link' fossils may be jumble of species, *New Scientist*, 2964: April 09, 2014.

39. Wong K., Is *Australopithecus sediba* the most important human ancestor discovery ever? *Scientific American* Blogs, April 24, 2014.

40. Balter M., Candidate human ancestor from South Africa sparks praise and debate, *Science* 328:154-155, 2010.

41. Barras C., Our closest ape-like ancestor went back to the trees, *New Scientist*, April 11, 2013. http://newscientist.com/article/dn23376-our-closest-ape-like-ancestor-went-back-to-the-trees/

42. de Ruiter D. *et al.*, Mandibular remains support taxonomic validity of *Australopithecus sediba*, *Science*, 340, 2013. DOI: 10.1126/science.1232997.

Sediba's Hip Bone is Human

Certain features of the human-looking hipbone (such as the *"sagittally oriented ilia"*) served as the basis for the researchers' claim that Sediba walked upright like humans, though with a pigeon-toed (hyperpronated) gait.[43] The researchers acknowledge that Sediba's inferred ability to walk upright was *"based primarily"* on the hip bone and lower limb (as well as the commingled vertebrae which we discussed previously), and *"to a lesser extent on the pedal* [partial foot and ankle bones] *morphology of MH2."*[44] If it were not for the human-shaped pelvis it would be difficult for the researchers to claim Sediba walked upright. However, the human-looking hip appears to have been mistakenly combined with australopith bones. This is likely, considering the mixed bone bed from which the fossils were recovered. The hipbone fits neatly within the genus *Homo*—it is markedly different from an ape hip. While examining a cast of the hipbone (a composite of MH-1 and MH-2), Ella Been couldn't help but notice its striking resemblance to that of modern human: *"It does look homo like."*[45] This is in agreement with published papers in *Science*. For instance, DeSilva and colleagues describe the pelvis attributed to Sediba as *"human-like."*[46] In the *Science* paper that focused specifically on the hipbones, evolutionary paleoanthropologists Kibii and colleagues report:

> The pelvis of early Pleistocene *Homo* share with modern humans a suite of features ... Many of these features are seen in the pelvic remains of two fairly complete individuals of *Australopithecus sediba* from Malapa.[47]

Evolutionary paleoanthropologist Christopher Ruff of Johns Hopkins University admitted, *"The pelvis does look more modern,"* though not exactly like a modern human pelvis, he adds.[48] Across the board, Sediba researchers acknowledge this. In talks held at The Paleoanthropology Society and American Association of Physical Anthropology in Minneapolis, Minnesota Lee Berger himself acknowledges:

> But the fossils also show some surprisingly modern traits usually found only in members of our genus ... The two pelvises, in particular, are capacious and elongated, resembling those of *Homo*.[49]

He writes elsewhere that the flaring of the iliac blade is *"derived"*—meaning its morphology is closely *"associated with later members of the genus Homo."*[50] To explain Sediba's human-looking hipbone that appears far too modern for an

43. DeSilva J. *et al.*, The lower limb and mechanics of walking in *Australopithecus sediba*, Science 340:1232999-1 –1232999-5, 2013.

44. DeSilva J. *et al.*, The lower limb and mechanics of walking in *Australopithecus sediba*, Science 340:1232999-1–1232999-5, 2013.

45. Personal communication, 2015.

46. DeSilva J. *et al.*, The lower limb and mechanics of walking in *Australopithecus sediba*, Science 340:1232999-1–1232999-5, 2013.

47. Kibii J. *et al.*, A partial pelvis of *Australopithecus sediba*. Science 333:1407-1411, 2011.

48. AAPA Meeting Briefs, Science, 2011.

49. Anonymous, A new ancestor for *Homo*? AAPA Meeting Briefs. Science 332:534, 2011.

50. Berger L.R., *Australopithecus sediba* and the earlist origins of the genus Homo J of Anthropol Sci 90:1-16, 2012.

australopith, the researchers assume that the pelvis must have rapidly evolved while other bones lagged behind. Again, they describe the phenomenon as "mosaic acquisition of traits." However, a more reasonable explanation for the "surprisingly modern" hipbone is that it belonged to a member of our own genus—not because Sediba was evolving in a mosaic fashion.

Sediba's Ribcage is Ape

The human-like hip not only influenced the researchers' claim that Sediba was a habitual upright walker; it also influenced their interpretation of the ribcage (thorax). The ribcage of Sediba was reconstructed with what Berger and researchers described as a "mosaic morphology"—looking partly human and partly ape—a convenient anatomy for an alleged transitional form. Schmid and colleagues discuss this in *Science*, writing:

> The thoracic shape of *Au. sediba* thus appears to be an unusual combination of the primitive condition of an ape-like upper thoracic shape, with a more derived, human-like shape to the lower thorax.[51]

The upper ribcage tapered inward toward the base of the neck in a funnel shape, which is characteristic of large-bodied apes.[52] Meanwhile, the lower ribcage was more cylindrical or barrel-shaped as in modern humans. The researchers note, *"In both skeletons, the upper thoracic region* [ribcage] *is better preserved than its lower parts."* The available remains allowed for a faithful reconstruction of the upper rib cage that is distinctly ape-like. They note, *"The overall shape of the upper thorax of Au. sediba is clearly more ape-like...."*[53] However, the lower ribcage that was supposedly "human-like" could not be reconstructed due to the fragmentary nature of the remains. All that was recovered from the lower thorax was a single, small rib fragment which was arguably human-like in structure. The researchers were not sure if it was the ninth or tenth rib. They claimed it belonged to the lower ribcage of the adult female (MH-2), though at least six other alleged hominin skeletons have since been recovered from the Malapa pit, and various bones have already been mistakenly included with the wrong skeleton (e.g., the tibia originally thought to belong to MH-1 was later reassigned to MH4). Therefore, the isolated lower rib fragment might be from a separate skeleton, one belonging to the genus *Homo*. Regardless, a single rib fragment is not sufficient to allow for a careful reconstruction of the lower ribcage, as the researchers freely confess. How then can they be confident the lower ribcage was barrel-shaped, like in humans? The honest answer is that they cannot. In fact, the most reasonable reconstruction of the lower ribcage would have been to make it anatomically compatible with

---

51. Schmid P. *et al.*, Mosaic morphology in the thorax of *Australopithecus sediba*, Science 340:1234598-1–1234598-5, 2013. DOI: 10.1126/science.1234598.
52. Schmid P. *et al.*, Mosaic morphology in the thorax of *Australopithecus sediba*, Science 340:1234598-1–1234598-5, 2013. DOI: 10.1126/science.1234598.
53. Schmid P. *et al.*, Mosaic morphology in the thorax of *Australopithecus sediba*, Science 340:1234598-1–1234598-5, 2013. DOI: 10.1126/science.1234598.

the comparatively better-preserved upper ribcage, which clearly resembles that of large-bodied apes. But the researchers understood that an ape-like lower ribcage would not be compatible with the *"surprisingly"* modern-looking hip (an anatomical contradiction). The researchers acknowledge that the inferred human-like, barrel-shaped reconstruction of the lower ribcage was primarily influenced by the human-shaped hip. Schmid and colleagues explain their reasoning:

> In both apes and humans, there is correspondence between the shapes of the inferior ribcage and the false pelvis (formed by the iliac blades). Thus, the derived, human-like vertical reorientation and greater curvature of the iliac blades of *Au. sediba* lead us to suggest that its lower thoracic shape [ribcage] could not be like that of an ape.[54]

It is true that there is an anatomical correspondence between the shape of the lower ribcage and iliac blades of the hipbone (as well as muscle attachments between them). The human lower ribcage wraps around the curvature of the iliac blades, whereas in apes the lower ribcage flares over the straighter iliac blades to form a funnel-shaped thorax. Thus the lower ribcage needed to be reconstructed to look human because of the loose assumption that the wider human-shaped hip also belonged to Sediba (not because the recovered rib bone fragments suggested this). But in consideration of the mismatched jawbones, and the mismatched vertebrae, it seems likely that the human-shaped hipbone was also mistakenly associated with the remains of MH-1 and MH-2. If Sediba reflects a mixture of *Homo* and australopith bones, then it is not surprising the reconstruction of the lower rib-cage was made to appear human (barrel-shaped), especially if it was modeled based on mismatched human hip bones (see above).

Sediba's Upper Limbs are Ape

Recovered remains of the upper limbs assigned to MH-1 and MH-2 include an assortment of complete and fragmentary bones—clavicles, humeri, ulna, radius, scapula, etc. In this suite of bones there is no evidence of a "mosaic" assemblage of "primitive and derived" traits; experts in the field are largely in agreement on this point. Consistent with the funnel-shaped upper thorax, the upper limb bones attributed to Sediba are unmistakably ape-like, revealing an anatomy perfectly suited for tree-dwelling life. The researchers involved in the analysis of the upper limb bones acknowledge this. Evolutionary paleoanthropologist Steven Churchill, first author of the published paper, is quoted in a *Live Science* article saying, *"Its scapula or shoulder blade is most similar in shape to that of orangutans...."*[55] He and his colleagues puzzled over this in their published *Science* paper writing:

> The importance of the Pongo-like scapular morphology of MH2 is unclear.

---

54. Schmid P. *et al.*, Mosaic morphology in the thorax of *Australopithecus sediba*, Science 340:1234598-1–1234598-5, 2013. DOI: 10.1126/science.1234598.
55. Choi C.Q., Humanity's closest ancestor was pigeon-toed, research reveals, *Live Science*, April 11, 2013. http://www.livescience.com/28656-closest-human-ancestor-was-pigeon-toed.html

Orangutans are the only large-bodied ape to retain a predominantly arboreal lifestyle, and they engage in the greatest amount of forelimb suspension during locomotion of any of the great apes.[56]

If Sediba is truly the immediate ancestor to upright-walking members of our genus *Homo*, why does it have an upper limb anatomy that indicates it spent most of its life in the trees? This conflicts with DeSilva and Berger's claim that *"Au. sediba was a habitual biped* [upright walker]."[57,58] Of course, they get around this by insisting Sediba could do both—preferring to spend most of its time in a terrestrial habitat as a biped, but still retaining *"substantial climbing and suspensory ability."*[59] Yet these types of contradictory anatomies (with some bones appearing distinctly ape and others appearing distinctly human) are expected of a chimeric skeleton that combines *Homo* and *Australopithecus* bones.

Other researchers have also pointed out the very ape-ish anatomy of the upper limbs. Schmid and colleagues report in *Science*: *"The morphology of the upper thorax and elements of the pectoral girdle suggest that Au. sediba had habitually elevated, "shrugged" shoulders like that of a chimpanzee."*[60] Berger writes further that Sediba had *"longer, more ape-like arms."*[61] Popular science writer, Ann Gibbons, summarizes the anatomy of the upper limbs in an article in *Science*:

The other new papers [in *Science*] tackle different parts of the anatomy, such as the shoulder and arm, which are primitive and chimplike. This shoulder and the long arm show that *Au. sediba* was still spending a lot of time climbing trees...[62]

If Sediba was a habitual biped as Berger claimed, it's very odd that the upper limbs appeared more arboreal and ape-like than any other australopith. The bottom line is that the bones of the upper limb are in every respect, fully ape.

Sediba's Human Hand

Paleo-expert Steven Churchill describes the hand and wrist attributed to the adult female (MH-2) as *"hyper human."*[63] Berger described the hand similarly: *"Sediba's hand is hauntingly similar to that of modern humans—with a fully opposable thumb. A chimpanzee's hand is excellent for grasping and swinging from trees. Sediba's*

---

56. Churchill S. *et al.*, The upper limb of *Australopithecus sediba*, *Science* 340 (2013); DOI: 10.1126/science.1233477.

57. Berger L. *et al.*, *Australopithecus sediba*: a new species of homo-like Austrolpith from South Africa, *Science* 328:195-204, 2010.

58. DeSilva J. *et al.*, The lower limb and mechanics of walking in *Australopithecus sediba*, *Science* 340:1232999-1–1232999-5, 2013.

59. Churchill S.E. *et al.*, The upper limb of *Australopthecus sediba*. *Science* 340, 2013. DOI: 10.1126/science.1233477.

60. Schmid P. *et al.*, Mosaic morphology in the thorax of *Australopithecus sediba*, *Science* 340:1234598-1 – 1234598-5. 2013. DOI: 10.1126/science.1234598.

61. Berger L.R., *Australopithecus sediba* and the earliest origins of the genus *Homo*, *J Anthropol Sci* 90:1-16, 2012.

62. Gibbons A., A human smile and funny walk for *Australopithecus sediba*, *Science* 340(6129):132-133, 2013.

63. Nuwer R. and Richards S., The mosaic pre-man, *The Scientist*, Sept 8, 2011.

hand could hold and use small objects.[64] Researchers were surprised to find such a modern-looking hand from what they believed to be a 1.97-million-year-old australopith. Humans have a longer thumb and shorter fingers when compared to apes (Figure 6). However, the perfectly human hand of Sediba is incompatible with the distinctly ape-like anatomy of the upper limbs. If Sediba swung through the trees, it could not do so with human hands.

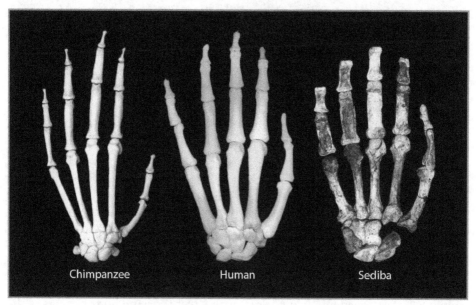

Figure 6. A comparison of Sediba's hand to that of a human and chimpanzee. Sediba's hand closely resembles that of modern humans, with longer thumbs relative to shorter fingers (the opposite of apes). Note: The finger tips (phalanges) of Sediba were not recovered.

Human hands give us the unique ability to grip and carefully manipulate objects between the thumb and fingers. Stone tools were recovered from the Malapa site where the remains of MH-1 and MH-2 were found. However, the stone tools were not found *in situ*, so researchers have not drawn any conclusions as to whether they were used by Sediba.[65] But in consideration of the mismatched fossils that demonstrate Sediba is a mixture of two different species (and is therefore a false taxon) it stands to reason that the hand of MH-2 and the stone tools belonged together, representing our genus, *Homo*.

Prior to Sediba, the most complete hand dating to the same time period (1.97 Ma) was assigned to *Homo habilis*. Habilis's recovered hand bones (OH 7) were said to display a human-like morphology, and were associated with stone tools. Interestingly the hand bones attributed to MH-2 appear to be even more human-like than those of Habilis. With this in mind, it is surprising that researchers do

64. Berger L.R. and Aronson M., *The Skull in the Rock*, National Geographic, Washington D.C., USA, pp. 51-52, 2012.
65. Churchill quoted in: Nuwer R. and Richards S., The mosaic pre-man, *The Scientist Magazine*, September 8, 2011.

not credit Sediba with the same tool-making ability. Kivell in the journal of *Science* comments on this writing:

> *Au. sediba* reveals that many of the manual morphological features commonly associated with stone tool production—even if *Au. sediba* itself was not a stone tool-maker—were present by 1.977 Ma, and most of these features are not present in OH 7. In light of this, *Au. sediba* may provide a better potential morphotype for basal *Homo* hand morphology than the hand fossils originally used to define the species *H. habilis*.[66]

Despite the overall similarity of the hand bones of MH-2 to humans, the researchers have been reluctant to ascribe Sediba with tool making. Why? The reason is because the ape-like anatomy of the upper limbs of Sediba is not compatible with a tool-making hominin. Long arms and chimpanzee-like upper thorax useful for suspensory behavior do not fit well with tool-making abilities (another apparent anatomical contradiction). Kivell and colleagues explain:

> Although arboreal features do not necessarily preclude the ability to make stone tools, the retention of arboreal features in MH2, together with its primitive australopith-like upper limb, suggest that *Au. sediba* still regularly engaged in arboreal behavior. Thus, *Au. sediba* does not have all of the morphological features commonly considered necessary to demonstrate a clear commitment to stone tool production.[67]

In other words, it is largely because of the ape-like upper limb anatomy that Sediba is assumed to be inconsistent with tool-making. But if Sediba is a mixture of bones from two different genera, then it is reasonable that the hand bone belongs in the genus *Homo* and the ape-like upper limb belongs to an australopith. This very nicely explains why the hand bones are described as *"hyper human"* and why the upper limb is considered *"like that of chimpanzee."*[68] It is not because Sediba is evolving to become human with a "mosaic" anatomy, but simply because it is a mixture of human and non-human bones that do not belong together.

Sediba's Skull and Braincase are Ape

When considering any putative ancestor to early man, there is the temptation for paleo-experts to highlight certain traits that might suggest an evolutionary vector toward the human condition. The skull and endocast (braincase) attributed to Sediba is no exception. Yet the Sediba cranium and endocast are fully ape, and resists efforts to humanize Sediba. This makes it difficult to argue that the skull represents anything other than an ordinary ape.

A partial cranium found at the Malapa site was assigned to the juvenile skeleton

---

66. Kivell T. *et al.*, *Australopithecus sediba* hand demonstrates mosaic evolution of locomotor and manipulative abilities, *Science* 333:1411-1417, 2011.

67. Kivell T. *et al.*, *Australopithecus sediba* hand demonstrates mosaic evolution of locomotor and manipulative abilities, *Science* 333:1411-1417, 2011.

68. Nuwer R. and Richards S., The mosaic pre-man, *The Scientist*, Sept 8, 2011.

(MH-1). The cranial capacity was small (~420 cm^3)—within the range of chimps.[69] But as we learned from Hobbit, Erectus, and modern humans, cranial capacity is not a definitive taxonomic indicator. In Berger's own assessment of the skull, *"The closest morphological comparison for Au. sediba is Au. africanus, as these taxa share numerous similarities in the cranial vault, facial skeleton, mandible, and teeth."*[70] Yet Berger points out other features that differ from *Au. africanus*. In particular *Au. africanus* has pronounced, flaring cheekbones, whereas in Sediba these are reduced. Berger considers the narrower face and other features (the shape of the cranium; the parietal, temporal, infraorbital region, etc.), to be "derived"— meaning more human-like. However, none of these features are outside the normal range of variation found in living apes. Consider a side-by-side comparison of the juvenile MH-1 skull attributed to Sediba with that of a juvenile chimpanzee and bonobo. In Berger's analysis of the skull in *Science*, he acknowledges that overall the skull aligns most closely with the ape-like australopithecines. He writes, *"we consider Au. sediba to be more appropriately positioned within Australopithecus."*[71] He then lists a suite of ape-like traits to support MH-1's inclusion into the genus *Australopithecus*. This is in keeping with the observation that the morphologies of australopithecine skulls overlap with living apes. In the *Journal of Human Evolution* (2017), William Kimbel and Yoel Rak reject Berger's claim that Sediba's skull (MH-1) is "derived" toward the human condition writing:

> We argue that MH 1 provides clear evidence that A. sediba was uniquely related to A. africanus [an extinct australopithecine ape] and that the hypothesis of an extensive ghost lineage connecting A. sediba to the root of the Homo clade is unwarranted.[72]

The cerebral cortex is the outer surface of the brain. Most people see it as a meaningless mush of folds and bumps, but it is informative.[73] In humans this region of the brain is involved with reasoning, learning, judging, planning, language, social skills, and creativity.[74] It also leaves an imprint on the inner walls of the braincase. Specialists known as paleoneurologists are able to make digital scans and internal molds of fossil braincases called endocasts. Some endocasts preserve the "wrinkles" of the brain (sulci) better than others. The skull of the juvenile specimen, MH-1, luckily produced a highly detailed endocast. Carlson

---

69. Berger L. *et al.*, *Australopithecus sediba*: a new species of homo-like Austrolpith from South Africa, *Science* 328:195-204, 2010.
70. Berger L. *et al.*, *Australopithecus sediba*: a new species of homo-like Austrolpith from South Africa, *Science* 328:195-204, 2010.
71. Berger L. *et al.*, *Australopithecus sediba*: a new species of homo-like Austrolpith from South Africa, *Science* 328:195-204, 2010.
72. Kimbel W.H. and Rak Y., *Australopithecus sediba* and the emergence of *Homo*: Questionable evidence from the cranium of the juvenile holotype MH 1, *J Hum Evol* 107:94-106, 2017.
73. Falk D., (2011-10-03). *The Fossil Chronicles: How Two Controversial Discoveries Changed Our View of Human Evolution* (Kindle Locations 1941-1942), University of California Press Berkeley, CA, Kindle Edition.
74. Falk D., Interpreting sulci on hominin endocasts: old hypotheses and new findings. *Frontiers in Human Neuroscience* 8(article 134):1-11, 2014.

and colleagues reported an analysis of the endocast in *Science* in 2011.[75] In their paper the researchers tried to emphasize certain parts of the brain that might suggest a more human-like brain-function. However, their research demonstrates that over-all the brain of MH-1 was fully ape.

The overall brain structure of humans and apes is similar. Dean Falk, a leading evolutionary paleoneurologist and expert in human and primate brains and cognition, explains:

> In keeping with their extraordinary cognitive abilities, humans have larger and more convoluted cerebral cortices than the other primates. Nevertheless, the basic organization of the entire cerebrum, including its arrangement of the major parts of the brain (lobes and the fissures that separate them), is similar in monkeys, apes, and people.[76]

Falk explains further that there are only two places in the brain where humans and apes differ markedly. The first is a large groove in the back of the brain that marks a structure known as the lunate sulcus, which is present in apes but absent from humans. Unfortunately, that portion of the skull of MH-1 was missing.[77] The second distinguishing feature is another large groove known as the fronto-orbital sulcus (*fo* for short), located toward the front of the brain in apes but not present in humans. As reported in the journal *Frontiers in Human Neuroscience*, "*Chimpanzee brains (and, indeed those of all great apes) have a fronto-orbital sulcus (fo), not seen in human brains....*"[78] In place of the ape *fo*, humans have two smaller grooves that make up a triangular region or *pars triangularis* called Broca's area which plays an essential role in speech and language.[79,80]

Falk notes that the fronto-orbital sulcus (*fo*) "*reproduces well on ape brains and, often, on their endocasts.*"[81] Does the endocast of MH-1 have a distinct *fo* that typifies apes or a Broca's speech area that typifies humans?[82] Carlson and colleagues acknowledge in *Science* that the endocast indicates the presence of the fronto-orbital sulcus (*fo*) and the absence of the human Broca's area. They showed that Sediba had the brain of an ape:

> A distinct fronto-orbital sulcus incises the lateral margin of the ... left inferior frontal lobe... This is a primitive condition that is present in apes and some other

75. Carlson K.J. *et al.*, The endocast of MH1, *Australopithecus sediba*, Science 333:1402-1407, 2011.
76. Falk D., (2011-10-03). *The Fossil Chronicles: How Two Controversial Discoveries Changed Our View of Human Evolution* (Kindle Locations 1941-1942), University of California Press Berkeley, CA, Kindle Edition.
77. Carlson K., *et al.*, The endocast of MH1, *Australopithecus sediba*, Science 333:1402-1407, 2011.
78. Falk D., Interpreting sulci on hominin endocasts: old hypotheses and new findings. *Frontiers in Human Neuroscience* 8(article 134):1-11, 2014.
79. Carlson K. *et al.*, The endocast of MH1, *Australopithecus sediba*, Science 333:1402-1407, 2011.
80. Falk D., Interpreting sulci on hominin endocasts: old hypotheses and new findings, *Frontiers in Human Neuroscience* 8(article 134):1-11, 2014.
81. Falk D., Interpreting sulci on hominin endocasts: old hypotheses and new findings, *Frontiers in Human Neuroscience* 8(article 134):1-11, 2014.
82. Falk D., Interpreting sulci on hominin endocasts: old hypotheses and new findings, *Frontiers in Human Neuroscience* 8(article 134):1-11, 2014.

South African australopiths but not typically expressed in *Homo*. Also similar to endocasts of apes and other australopiths, the MH1 endocast exhibits no evidence of … Broca's area. … In this respect, the inferior frontal region of MH1 clearly appears more ape-like than humanlike.[83]

The Sediba team claims the endocast represents an evolutionary intermediate; they point to a bulge on the left hemisphere of MH-1's endocast, located just in front of the *fo* called the inferior frontal gyrus, in the region that corresponds to Broca's speech area. In their assessment, the bulge is slightly larger on the left hemisphere than the right. They claim the asymmetrical bulge is atypical of apes and could be evidence of further developed neural connectivity.[84] Carlson and colleagues hypothesize that *"the bulge on the MH1 endocast could represent early stages of bolstering local neural interconnectivity in area 45, but not yet to the point that more advanced interconnectivity had established true outward folding."*[85] This evidence is unconvincing and very speculative. What does it mean to say a slight bulge *"bolstered neural interconnectivity"*? An article in *National Geographic* brings Falk into the discussion who adds caution to this claim:

Pronounced asymmetry between right and left brain hemispheres is a hallmark of humans, because our cerebrum has become specialized, with the left side more involved in language. On that side Carlson sees hints of a protrusion in the region of Broca's area—a part of the brain linked to language processing in modern humans. But Dean Falk from the School for Advanced Research in Santa Fe, an expert on fossil endocasts, adds the caution that Broca's area is defined by specific creases in the brain, and "it would be quite a reach" to identify it based only on a bulge.[86]

Other criticisms have been raised. Recent studies have called into question the long-held assumption stated above—that there exists a structural asymmetry in the Broca's speech area found on the left hemisphere of the human brain (which corresponds to the inferior frontal gyrus in apes and in the endocast of MH-1).[87] For instance, in the *Journal of Neuroscience*, Simon Keller and colleagues report, *"The findings presented here suggest that there is no population-based interhemispheric macroscopic asymmetry of Broca's area in humans or Broca's area homolog in chimpanzees."*[88] This invalidates the claim of Carlson *et al.*, that an asymmetric bulge in the endocast of MH-1 is evidence that Sediba was evolving toward a human brain.

Moreover, in the study by Carlson and colleagues in *Science*, the endocast of Sediba was compared to just two other australopithecine endocasts (Sts 5 and

---

83. Carlson K. *et al.*, The endocast of MH1, *Australopithecus sediba*, *Science* 333:1402-1407, 2011.
84. Gibbons A., Skeletons present an exquisite Paleo-puzzle, *Science* 333:1370-1372, 2011.
85. Carlson K. *et al.*, The endocast of MH1, *Australopithecus sediba*, *Science* 333:1402-1407, 2011.
86. Fischman J., Malapa fossils part ape, part human, *National Geographic*, August, 2011
87. Schenker N.M. *et al.*, Broca's area homologue in chimpanzees (*Pan troglodytes*): probabilistic mapping, asymmetry, and comparison to humans, *Cerebral Cortex* 20:730-742, 2010.
88. Keller S. *et al.*, A comparative magnetic resonance imaging study of the anatomy, variability, and asymmetry of Broca's area in the human and chimpanzee brain, *J Neuroscience* 29(46):14607-14616, 2009.

Sts 60). They excluded other australopithecine endocasts that are more variable. Commenting on this Falk says, *"To make a convincing case you need to look at all the australopithecines in South Africa."*[89] In a follow-up study in the journal *Frontiers in Human Neuroscience*, Falk includes an additional australopithecine endocast (Taung) for further comparative analysis of MH-1's endocast. In her analysis, Falk did not find that the specified sulcal pattern by Carlson *et al.* was unique to MH-1. Instead it appears that *"All of the australopithecine endocasts that reproduce sulci in the frontal lobe have similar sulcal patterns...."*[90]

There are still more problems. Compared to other australopithecine specimens, the brain size of Sediba is noticeably smaller (~420 cm^3). Carlson and colleagues describe the small brain size as "primitive." Considering the human-like bones of the hand and pelvis, they were intrigued by this.[91] They write:

> Retained australopith (primitive) brain size in *Au. sediba* is intriguing given the appearance of derived morphology elsewhere in the cranium and postcranial skeleton, particularly within the pelvis and hand. Presumed selective pressures (such as complex object manipulation and tool use) favoring more derived hand morphology in a species that may be ancestral to *H. erectus sensu lato* would seem inconsistent with retention of a small brain size.[92]

First, the so-called "derived" (meaning human-like) morphology of the cranium is highly questionable and overall most closely resembles that of apes, as discussed above. The modern hands and pelvis are best understood in terms of mixed bones, and so do not need to be reconciled with an ape-like brain. However, the discovery team tries to reconcile human hands and hips with an ape skull and brain by saying, *"The possibility exists, however, that neural reorganization, independent of overall size increase could explain such discrepancies."*[93] The problem with this is that the endocast studies of MH-1 do not support neural reorganization. It is pure conjecture. This also puts them in a difficult position because they must reject the traditional hypothesis that australopith brain size increased gradually over time in favor of a rapid reorganization of the brain (that preceded brain size increase) in a tiny slice of geologic time. This is one of the reasons many experts in the field are not convinced Sediba is ancestral to the genus *Homo*, one of the world's leading evolutionary paleoanthropologists, poses this as a serious objection against the proposed ancestral status of Sediba:

> Dr. Wood gave little credence to Dr. Berger's arguments that *Australopithecus* is a direct ancestor of the human group, saying there was too little time for the small-

89. Gibbons A., Skeletons present an exquisite Paleo-puzzle, *Science* 333:1370-1372, 2011.
90. Falk D., Interpreting sulci on hominin endocasts: old hypotheses and new findings, *Frontiers in Human Neuroscience* 8(article 134):1-11, 2014.
91. Carlson K., *et al.*, The endocast of MH1, *Australopithecus sediba*, *Science* 333:1402-1407, 2011.
92. Carlson K., *et al.*, The endocast of MH1, *Australopithecus sediba*, *Science* 333:1402-1407, 2011.
93. Carlson K., *et al.*, The endocast of MH1, *Australopithecus sediba*, *Science* 333:1402-1407, 2011.

brained, tree-climbing ape to evolve into large-brained *Homo erectus*.[94]

In summary, Carlson and colleagues describe the endocast attributed to Sediba in their *Science* report as "intermediate." They state that the brain of MH-1 *"reveals generally australopiths-like convolutional patterns on the frontal lobes but also some foreshadowing of features of the human frontal lobes..."* suggesting *"the transition from Australopithecus to Homo."*[95] Contrary to these claims, the ape-like aspects of the endocast are uncontested among paleoanthropologists, and the supposed *"foreshadowing"* of other features toward the human condition is pure speculation.

Sediba's Puzzling Mixed Bone Bed

Sediba bones were found in a shallow, open pit about 11 ft by 14.5 ft in size and 13 ft deep, located on the side of a low hill (marked "Malapa site" below the dotted line in Figure 7). In describing the geological context, Dirks and colleagues reported in *Science* that, *"Minor limestone mining* [by hand] *took place at Malapa in the early 20th century,"*[96] which exposed Sediba bones (and many other bones) in the pit.[97] Most of the bones were found in loose anatomical association. Other remains were found separately, as unarticulated, stray bones—such as the collarbone that was embedded in a block of calcified sediment removed by the miners, and found by Matthew Berger lying by itself on the ground above the pit. Looking at the exposed strata from within the pit, the bulk of the remains of MH-1 and MH-2 were found at mid-depth in the deposit. The Sediba bones were buried in a mixed bone bed with thousands of other bones from at least 18 different species, including primates.[98] Researchers in *Science* reported that the fossils were encased in *"water-laid clastic sediments that were deposited along the lower parts of what is now a deeply eroded cave system... The two hominin specimens were buried together in a single debris flow that lithified soon after deposition in a phreatic* [cave] *environment inaccessible to scavengers."*[99] Researchers assume that what is now a shallow open pit was once the bottom of a deep cave system 100 feet *above* the present ground level. Dirks and colleagues drew a cartoon of a hypothetical cave system and what it might have looked like before it was allegedly eroded down to the shallow pit seen today (Figure 7).

Everything drawn above the dotted line—the death traps, the overlying cave

---

94. Wade N., New Fossils May Redraw Human Ancestry, New York Times Science, September 9, 2011. http://www.nytimes.com/2011/09/09/science/09fossils.html?pagewanted=all&_r+0
95. Carlson K. *et al.*, The endocast of MH1, *Australopithecus sediba*, *Science* 333:1402-1407, 2011.
96. Dirks P. *et al.*, Geological setting and age of *Australopithecus sediba* from southern Africa, *Science* 328:205-208, 2010.
97. Val A. *et al.*, Taphonomic Analysis of the Faunal Assemblage Associated with the Hominins (*Australopithecus sediba*) from the Early Pleistocene Cave Deposits of Malapa, South Africa, *PLOS ONE*, July 23, 2013. DOI:10.1371/journal.pone.0126904
98. Val A. *et al.*, Taphonomic Analysis of the Faunal Assemblage Associated with the Hominins (*Australopithecus sediba*) from the Early Pleistocene Cave Deposits of Malapa, South Africa, *PLOS ONE*, July 23, 2013. DOI:10.1371/journal.pone.0126904
99. Dirks P. *et al.*, Geological setting and age of *Australopithecus sediba* from southern Africa, *Science* 328:205-208, 2010.

system, the water flow, the shear zone, etc—is all imagined. No one knows what the terrain looked like two million years ago. Berger *et al.* hypothesized the idea of a death trap to explain the mystery of how the remains of so many species could have been buried together in a small pit. Here is the standard explanation:

> On the ground above the cave are a number of 'death traps', or longer vertical shafts, down which the animals fell, probably attracted by the smell of damp. The pair—possibly mother and son—might have fallen to their deaths while searching for water. The sediments imply that subsequent high-volume water inflow, perhaps the result of a large storm, caused a debris flow. This carried the bodies deeper into the cave, to deposit them along a subterranean stream.[100]

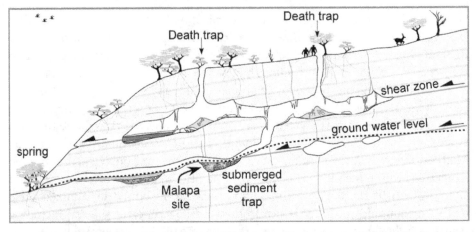

Figure 7. Hypothetical cave system showing possible features of the landscape prior to erosion. Everything drawn above the dotted line is an imaginary reconstruction of a complex cave system. Today all that is seen is a shallow pit assumed to be the remnant of a former cave system.

It should be obvious that this is not a testable hypothesis, but is a "just so" story. There are numerous alternative scenarios which could explain a mixed bone bed like the Malapa pit. The flowstone observed in the pit does not necessarily indicate an ancient cave; flowstone is also observed around hot water springs. Flowstone is just a localized deposit of lime, deposited by lime-saturated flowing water.[101] Hot water springs could also be associated with a natural gas seep—where animals would come to drink and become asphyxiated. The pit of bones could also reflect a sinkhole (a deep pond with steep sides), where animals would drown. Another possibility is that the animals were hunted by humans, and after consumption the remains were conveniently cast into an existing pit. This would neatly explain why nearly all of the species represented are common game animals.[102] Lastly, the pit,

100. Seddon C. (2014-03-03). *Humans: from the beginning: From the first apes to the first cities,* (Kindle Locations 13892-13893). Glanville Publications. Kindle Edition.
101. Dirks P. *et al.,* Geological setting and age of *Australopithecus sediba* from southern Africa, *Science* 328:205-208, 2010.
102. Val A. *et al.,* Taphonomic Analysis of the Faunal Assemblage Associated with the Hominins (*Australopithecus sediba*) from the Early Pleistocene Cave Deposits of Malapa, South Africa, *PLOS ONE,* July 23, 2013. DOI: 10.1371/journal.pone.0126904

being near a river, may have been filled with debris from a local flash flood. The Malapa pit is located in a flood plain between three converging tributaries of the Magaliesberg River.

All we can honestly infer from the existing evidence is that the bones of many creatures of all sorts accumulated in a small pit, resulting in a jumble of mixed bones. This made reassembly of the original skeletons, as Berger noted, *"the most taxing jigsaw puzzle."*[103]

Conclusion—Sediba is a Jumble of *Homo* and *Australopithecus* Bones

The bones that have been called Sediba do not appear to represent a "transitional form" at all. What Berger and colleagues reconstructed is not a new species but rather appears to be a chimeric skeleton (a mixture of human and non-human bones). It is not uncommon for paleo-experts to unintentionally mix bones belonging to different species. This is especially true when they are highly motivated to find an "in-between" creature. Berger admits that this was always his life-long ambition.[104] Berger (like his role model Donald Johanson) seem to have spent a lifetime chasing after the honor of finding the missing link that would validate human evolution. Given a jumble of bones from all kinds of African animals (including apes and men), all found in one small pit, and given a strong desire to discover an "in-between" ape-human skeleton, it is easy to see how bones and bone fragments might be assembled to resemble an incomplete "ape-man" skeleton. This explains why some of Sediba's bones appear distinctly ape, while others appear distinctly human.

Berger and colleagues repeatedly refer to Sediba as a mosaic of primitive (ape-like) or derived (human-like) traits.[105] Some bones were distinctly ape, whereas others were distinctly human. The researchers' explanation for the mishmash of traits is that Sediba is a snapshot of ape evolving into man. However, a number of leading paleoanthropologists such as Bernard Wood, Donald Johanson, and others reject this view of Sediba. Other paleo-experts argue that Sediba is an artificial species —the accidental mixture of human and non-human bones. This would mean that Sediba is essentially the same as Habilis—an artificial taxon consisting of a loose collection of human and ape bones. Evolutionary paleo-experts Ella Been and Yoel Rak of Tel Aviv University hold this view, and show that the Sediba lumbar vertebrae and jawbones derive from two different genera—*Australopithecus* and *Homo*. Based on this evidence, Been and Rak claim that Sediba is not a legitimate hominin ancestor but is actually a combination of *Australopithecus* and *Homo* bones. This explains why the discovery team was so puzzled over how it was possible for Sediba to have a suite of bones with what were described as "anatomical

103. Berger L.R. and Aronson M., *The Skull in the Rock*, National Geographic, Washington D.C., USA, 2012.
104. Berger L.R. and Aronson M., *The Skull in the Rock*, National Geographic, Washington, D.C., USA, 2012.
105. Berger L. *et al.*, *Australopithecus sediba*: a new species of homo-like Austrolpith from South Africa, *Science* 328:195-204, 2010.

contradictions" (i.e., upper limb and shoulder anatomy just like arboreal-dwelling orangutans but with hands indistinguishable from modern humans). This is certainly not the first time paleo-experts have mixed human bones with ape bones to create the appearance of an "ape-man." The most famous example of this was the "Piltdown Man", which was just an ape jaw that was force-fitted to a human skull (unlike Sediba, Piltdown Man was a deliberate scientific fraud). The bones of Piltdown Man received the same type of popular acclaim as Sediba, and for decades was lifted up by many prestigious scientists as being the best evidence of human evolution.

After Piltdown Man was discredited, the bones called *Homo habilis* took center stage (see chapter 8). Arguably, Sediba is really just Habilis renamed. Sediba was given the same timeframe as Habilis, and was placed in the same position within the hominin family tree (directly preceding Erectus). Most significantly, Habilis bones were extracted from mixed bone beds, and resulted in a chimeric mixture of ape and human bones; exactly the same can be said of Sediba.

As this book goes to press, much of the buzz surrounding Sediba as a candidate ancestor to the genus *Homo* has gone silent. A *Science* article published in 2017 carried the headline: *"A famous 'ancestor' may be ousted from the human family tree."*[106] Ann Gibbons summarizes a recent analysis presented by Bill Kimbell at the annual meeting for the American Association of Physical Anthropologists. Working together with Yoel Rak, Kimbel notes that Sediba (MH-1 juvenile skull) shares a striking resemblance to an already recognized species *Au. africanus*, and is therefore, not our ancestor: *"We do not believe... that Au. sediba has a unique relationship to the genus Homo."* Bernard Wood, who has always been skeptical of Sediba, whole-heartedly agreed with Kimbel's analysis, as did Ian Tattersall. Gibbons says it best: *"A remarkably complete skeleton introduced in 2010 as "the best candidate" for the immediate ancestor of our genus Homo may just be a pretender."*[107]

Team leader John Hawks and even discoverer Lee Berger himself, appear to have given up on Sediba. As Hawks reflects, *"It's not everything the rumor mill said it was going to be. It's not a missing link."*[108] From the beginning, the paleo-community was suspicious of Berger's sensationalized claims, and has since dismissed Sediba as a credible transitional "bridge species" to early *Homo*. An article in *National Geographic* by science writer James Shreeve captures the current sentiment of the paleo-community regarding the claims made about Sediba:

> Though the doyens of paleoanthropology credited him with a "jaw-dropping" find, most dismissed his interpretation of it. *A. sediba* was too young, too weird,

106. Gibbons A., A famous 'ancestor' may be ousted from the human family, *Science*, April 23, 2017. DOI: 10.1126/science.aal1099

107. Gibbons A., A famous 'ancestor' may be ousted from the human family, *Science*, April 23, 2017. DOI: 10.1126/science.aal1099

108. John Hawks quoted in Choi C.Q., Fossil skeletons may be human ancestor, https://www.livescience.com/6313-fossil-skeletons-human ancestor.html.

and not in the right place to be ancestral to *Homo*: It wasn't one of us. In a sense neither was Berger. Since then, prominent researchers have published papers on early *Homo* that didn't even mention him or his find.[109]

On the heels of disappointment with his discovery of Sediba, Berger stumbled upon yet another remarkable finding hidden deep within a South African cave. In 2015 Berger announced to the world his latest claim of a new "almost human" species, which he has named *Homo naledi* (see next chapter). Could "Naledi" be the long-sought-after transitional bridge species to link australopith and man—or will the "middle" forever remain muddled?

---

109. Shreeve J., Mystery Man, *National Geographic*, October 2015, p. 30-57.

CHAPTER 10

Homo naledi
"Almost Human" or Fully Human?

White is not alone in his uneasiness over H. naledi. Reviewers at top scientific journals also found evidence for the new hominin species to be suspect. Berger and his team originally submitted multiple papers on H. naledi to the prestigious journal Nature, which rejected them.[1]

University of California Berkeley article: *Bones of Contention: Cal Paleo Expert Doubts Homo Naledi is New Species*

Background and Discovery of "Naledi"

In 2013 two cave explorers climbed 90 feet underground into the Rising Star cave system near the Cradle of Humankind World Heritage Site of Gauteng Province, South Africa. In a nearly inaccessible region of the cave, known as the Dinaledi Chamber, the cavers stumbled upon a collection of human bones. They contacted paleo-expert Lee Berger, who had discovered Sediba just five years earlier.[2] Shortly after, Berger called National Geographic and began to celebrate. The disappointments associated with Sediba were quickly forgotten. A childhood dream of Berger was to someday find a hominin ancestor such as Lucy.[3] His hopes had been high with the discovery of Sediba; however, the paleoanthropological community had largely rejected his finding for a number of reasons (see chapter 9). Berger's hopes must have been rekindled with the bones in the Rising Star cave that might possibly represent the bridge species linking ape to man. What did the cave explorers find and how did Berger and his team interpret the bones?

Description of the Fossils and Evolutionary Claims

The Dinaledi Chamber yielded a total of 1,550 bones or bone fragments, belonging to 15 very incomplete individuals (Figure 1). The finding was described as *"the*

1. Martin G., Bones of Contention: Cal paleo expert doubts *Homo naledi* Is new species, 1 October 2015: http://alumni.berkeley.edu/california-magazine/just-in/2015-12-29/bones-contention-cal-paleo-expert-doubts-homo-naledi-new
2. Berger L.R., *Australopithecus sediba* and the earliest origins of the genus *Homo*, J Anthropol Sci 90:1-16, 2012.
3. Berger L.R. and Aronson M., *The Skull in the Rock*, National Geographic, Washington D.C., USA, 2012.

Figure 1. The October 2015 *National Geographic* cover story on the reputed new species, Naledi.

richest assemblage of associated fossil hominins ever discovered in Africa."[4] The remains were found scattered throughout the Dinaledi Chamber with only a few of the bones in articulation (physically connected to other bones).[5] None of the individuals were complete skeletons, so a single composite skeleton was assembled from the available remains from different individuals (Figure 2).[6] The recovered bones included broken upper and lower limbs, some vertebrae, partial ribs, an almost complete hand and foot, pieces of the hip, an upper jaw, one complete lower jaw, and skull fragments from four individuals.[7] The bones were un-mineralized (i.e., true bones), were well preserved, and were easily exposed (buried no more than eight inches deep within a fine clay sediment).[8] In fact, many bones were found lying exposed on the surface of the cave floor. Some were freshly broken, suggesting they had been tampered with.[9] No skeletons of other animals were found, with the exception of a trapped bird and a few rodent skeletons (and more recently a single baboon tooth). The remains appeared to belong to a single hominin population representing all ages, from infants to adults, with the latter being about five feet tall. It appeared as though the bodies were deliberately deposited in the cave chamber, (this possibility, and its implications, are discussed later). Researchers observed that certain distinct anatomical features were repeatedly observed among the samples. This suggested that there was only one species represented. For instance, similarities included short stature and body proportions, similar skulls, similar teeth, and other distinctive features found in multiple specimens. Very little morphological variation was observed between the 15 individuals (apart from age and size). Berger and colleagues made note of this

4. Berger L.R. *et al.*, *Homo naledi*, a new species of the genus *Homo* from the Dinaledi Chamber, South Africa, *eLife* 4:e09560, 2015 p. 24.

5. Berger L.R. *et al.*, *Homo naledi*, a new species of the genus *Homo* from the Dinaledi Chamber, South Africa, *eLife* 4:e09560, 2015 p. 2

6. Berger L.R. *et al.*, *Homo naledi*, a new species of the genus *Homo* from the Dinaledi Chamber, South Africa, *eLife* 4:e09560, 2015 p. 2, figure 1.

7. Berger L.R. *et al.*, *Homo naledi*, a new species of the genus *Homo* from the Dinaledi Chamber, South Africa, *eLife* 4:e09560, 2015 p. 3

8. Dirks P. *et al.*, Geological and taphonomic context for the new hominin species *Homo naledi* from the Dinaledi Chamber, South Africa, 2015. DOI: 10.7554/eLife.09561.001

9. Shreeve J., This Face Changes the Human Story. But How? *National Geographic*, 10 September 2015.

in their paper published in the journal *eLife* (2015).[10] They describe the fossils as a *"morphologically homogeneous sample"* and assigned the remains to a new species, *Homo naledi* ("Naledi"):

> The collection is a morphologically homogeneous sample that can be attributed to no previously-known hominin species. Here we describe the new species, *Homo naledi.*[11]

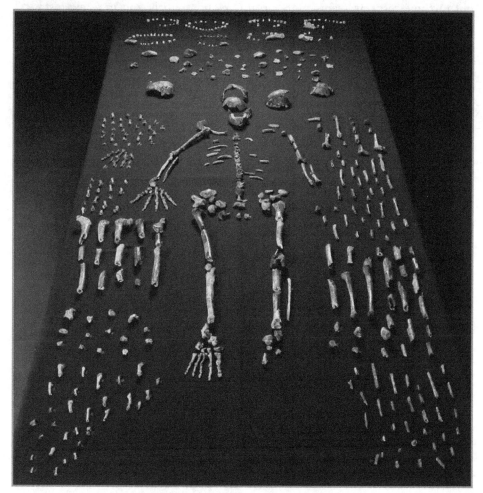

Figure 2. Out of the 1,550 recovered partial and complete bones, 737 of them (shown in this picture) were analyzed and reported in the *eLife* discovery paper.[12] The holotype—the most complete Naledi skeleton to date—is shown in the center. It represents a composite skeleton assembled from bones belonging to multiple individuals.

10. Berger L.R. *et al.*, *Homo naledi*, a new species of the genus *Homo* from the Dinaledi Chamber, South Africa, *eLife* 4:e09560, 2015.
11. Berger L.R. *et al.*, *Homo naledi*, a new species of the genus *Homo* from the Dinaledi Chamber, South Africa, *eLife* 4:e09560, 2015 p. 2.
12. Berger L.R. *et al.*, *Homo naledi*, a new species of the genus *Homo* from the Dinaledi Chamber, South Africa, *eLife* 4:e09560, 2015.

"Naledi" in the South African Sotho language, translates as "star." It was named after the Rising Star cave where the remains were found. The researchers felt that assigning the bones to *Homo* was appropriate, considering its overall anatomy was very human—with the exception of a few features—hence *National Geographic's* headline: *"Almost Human"* (Figure 1).[13] According to Berger, Naledi exhibited an unusual combination of traits. In most respects, Naledi is unquestionably human, but in some respects seems more primitive and ape-ish, and in a few instances seemed to show traits never seen before. In the *eLife* publication Berger and colleagues describe Naledi as an "anatomical mosaic":

> This anatomical mosaic is reflected in different regions of the skeleton. The morphology of the cranium, mandible, and dentition is mostly consistent with the genus *Homo*, but the brain size of *H. naledi* is within the range of *Australopithecus*. The lower limb is largely *Homo*-like, and the foot and ankle are particularly human in their configuration, but the pelvis appears to be flared markedly like that of *Au. afarensis*. The wrists, fingertips, and proportions are shared mainly with *Homo*, but the proximal and intermediate manual phalanges are markedly curved, even to a greater degree than in any *Australopithecus*. The shoulders are configured largely like those of australopiths. The vertebrae are most similar to Pleistocene members of the genus *Homo*, whereas the ribcage is wide distally like *Au. afarensis*.[14]

This is very similar to how Berger described Sediba—a mosaic of "primitive" and "derived" traits. "Primitive" refers to ape-like, and "derived" refers to anatomically human traits. Naledi does *not* appear to be an accidental mixture of human and non-human bones (unlike Sediba and Habilis). All of the bones recovered from the Dinaledi Chamber appear to belong to a single population. In this chapter we will argue that Naledi, from this particular cave chamber of bones,[15] is fully human and not significantly different from Erectus, and that both should be folded into *Homo sapiens* (as "lumper" paleo-experts have insisted).

Did Naledi Have Ape-like Bones?

The claim that Naledi was a precursor species of the other *Homo* types (*H. sapiens, H. erectus*, etc.) ultimately rests upon those few bones that were viewed as less than fully human. So which bones did Berger and colleagues describe as anatomically human, and which were said to be more like *Australopithecus*? Berger and colleagues in the journal *eLife*, offer their interpretation:

> *H. naledi* presents yet a different combination of traits [compared to Sediba]. This species combines a humanlike body size and stature with an australopith-sized brain; features of the shoulder and hand apparently well-suited for climbing with humanlike hand and wrist adaptations for manipulation; australopith-like hip

13. Shreeve J., Mystery Man, *National Geographic*, October pp. 30-57, 2015. Issue title: *Almost Human*.

14. A separate chamber in the Rising Star cave system has yielded additional bones that have been attributed to *H. naledi*: Hawks J. et al., New fossil remains of *Homo naledi* from the Lesedi Chamber, South Africa, *eLife*, 2017. DOI: 10.7554/eLife.24232.001

15. Hawks J. et al., New fossil remains of *Homo naledi* from the Lesedi Chamber, South Africa, *eLife*, 2017. DOI: 10.7554/eLife.24232.001

mechanics with humanlike terrestrial [ground] adaptations of the foot and lower limb; small dentition [teeth] with primitive dental proportions.

The australopith-like features of the postcranium [skeleton from the neck down], including the ribcage, shoulder, proximal femur, and relatively long, curved fingers, also depart sharply from the morphology present in MP humans and *H. sapiens*. The similarities of *H. naledi* to earlier members of *Homo*, including *H. habilis, H. rudolfensis,* and *H. erectus,* suggest that this species may be rooted within the initial origin and diversification of our genus.[16]

All parties agree that most of the Naledi bones are unambiguously human. The clearly human bones of Naledi include the vertebrae, the hands, the wrists, the feet, the upper and lower limbs (excluding the shoulder), the limb proportions, the body size, and the shape of the skull, jaw, and teeth (Figure 3). However, Berger's list of Naledi's "less-than-human" bones is shorter; small brain, smaller shoulders, slight curvature of fingers, details of hip mechanics, exact dental proportions, and widening of the lower ribcage.

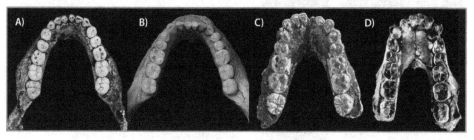

Figure 3. Mandible and dentition of *H. naledi* (A); modern *H. sapiens* (B); *Au. afarensis* from Ethiopia (C); and *Au. anamensis* from Kenya (D). The overall morphological similarity between the mandible of *H. naledi* and that of modern humans is clearly seen. The teeth are arranged in a parabolic or rounded arc shape typical of humans. It is markedly different from the U-shaped mandibles of australopiths.

It is because of these alleged ape-like features that the discovery team argues that Naledi was at the root of the genus *Homo.* As Berger told *National Geographic,* *"The message we're getting is of an animal right on the cusp of the transition from Australopithecus to Homo."*[17] Not surprisingly, this interpretation is consistent with Berger's life-long dream of finding a crucial "missing link," and so his view is potentially colored by personal bias (as are everybody's).[18] Even before Naledi was assigned an age, Berger had already proclaimed his finding to the world as the root

16. Berger L.R. *et al., Homo naledi,* a new species of the genus *Homo* from the Dinaledi Chamber, South Africa, *eLife* 4:e09560, 2015, p. 23. DOI: 10.7554/eLife.09560.

17. Shreeve J., Mystery Man, *National Geographic,* October pp. 30-57, 2015.

18. Even before *Homo naledi* was assigned an age Berger had already proclaimed his finding to the world as the root ancestor to the genus *Homo* (Berger *et al., eLife,* p. 23, 2015). Yet without a date, there is no way he could possibly be sure of this. Shreeve tells of Berger's motivation to find a root ancestor in *National Geographic:* *"What he wanted to find were fossils that could shed light on the primary outstanding mystery in human evolution: the origin of our genus, Homo, between two and three million years ago."* (Shreeve J., Mystery Man, *National Geographic,* October pp. 30-57, 2015).

ancestor to the genus *Homo* (just as he had claimed about Sediba).[19] In light of new developments, Berger's claims regarding the significance of Naledi now appear to have been premature.

Naledi's morphological differences from modern humans are real. However, these differences are relatively minor and their significance seems to have been exaggerated. These "australopith-like" characteristics are not inconsistent with the bones of modern human beings. Naledi bones, like those of Erectus, have some features that are atypical, but still overlap with modern human variation.

Naledi's Human Skull and Braincase

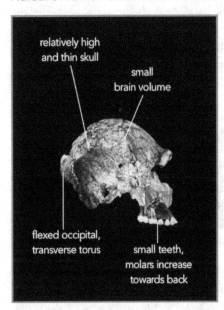

relatively high and thin skull

small brain volume

flexed occipital, transverse torus

small teeth, molars increase towards back

Figure 4. A composite reconstruction of Naledi skull. Paleo-experts such as Chris Stringer regard the Naledi material (including the skull) as most closely resembling Erectus. Image from Stringer, *eLife*, 2015.

The primary basis for declaring Naledi to be "almost human" is its small cranial capacity, although no complete skull was actually recovered.[20] Four partial skull fragments were recovered and digitally pieced together into two composite skulls via a CT scanner (composite means they combined broken pieces of the skulls from different individuals—this was the only way they could get a very rough approximation of the average brain volume in the population). Because they used skulls of different sizes, ages, and likely different genders, to make the composite, and because large fractions of the skulls were missing, the digital reconstruction is of limited value. Obviously, if three of four skull fragments were from juveniles or small children, the estimated brain volume would be misleading. The researchers point out, *"In order to obtain a volume calculation the model has to be a closed surface, meaning that all the holes in the surface model had to be filled."*[21] When they say they *"filled the holes,"* they mean they only filled the holes in a virtual (conceptual) sense.

Though there was quite a bit of guesswork and possible bias in the reconstruction

19. Berger L.R. *et al.*, *Homo naledi*, a new species of the genus *Homo* from the Dinaledi Chamber, South Africa, *eLife* 4:e09560, 2015, p. 23. DOI: 10.7554/eLife.09560.

20. The latest cranial capacity estimate from a better-preserved, non-composite Lesedi cranium (LES1) is 610 cc—notably larger than the composite reconstructions. The latest cranial capacity estimate overlaps with those of modern humans (see chapter 5). Hawks J. *et al.*, New fossil remains of *Homo naledi* from the Lesedi Chamber, South Africa, *eLife*, 2017. DOI: 10.7554/eLife.24232.001

21. Berger L.R. *et al.*, *Homo naledi*, a new species of the genus *Homo* from the Dinaledi Chamber, South Africa, *eLife* 4:e09560, 2015, p. 29. DOI: 10.7554/eLife.09560.

process due to these uncertainties, the adult cranial capacity of Naledi was estimated to range between 466 cm^3 and 560 cm^3.[22] The larger skulls were assumed to belong to males and the smaller skulls to females. With a brain size less than half that of the average modern human (which is around 1350 cm^3), the researchers regarded this as being strong evidence that Naledi was not fully human. However, the Naledi people were very small, and smaller people consistently have smaller heads and brains. Furthermore, brain size differences do not directly correlate with intelligence (see chapter 4). It is well known among neurologists that when it comes to intelligence, neural organization is much more important than brain size. Certainly small people, while they generally have smaller brains than average, are not less intelligent. Very obviously, small people cannot be assumed to be a different species.

Nevertheless, Naledi seems to have a disproportionately small skull and braincase. It was described in a number of popular press articles as a *"pinhead."*[23,24] This is interesting, because the term "pinhead" has been used as a derogatory term to describe people who suffer from a pathology called "microcephaly." Such people can have brain volumes that are one third smaller than normal, and they may or may not display varying degrees of mental retardation. Modern people with microcephaly have reductions in brain volume that are very similar to what is seen in Naledi. Significantly, *Homo erectus* and *Homo floresiensis* ("Hobbit") also share this characteristic, even though they are fully human. Indeed, the Hobbit had an even smaller brain size than Naledi (a mere 426 cm^3).[25] Using the same logic one might assume the Hobbit could not possibly be a modern human. But a number of leading paleo-experts regard Hobbit as being fully human, though suffering from pathology (see chapter 5). We have argued that these extinct people groups were suffering from genetic isolation, inbreeding, and subsequent genetic degeneration (as experts in the field have also suggested).

Endocast scans of the interior of a skull's braincase (reflecting the outer surface of the brain) can be used to understand the structure of the brain. This was done with the Hobbit skull by evolutionary paleoneurologist Dean Falk. She found that the Hobbit's brain was remarkably similar to a modern human brain—fully equipped with Brodmann's area 10, a region of the brain not found in apes and associated with higher cognition typical of modern humans (see chapter 5). Endocast scans of the interior surface of the Naledi braincase were published in the journal *eLife*. Like the Hobbit, Naledi appears to have had a fully human brain. As *New Scientist* states:

22. Stringer C., Human Evolution: The many mysteries of *Homo naledi*, eLife, 2015. DOI: 10.7554/elife.10627
23. Drake N., Mystery Lingers Over Ritual Behavior of New Human Ancestor, *National Geographic*, http://news.nationalgeographic.com/2015/09/150915-humans-death-burial-anthropology-Homo-naledi/
24. Shreeve J., Mystery Man, *National Geographic*, October 2015.
25. Than K., Hobbit's Brain Size Holds Clues About Its Ancestor, *National Geographic News*, 18 April 2013. http://news.nationalgeographic.com/news/2013/13/130418-Hobbit-homo-floresiensis-brain-size-hominin-human-evolution/

Dean Falk at Florida State University in Tallahassee is especially excited by the fact that Berger's team has produced a cast of *Homo naledi's* small brain. Images of it hint at interesting features close to one brain region associated with speech in modern humans, she says. Berger says it's possible that for the first time, we have found another creature not that closely related to us, yet with a cognitive ability "different but essentially equal to ours."[26]

Regardless of what we call these different early variants of man, all members of the genus *Homo* share a unique part of the brain called Broca's speech area (which is absent in apes). Broca's speech area is seen in all three of the smaller-brained people groups (Naledi, Erectus, and Hobbit). The presence of Broca's speech area in Naledi further indicates that Naledi was fully human. Only true humans have speech and can share concepts through language. Only human speech, language, and cognition can explain why the Naledi bones were deliberately deposited in the Dinaledi Chamber (suggesting belief in an afterlife). The only way Naledi could have carried their dead deep into the Rising Star cave was if they had fire (see below). All these types of behavior are unique to humans. Naledi, like Erectus and Hobbit, must have had abstract reasoning, language, art, fire, and a belief in an afterlife. In other words, they must have been fully human.

Why did Naledi, Erectus, and Hobbit all have abnormally small braincases and other genetic anomalies? And why did these small and anomalous populations disappear? A very strong case can be made that they suffered from inbreeding, which led to their morphological oddities and eventual extinction. All hunter-gathering people live in small tribes, typically of fewer than 100 people. If such tribes are isolated and do not interbreed with other tribes, over time they must always undergo genetic inbreeding. In such cases, genetic drift will cause many bad mutations to arise and they will escape removal by natural selection. These accumulating bad mutations will then drift through the tribe to the point where everyone carries the same bad mutations. We know the result of inbreeding is that the group will eventually develop distinctive and anomalous morphologies, reduced fertility, and reduced intelligence. Reduced intelligence will sometimes be coupled with reduced brain size. In addition, if a tribe starts from just a few individuals (which is how many new tribes start), and remain isolated, then there will be a very strong "genetic founder effect," such that every such tribe would tend to have its own unique appearance. This would explain the great diversity of morphologies seen both among the australopithecines and also the early human tribes (described by experts in the field as having "luxuriant diversity"). Population geneticists know that if a human population remains small and isolated, it must degenerate continuously all the way to extinction. Therefore, the inbreeding hypothesis can explain why in early human history tribes were diverse, often very strange, and often genetically deformed (see chapter 14).

26. Barras C., New species of extinct human found in cave may rewrite history, *New Scientist* 3038 (12 September), 2015.

Given a small and isolated hunter-gathering tribe, not only might there be degenerative inbreeding, there might simultaneously be a limited amount of natural selection for a smaller brain volume (see chapter 4). This applies not only to Naledi, but also to Erectus, Hobbit, and any other small population where insufficient food is a persistent problem. Given starvation conditions, mutations that reduce required caloric intake would be strongly favored—even at the cost of some otherwise important functions. This type of tradeoff is called reductive evolution (short-term gain at the cost of long-term genetic degeneration). The human brain burns calories much more quickly than any other organ, and so under starvation conditions those people with small brains will survive while all others will die. Energetically, the brain is a very costly organ, consuming as much as 20% of the body's total energy need. In the *Yearbook of Physical Anthropology*, evolutionary scientists believe there would be strong selection for smaller brain size in small populations with limited resources due to the cost of larger brains:

> As has been widely noted, the brain is an extremely costly organ from a nutritional perspective, consuming about 16 times as much energy as does muscle by weight. Thus sustaining trends in brain size increase requires additional energetic resources...[27]

Paloeanthropologists have suggested that reductive selection is part of the "island dwarfing" seen in man and other mammals. In fact, Michael Morwood, Peter Brown, *et al.* offered this very explanation to describe the Hobbit's small brain size (and short stature) in their original *Nature* (2004)[28] report, summarized below:

> Brown *et al.* suggest insular dwarfing of *H. erectus* as a result of selective pressures acting on island populations. This theory posits that the tropical rainforests present on the island tend to be a calorically impoverished environment, causing a dietary strain on hominins, especially in the absence of agriculture. Because of reduced resources, an advantage is placed on individuals who are smaller with lower energy requirements. This selection can also greatly affect sensory organs such as the brain, which could explain the small endocranial volume present in *H. floresiensis*.[29]

In a study published in *Nature*, Eleanor Weston and Adrian Lister found that the brain size of the pygmy hippopotamus was reduced by 30% beyond the normal body-scaling effects of decreased body size.[30] These researchers concluded that island-dwarfing could adequately explain the reduced brain volume of Hobbit:

> This study demonstrates empirically that it is mechanically possible for dwarf mammals on islands to evolve significantly smaller brains than would be predicted from a model of dwarfing based on the intraspecific scaling of the

27. Anton S.C., Natural History of *Homo erectus*, *Yearbook of Physical Anthropology* 46:126-169, 2003. (p.155)
28. Brown P. *et al.*, A new small-bodied hominin from the Late Pleistocene of Flores, *Nature* 431:1055-1061, 2004.
29. https://en.wikipedia.org/wiki/Homo_floresiensis
30. Weston E.M. and Lister A.M., Insular dwarfism in hippos and a model for brain size reduction in *Homo floresiensis*. *Nature* 459:85-88, 2009. DOI: 10.1038/nature07922

mainland ancestor. Our findings ... suggest that the process of dwarfism could in principle explain small brain size, a factor relevant to the interpretation of the small-brained hominin found on the Island of Flores, Indonesia.[31]

By extension, the same argument can be made for the small brain size of Naledi. Lee Berger himself analyzed skeletons of small-bodied humans found on the Rock Islands of Palau, Micronesia.[32] That population appears to represent another example of *Homo sapiens* being subjected to insular ("island") dwarfism and inbreeding. Berger *et al.* noticed a pattern of reduction in the face and skull of the Palauan sample similar to what was observed in the Hobbit skull (LB1). It is increasingly realized that many generations of inbreeding, and long-term starvation produces human populations that will display pathologies, dramatically reduced body size, and very dramatically reduced brain size. Naledi appears to be an example of this process happening within an Erectus (fully human) population. In this light, the small cranial capacity of Naledi is not a valid reason to assign it to a new species, or deny its human status.

Finally, the shape (not size) of Naledi's skull is further evidence that it is fully human. Its shape appears even more modern than the skulls of most *Homo erectus*.[33] Rather than a low sloping or absent forehead, Naledi had a higher vaulted dome and a rounded skull similar to those of modern humans (Figure 4).[34] In addition, the skull had less pronounced chewing muscle attachments, a more human-shaped jaw, small teeth, and a flatter face.[35] Berger and colleagues affirm this in their *eLife* report: "*The morphology of the cranium, mandible, and dentition* [teeth] *is mostly consistent with the genus Homo, but the brain size of Naledi is within the range of Australopithecus.*"[36] It was primarily on the basis of small brain size that Naledi was demoted to less than human. Yet as discussed above, neural organization is a better indicator of intelligence and humanness than is brain size. Brain size is not what defines humanness.[37] As Willerman and researchers note in the journal *Intelligence*, "*there is no strong direct relationship between brain size and intelligence among modern humans.*"[38]

Naledi's Human Feet

The clearest anatomical distinction that separates all apes from humans is the

31. Weston E.M. and Lister A.M., Insular dwarfism in hippos and a model for brain size reduction in *Homo floresiensis. Nature* 459:85-88, 2009. DOI: 10.1038/nature07922

32. Berger L.R. *et al.*, Small-Bodied Humans from Palau, Micronesia, *PLOS ONE* 3(3):e1780, 2008. DOI: 10.1371/journal.pone.0001780.

33. Berger L.R. *et al.*, *Homo naledi*, a new species of the genus *Homo* from the Dinaldi Chamber, South Africa, *eLife* 4:e09560, 2015, p. 10. DOI:10.7554/eLife.09560.

34. Gibbons A., New human species discovered, September 10, 2015, http://www.sciencemag.org/news/2015/09/new-human-species-discovered. This article describes the skull as "globular" in shape, "*like a member of our genus Homo.*"

35. Howley A., What Can We Learn From *Homo naledi's* Skull? *National Geographic*, 17 September 2015.

36. Berger L.R. *et al.*, *Homo naledi*, a new species of the genus *Homo* from the Dinaldi Chamber, South Africa, *eLife* 4:e09560, 2015, p. 17. DOI: 10.7554/eLife.09560.

37. Shreeve J., Mystery Man, *National Geographic*, October 2015, p. 30-57.

38. Willerman L. *et al.*, *In vivo* brain size and intelligence, *Intelligence* 15: 223–228, 1991.

structure of the foot; the human foot is truly unique. The most obvious difference is seen in the grasping nature of the feet of non-human primates. This involves not just the size and angle of the great toe, but the form and function of the bottom of the foot. In all humans the big toe falls in line with the other four toes. This is markedly different from primates, all of which have an opposable "thumb-like" great toe that juts out to the side, and is called the "hallux."

After over a century-and-a-half of cataloguing many thousands of hominin fossils, no one has ever found an ape-like foot physically associated with a human skeleton or a human-like foot physically associated with an ape skeleton. Nor have any intermediate ape/human feet been found in the fossil record. All the alleged "ape-man" intermediates—wherein the intact feet are unambiguously associated with the rest of the skeleton—have feet that are clearly either human or ape. Naledi is no exception. Consistent with its overall human anatomy, the only foot that is almost complete has a big toe that falls in line with the other four toes, and a human arch, and is virtually indistinguishable from modern humans (Figure 5). The researchers who conducted the analysis of the Naledi foot acknowledge this in the *Nature* publication, as does the paleo-community as a whole.[39] For instance, a paleo-expert from Duke University compared Naledi's foot to that of a modern Kenyan Bushman and commented, *"If you found the foot by itself, you'd think some Bushman had died."*[40] Dan Lieberman, paleoanthropologist of Harvard University agrees, stating, *"The foot is indeed strikingly human... and suggests it walked and possibly ran much like modern humans."*[41] Finally, William Harcourt-Smith who led the study of Naledi's feet acknowledged that they were *"virtually indistinguishable from those of modern humans."*[42]

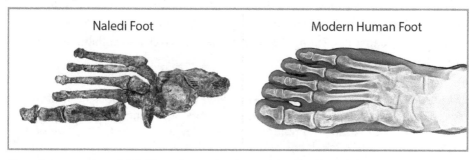

Naledi Foot   Modern Human Foot

Figure 5. A comparison of Naledi's nearly complete foot and a modern human foot. Wood cautioned that the modern-looking feet and hands suggest Naledi's primitive features may be misleading. Image of Naledi's foot from Berger *et al.*, *eLife*, 2015.

39. Harcourt-Smith W.E.H. *et al.*, The foot of *Homo naledi*, *Nature* 6:8432, 2015. DOI: 10.1038/ncomms9432.
40. Shreeve J., Mystery Man, *National Geographic*, October p. 43, 2015.
41. Gibbons A., New human species discovered, *Science*, 2015; DOI: 10.1126/science.aad1728. http://news.sciencemag.org/archaeology/2015/09/new-human-species-discovered
42. Knapton S., *Homo naledi* a new species of human discovered in a cave in South Africa, *Telegraph UK*, 10 September 2015; http://www.telegraph.co.uk/news/science/science-news/11855405/how-a-new-species-of-human-discovered-in-a-cave-in-South-Africa.html

The only difference in the foot of Naledi was a slight curvature of the toes. The researchers described them as slightly more curved than is typically seen in modern humans.[43] As Berger notes, the *"toes were also slightly curved—not as much as a chimp's toes—but more than in humans"*[44] This trivial difference (slight curvature), would add negligible functional advantage in climbing.[45]

Naledi exhibited a slightly flatter foot than the average human. Again, this is not evidence of a sub-human species. Modern humans quite commonly have flat feet, which can be inborn or caused by a number of circumstances. The diseased modern human from Flores (LB1) displayed a remarkably human-looking foot, yet had even flatter feet than Naledi. Neurologist Peter Line addresses the claim in greater detail, citing medical journals, in an online report:

> According to these specialists "adult flatfoot is defined as a foot condition that persists or develops after skeletal maturity and is characterized by partial or complete loss (collapse) of the medial longitudinal arch".[46] It is said to encompass "a wide variety of pathologic etiologies" and to often be "a complex disorder with a diversity of symptoms and various degrees of deformity".[47] The point is that if less developed longitudinal foot arches are not regarded as 'primitive' in the modern human foot, then neither should it be in the foot of *Homo naledi*, described as "essentially the foot of a modern human", but having "features that may signal a relatively low medial longitudinal arch, at least in Foot 1".[48]

Naledi's Human Hands

The human hand is also very distinctive, which reliably distinguishes man from apes. In a study published in the journal *Nature* (2015), researchers acknowledge, *"The hand is one of the most distinctive traits of humankind…. The human hand can be distinguished from that of apes by its long thumb relative to fingers."*[49] In a separate *Nature* (2015) paper describing the hand of Naledi, Kivell and collaborators affirm this:

> Modern humans and archaic humans (as represented here by Neandertals) differ from other apes in having short fingers relative to a long and robust thumb with well-developed thenar musculature [group of muscles on the palm of the human hand at the base of the thumb] that facilitates forceful precision and precision-pinch grips between the thumb and fingers.[50]

43. Harcourt-Smith W.E.H. *et al.*, The foot of *Homo naledi*, *Nature* 6:8432, 2015. DOI: 10.1038/ncomms9432.

44. van Wyk E., The science speaks, University of the Witwatersrand, Johannesburg, 2015.

45. Line P., The puzzling *Homo naledi*: a case of variation or pathology in *Homo erectus*, 19 November 2015, creation.com/puzzling-homo-naledi

46. Lee M.S. *et al.*, Diagnosis and treatment of adult flatfoot, *J Foot Ankle Surg.* 44(2):78–113, 2005 | PMID: 15768358.

47. Lee M.S. *et al.*, Diagnosis and treatment of adult flatfoot, *J Foot Ankle Surg.* 44(2):78–113, 2005 | PMID: 15768358.

48. Line P., The puzzling *Homo naledi*: a case of variation or pathology in *Homo erectus*, 19 November 2015, creation.com/puzzling-homo-naledi

49. Almécija S. *et al.*, The evolution of human and ape hand proportions, *Nature Commun* 6:7717, 2015.

50. Kivell T.L. *et al.*, The hand of *Homo naledi*, *Nature Commun* 6:8431, 2015.

What these evolutionary anatomists are referring to is the human thumb-to-fingers length proportion. The length of the human thumb is longer relative to the other four digits when compared to apes. This is an important distinction because it is the longer thumb relative to the other fingers that allow humans to have pad-to-pad precision grasping. This, in combination with well-developed palm muscles at the base of the thumb, gives humans the ability to exert force on objects in the precise ways necessary for manufacturing and manipulating tools. All apes, on the other hand, have much shorter thumbs, and less-developed palm muscles at the base of the thumb. This anatomy does not enable them the ability to forcefully grip objects between the thumb and finger pads. Instead, apes have a weak tip-to-tip precision grip. So what about the hands of Naledi? Does the fossil evidence reveal a human hand, an ape hand, or perhaps a never-before-seen mixture of both?

A total of 150 hand bones have been recovered from the Dinaledi Chamber to date, 26 of which make a nearly complete right hand of an adult individual. The hand was reportedly found *"partially articulated with the palm up and fingers flexed."*[51] In the published *Nature* paper describing the hand morphology attributed to Naledi; Kivell and colleagues acknowledge the hand bones are overwhelmingly human:

> …the full suite of features in *H. naledi* suggests it had a well-developed flexor pollicis longus muscle and a very broad, human-like palmar pad with a mobile proximal pulp. These features facilitate forceful pad-to-pad gripping between the thumb and fingers.[52]

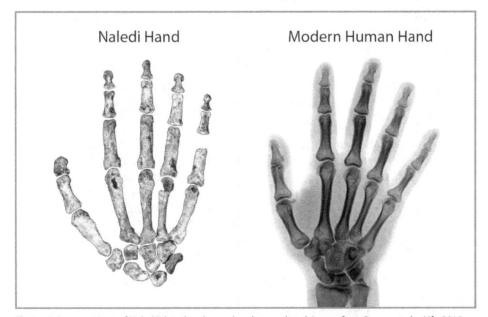

Naledi Hand   **Modern Human Hand**

Figure 6. A comparison of Naledi's hand and a modern human hand. Image from Berger *et al.*, *eLife*, 2015.

51. Kivell T.L. *et al.*, The hand of *Homo naledi*, *Nature Commun* 6:8431, 2015.
52. Kivell T.L. *et al.*, The hand of *Homo naledi*, *Nature Commun* 6:8431, 2015.

Put simply, Naledi's hand reveal distinctly human features, including large thumb muscle attachments and broad palms. Naledi had a human hand capable of pad-to-pad precision gripping just like in modern man.

Compared to apes, the four fingers of Naledi are relatively shorter and the thumb is relatively longer. This diagnostic feature can be clearly seen in a side-by-side comparison with a modern human hand (Figure 6). Berger himself states that the thumb-and-finger-length proportions are *"humanlike and visually apparent."*[53] Moreover, the first thumb bone (the pollical metacarpal, Mc1) is robust, just like in modern humans. It is different compared to the corresponding bones in living apes and australopiths. Kivel *at al.* mention this, stating:

> The pollical (thumb) metacarpals (Mc1), is also robust and markedly different than living apes ... Overall, the well-developed thenar [base of thumb] muscle attachments are most similar to those seen in modern humans... they are unlike the weakly developed muscle attachments of gracile australopiths and Ardipithecus ramidus.[54]

These researchers acknowledge that the wrist, palm, and thumb share an overall morphology with that of modern humans. Shreeve in *National Geographic*, notes this as well: *"The thumb, wrist, and palm bones all look remarkably modern."*[55] This leads to the question: if the general anatomy of the hand is admittedly human, then what exactly made the researchers claim Naledi possessed *"a combination of primitive and derived features not seen in the hand of any other hominin"*?[56] What features were supposedly more ape-like and "primitive"? In the discovery paper, Berger and researchers provide the answer, *"The wrists, fingertips, and proportions of the fingers are shared mainly with Homo, but the proximal and intermediate manual phalanges are markedly curved, even to a greater degree than in any Australopithecus."*[57] This is interesting—the finger bones of Naledi are said to be curved more than the tree-climbing australopithecines. Kivell *et al.* discuss this in more detail in their *Nature* report:

> This hand reveals a long, robust thumb and derived wrist morphology that is shared with Neanderthals and modern humans, and considered adaptive for intensified manual manipulation. However, the finger bones are longer and more curved than in most australopiths, indicating frequent use of the hand during life for strong grasping during locomotor climbing and suspension. These markedly curved digits in combination with an otherwise human-like wrist and palm indicate a significant degree of climbing, despite the derived [human] nature of many aspects of the hand and other regions of the postcranial skeleton in *H.*

53. Berger L.R. *et al.*, *Homo naledi*, a new species of the genus *Homo* from the Dinaledi Chamber, South Africa, *eLife* 4:e09560, 2015.
54. Kivell T.L. *et al.*, The hand of *Homo naledi*, *Nature Communications* 6:8431, 2015.
55. Shreeve J., Mystery man, *National Geographic* 228:39, October 2015.
56. Berger L.R. *et al.*, *Homo naledi*, a new species of the genus *Homo* from the Dinaldi Chamber, South Africa, *eLife* 4:e09560, 2015, p. 10. DOI: 10.7554/eLife.09560.
57. Berger L.R. *et al.*, *Homo naledi*, a new species of the genus *Homo* from the Dinaledi Chamber, South Africa, *eLife* 4:e09560, 2015.

naledi.[58]

The researchers used the curved fingers to support their interpretation that Naledi was still in the process of losing it's ape-like characteristics before becoming fully human. Supposedly, Naledi still spent considerable time in the trees. *National Geographic* expresses this view, stating: *"Long, curved fingers, useful for climbing in trees, could be a trait retained from a more apelike ancestor."*[59] The idea that slight finger curvature is *"retained from a more apelike ancestor"* is not logical, because in that case, the australopithecines should have more finger curvature than Naledi (but have less). More importantly, finger curvature and many other bone alterations can be explained solely through physiological adaptation. By "physiological adaptation" we mean a physical alteration to the bone caused by continuous use, not by genetics, having nothing to do with evolution.

It is widely understood that bones change their shape and density based upon their use and the physical stresses they experience. For example, weight lifters develop thicker and denser bones. Even in baby apes, finger curvature does not occur until they engage in suspensory and limb-grasping locomotory behavior. Studies by evolutionary paleoanthropologists Paciulli and Richmond have shown, as noted in *The Human Lineage*, that *"phalangeal* [finger] *curvature reflects use, not genetic predisposition."*[60] Ironically, a separate *National Geographic* article offers this exact explanation for Naledi's curved fingers:

> We might tend to think of a skeleton as basically a steel superstructure our muscles are draped over, but our bones are living, growing, and changing based on use, just as much as the rest of us. For climbers of all sorts, the suspension of weight and the repeated strong gripping applies stresses that induce the digits of the fingers to curve. This is visible in x-rays of athletes, and is visible in the bones of naledi's fingers as they rest in your hand.[61]

Modern humans naturally have longitudinal curvature on the palm side of the finger bones. However, athletes that habitually apply strong gripping forces on a sporting implement or in climbing can develop curved fingers that exceed normal variation. A paleo-expert published a report in the *Journal of Human Evolution* on the effects of mechanical stress on the shape of finger bones. Brian Richmond found that finger curvature can occur due to certain habitual behaviors and therefore has nothing to do with genetic changes caused by evolution. Richmond writes:

> ...the strain differences between curved and straight phalanges illustrated here support the common assertion that phalangeal shaft curvature is related to the strains associated with arboreal and especially suspensory activity ... and may underlie changes in curvature during ontogeny in response to changes in

---

58. Kivell T.L. *et al.*, The hand of *Homo naledi*, *Nature Commun* 6:8431, 2015.
59. Shreeve J., Mystery man, *National Geographic* 228:49, October 2015.
60. Cartmill M. and Smith F.H., *The Human Lineage*, Wiley-Blackwell, Hoboken, NJ, p. 182, 2009. These authors reference a study by Paciulli L. (*Am J Phys Anthro*, Suppl 20.:165, 1995) and Richmond B., (*Am J Phys Anthro* Suppl 24:197, 1997).
61. Howley A., *Homo naledi's* powerful hand up close, *National Geographic*, 16 September 2015.

mechanical environments of arboreal and terrestrial supports.[62]

If finger curvature can be accentuated in modern humans due to habitual, mechanical stresses applied during gripping forces, then on what grounds can it be considered an evolutionary trait "retained" from an ape-like ancestor? Curved fingers could arise by habitual tree climbing, or rock climbing, or habitual tool use. The slightly curved fingers of Naledi are not credible evidence that it was a less-than-human transitional form.

Other theories have been offered to explain Naledi's markedly curved fingers. For instance, a vitamin D deficiency results in soft, curved bones (rickets). Neurologist Peter Line writes that, if Naledi spent considerable time in the safety of caves when they were children, they could have developed vitamin D deficiency due to little sunlight exposure.[63]

The Flores Hobbit (assigned to *Homo floresiensis*) was also found to have highly curved fingers. The hand bones belonging to skeleton LB6 was described by Kivell in the *Philosophical Transactions of the Royal Society B* as follows: *"...although H. floresiensis has a broad pollical distal phalanx with a human-like FPL attachment, the proximal phalanges are curved to a similar degree as in Au. afarensis..."*[64] Like Naledi, the overall anatomy of the Hobbit hand appeared human yet with more curved fingers. Rather than accepting the conclusion it must therefore be a new sub-human species, other experts in the field believe the Hobbit was *Homo sapiens* and attributed the curvature of the fingers and other unique features to a disease known as cretinism.[65] All things considered, there is no reason to assume curved fingers are evidence Naledi is a bridge species between ape and man. Naledi appears to be a variant of *Homo erectus* (which "lumpers", including ourselves, put in synonymy with *H. sapiens*).

Naledi's Human Shoulders and Ribs

In the Naledi discovery paper, Berger and colleagues describe the shoulder of Naledi as being *"configured largely like those of australopiths"*[66]—a shoulder anatomy allegedly retained from an ape-like ancestor. The Naledi research team explains, *"The shoulder of H. naledi is configured with the scapula situated high and lateral on the thorax, short clavicles, and little or no torsion of the humerus."*[67]

62. Richmond B.G., Biomechanics of phalangeal curvature, *J Hum Evol* 53(6):678-690, 2007. DOI: 10.1126/science.1202625. Supporting Online Material, pp. 16-17.

63. Line P., The puzzling *Homo naledi*: a case of variation or pathology in *Homo erectus*, 19 November 2015. creation.com/puzzling-homo-naledi

64. Kivell T.L., Evidence in hand: recent discoveries and the early evolution of human manual manipulation. *Phil Trans R Soc B* 370: 20150105, 2015. http://dx.doi.org/10.1098/rstb.2015.0105

65. Oxnard C., Obendorf P.J. and Kefford B.J., Post-cranial skeletons of hypothyroid cretins show a similar anatomical mosaic as *Homo floresiensis*, *PLOS ONE* 5(9):e13018, 2010. DOI: 10.1371/journal.pone.0013018.

66. Berger L.R. *et al.*, *Homo naledi*, a new species of the genus *Homo* from the Dinaldi Chamber, South Africa, *eLife* 4:e09560, 2015 p. 28. DOI: 10.7554/eLife.09560.

67. Berger L.R. *et al.*, *Homo naledi*, a new species of the genus *Homo* from the Dinaledi Chamber, South Africa, *eLife* 4:e09560, 2015, p. 22.

Berger *et al.* write, "*The vertebrae are most similar to Pleistocene members of the genus Homo, whereas the ribcage is wide distally like Au. afarensis.*"[68] The claim here is that Naledi must be a new species since these traits are not commonly found in modern humans. An explanation of the key differences between living apes (as well as the similar, extinct australopithecines) versus human shoulders will help us to critically examine these claims.

The shoulders of apes are different when compared to humans. In living apes like baboons and chimpanzees, the shoulder blade (scapula) is positioned higher on the body and more laterally, toward the side of the ribcage. A shorter and thinner collarbone (clavicle) is usually associated with this morphology. This positions the socket of the shoulder joint (glenoid cavity) toward the head (cranially or superiorly orientated). Imagine a permanent shrugged shoulder look with shoulders lifted toward the ears. This anatomy is conducive for above-head arm postures used in tree-climbing and suspensory behavior. These features are typically found in the ape-like australopithecines. Modern humans, on the other hand, usually have their scapula positioned lower on the body and more toward the back of the ribcage with a longer, more robust clavicle. In humans the glenoid cavity (the shallow depression in the scapula where the head of the humerus fits into) is positioned lower and closer to the side, which allows the arms to swing freely when walking.

The ribcage of apes are also generally different when compared to humans, as mentioned earlier. The australopithecines have a funnel-shaped ribcage: the upper thorax is narrower where the ribcage connects to the shoulder girdle whereas the lower thorax fans out wider. Modern humans, on the other hand, commonly display a barrel-shaped ribcage. Let's consider each of these traits in Naledi individually to see if they are also found in anatomically modern humans. If they are, then these features cannot be cited as evidence that Naledi is less than human. We suggest that Berger and collaborators may have underestimated the possible extent of variation in the human form.

High-placed Shoulder with Funnel-shaped Ribcage: Berger and colleagues claim this feature is characteristic of australopithecines, and thus suggest Naledi is a bridge species. But a high and more laterally positioned shoulder blade is not exclusive to australopiths and living apes, but can be found in anatomically modern humans. This trait correlates with the shape of the upper ribcage. So for humans with a narrow upper ribcage, the scapula would naturally rest higher on the thorax. Researchers reporting in *Journal of Human Evolution* (2015) found this to be the case with Turkana Boy (*H. erectus*):

> Clavicle shape and curvature in *H. erectus* are also consistent with a modern-human like form. The single exception to this is Nariokotome's [Turkana Boy] increased superior clavicle curvature, which could result in a slightly more

---

68. Berger L.R. *et al.*, *Homo naledi*, a new species of the genus *Homo* from the Dinaledi Chamber, South Africa, *eLife* 4:e09560, 2015, p. 18.

superiorly placed acromial facet and a scapula that sits higher on the thorax.[69]

The Flores Hobbit (a dwarfed *Homo sapiens*—see chapter 5), also appears to have had a slightly higher scapula, positioned more toward the side.[70] This feature is known to occur in modern humans suffering from Laron syndrome—a congenital deficiency of insulin-like growth factor, I (IGF-I), and the same disease some experts believe afflicted Hobbit. Hershkovitz *et al.* report in *American Journal of Physical Anthropology*: "*Radiographs and CT reconstruction suggest a slightly protracted scapular position. The clavicles are short relative to the humeral length with shallow arcs (Fig. 6). Similar characteristics have been reported for LB1.*" The same researchers write, "*The ribcage of LS patients manifests a "fan-shaped" appearance, which is expressed as a pronounced deep (dorsoventrally) funnel-shaped thorax (rather than the "barrel-shape" that is characteristic of modern humans) with obliquely oriented ribs and a narrow sternum.*"[71] Neanderthals are fully human (see chapter 3), and they also display a funnel-shaped thorax. Leading evolutionary paleo-expert Ian Tattersall, states that a complete Neanderthal skeleton "*boasted a conical thorax* [cone-shaped ribcage] *that tapered upward from the broad pelvis to a narrow top, giving it an incredibly distinctive look.*"[72]

Short Clavicle: Despite the claims of Berger and colleagues, a shorter clavicle cannot be used as evidence that Naledi is a new species. Shorter clavicles are simply a consequence of ribcage (thorax) shape, and are found in humans. For instance, Erectus (Turkana Boy) has a shorter clavicle because of the narrower upper ribcage.[73] The modern human dubbed Hobbit also displayed this feature. Hershkovitz *et al.* insist Hobbit was a small-bodied modern human subject to a type of dwarfism known as Laron syndrome. These researchers notice many skeletal abnormalities that LB1 (Hobbit) shares with modern humans:

> Ignoring the possibility that LB1 is derived from a small stature population (Rampasasa pygmies are good candidates, as suggested by Jacob *et al.* in 2006) with its own distinct morphological features may lead to erroneous conclusions. For example, recently Larson *et al.* (2006) reported on a clavicle (short relative to humeral length) and scapula (normal) of LB1 and suggested that... [a] short clavicle may indicate a more protracted scapular position, raising the possibility of a previously unsuspected transitional stage in the course of hominin pectoral girdle evolution" (p A21). However, the length of the clavicle is mainly dictated by the shape and diameter of the upper thoracic cage. This is why both LS patients and KNM-WT 15000 *H. erectus* (both manifesting a very similar fan-shaped thorax)

69. Roach N.T. and Richmond B.G., Clavicle length, throwing performance and the reconstruction of the *Homo erectus* shoulder, *J Hum Evol* 80:107-113, 2015. DOI: 10.1016/j.jhevol.2014.09.004.

70. Hershkovtiz *et al*, Comparative Skeletal Features Between *Homo floresiensis* and Patients With Primary Growth Hormone Insensitivity (Laron Syndrome), *Am J Phys Anthropol*, 134:198-208, 2007.

71. Hershkovitz *et al.*, Comparative Skeletal Features Between Homo floresiensis and Patients With Primary Growth Hormone Insensitivity (Laron Syndrome), *Am J Phys Anthropol* 134:198-208, 2007.

72. Tattersall, I., *The Strange Case of the Rickety Cossack*, Palgrave Macmillan, New York, NY, pp. 203-204, 2015.

73. Larson S.G., Evolutionary Transformation of the Hominin shoulder, *Evol Anthropol* 16(5):172-187, 2007. DOI: 10.1002/evan.20149

have a relatively short clavicle.[74]

Humeral Torsion Angle: Larson *et al.* define this feature carefully as follows: *"Humeral torsion refers to the orientation of the head relative to the distal end of the humerus. Modern humans display a high degree of torsion..."*[75] Only African apes and modern humans display a high degree of humeral torsion. In apes, this anatomical feature is well suited for walking on all fours (quadrupedal locomotion). Gibbons have a low degree of torsion and orangutans have a moderate degree; the australopiths also fall in this range.[76] Little or no humeral torsion is regarded by Berger *et al.* as one of Naledi's unique traits not found in modern humans: "[*H. naledi* displays] *little or no torsion of the humerus.*" This was used to justify its assignment to a new species. However, low humeral torsion has been found in other humans such as Erectus (chapter 4). In *The Paleobiology of Australopithecus*[77] researchers cite analyses performed by Larson and Lordipinski who have found this trait displayed in Erectus specimens from Northern Kenya (Turkana Boy) and from the Republic of Georgia in Dmanisi, as noted by paleo-expert Peter Brown in the *Journal of Human Evolution* (2012).[78]

In further support, paleoanthropologist John Hawks noted, *"There's a huge range of torsion included within normal human populations, now—extending as low as macaque values."*[79] Furthermore, modern athletes have lower humeral torsion angles than most people. Roach *et al.* in the *Journal of Anatomy* state, *"Several recent studies have found that throwing athletes typically have lower humeral torsion (retroversion) and a greater range of external rotation at the shoulder than non-athletes."*[80] The abnormalities found in Hobbit are especially relevant to this discussion. Just like Naledi, the Hobbit exhibited an overall modern human anatomy except for a few traits such as low humeral torsion angle.[81] Morwood, leader of the Hobbit team, was responsible for the original measurements.[82]

---

74. Hershkovitz I. *et al.*, Comparative Skeletal Features Between *Homo floresiensis* and Patients With Primary Growth Hormone Insensitivity (Laron Syndrome), *Am J Phys Anthropol* 134:198-208, 2007.

75. Larson S.G., Evolutionary Transformation of the Hominin Shoulder, *Evol Anthropol* 16(5):172-187, 2007. DOI: 10.1002/evan.20149.

76. Larson S.G., Shoulder morphology in early hominin evolution, in Reed K., Fleagle J.G. and Leakey R.E. (eds.), *The Paleobiology of Australopithecus*, Springer, New York USA, pp. 247-262, 2013.

77. Larson S.G., Shoulder morphology in early hominin evolution, in Reed K., Fleagle J.G., Leakey R.E. (eds), *The Paleobiology of Australopithecus*, Springer, New York USA, p. 247-262, 2013.

78. Brown P., LB1 and LB6 *Homo floresiensis* are not modern human (*Homo sapiens*) cretins, *J Hum Evol* 62(2):201-224, 2012.

79. Hawks J., Another Diagnosis for a Hobbit, http://johnhawks.net/weblog/fossils/flores/hershkovitz_laron_syndrome_2007.html

80. Roach N.T. *et al.*, The effect of humeral torsion on rotational range of motion in the shoulder and throwing performance, *J Anat* 220:293-301, 2012.

81. Larson S.G. *et al.*, *Homo floresiensis* and the evolution of the hominin shoulder, *J Hum Evol* 53(6):718-731, 2007.

82. Morwood, M.J. *et al.*, Further evidence for small-bodied hominins from the Late Pleistocene of Flores, Indonesia, *Nature* 437:1012-1017, 2005. *"... the norm for Hylobates and quadrupedal primates such as Macaca, but is significantly less than in large-bodied apes, modern humans (141°-178°) and other known hominids, including Australopithecus'."*

Other researchers cited this as evidence Hobbit was a modern human based on earlier studies showing this feature has been found in modern pygmy populations—though Larson *et al.* questioned this interpretation. A low humeral torsion angle cannot be used as evidence Naledi was subhuman, because the humeral torsion range varies widely among modern humans. John Hawks, a lead member of the Naledi team states, *"The humeral torsion in particular has turned out to be a red herring, since Jungers and Larson have presented that LB1 is within the range of recent Australians."*[83]

Naledi's Human Hip

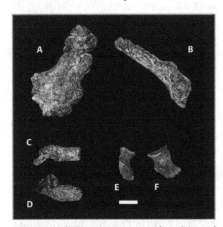

Berger *et al.* write in their published report that *"the pelvis appears to be flared markedly like that of Au. afarensis [Lucy]...."*[84] The hip is described similarly in a *National Geographic* article: *"the widely flaring blades of the pelvis were as primitive as Lucy's—but the bottom of the same pelvis looked like a modern human's."*[85] Here the authors are emphasizing the top part of the hip called the iliac blades that you can feel just under your belt. In Lucy, the hips flare out more widely than in modern humans, the hips of which curve around the body more. This is cited as additional evidence that Naledi retained primitive australopithecine traits, a requisite for its proposed status as a transitional ancestor to the genus *Homo*.

Figure 7. Naledi's pelvis consists of small bits of broken bone from multiple individuals. Among the better preserved specimens are portions of the ilium (A,B), sacrum (C,D), and ischium (E,F). Different views of the same three pieces are shown. Image from Berger *et al.*, *eLife*, 2015.

Let's carefully consider this claim. First, the hip of Naledi consists of fragmentary bits and pieces of bone with only a few features preserved that can be compared to other specimens (Figure 7).[86] Paleo-expert Caroline VanSickle explains in *The Anatomical Record* (2017) how researchers cannot seem to agree on the proper way to measure the degree of lateral flaring. Confounding this issue has to do with the fragmentary record. She writes:

> Orienting the ilium in anatomical position relative to the sagittal plane [to measure iliac flare] requires much of the pelvis to be preserved, which is rare among fossils. ... An example of how these problems manifest can be found in the newly discovered hominin species, *Homo naledi* (Berger *et al.*, 2015). The *H. naledi* pelvis is represented by multiple small fragments of bone that come from different individuals (Berger

83. http://johnhawks.net/weblog/fossils/flores/culotta_flores_meeting_report_2007.html
84. Berger L.R. *et al.*, *Homo naledi*, a new species of the genus *Homo* from the Dinaledi Chamber, South Africa, *eLife* 4:e09560, 2015 p. 17. DOI: 10.7554/eLife.09560.
85. http://news.nationalgeographic.com/2015/09/150910-human-evolution-change/
86. VanSickle C. *et al.*, *Homo naledi* pelvic remains from the Dinaledi Chamber, South Africa, *J Hum Evol*, 2017.

et al., 2015: VanSickle *et al.*, 2017, in press). The largest fragment in the sample is U.W. 101-1100... It is unclear which method should be used to measure the lateral iliac flare of U.W 101-1100. Many different techniques have been proposed in the literature for measuring flare in fossils (McHenry, 1975; Arsuaga *et al.*, 1999; Lovejoy *et al.*, 2009; Kibii *et al.*, 2011), yet in this case, U.W. 101-1100 does not preserve the necessary landmarks for any of these techniques.[87]

VanSickle concludes:

> ... overly simplified models of the ilium have resulted in confusing, contradictory definitions for lateral iliac flare and its evolutionary significance. Lateral iliac flare is the angle of the iliac blade relative to the sagittal plane, yet this is challenging to measure because it requires correct anatomical orientation of the pelvis, a fairly complete pelvis, and the ability to model the iliac blade as a plane in all hominins.

Thus in order to make meaningful comparison to Lucy's half hipbone, one must further grant that the precise orientation and degree of lateral flaring in Lucy's hip is accurate.[88] However, evolutionary anatomists, Jack Stern and Randal Susman, have challenged Lovejoy's reconstruction of this part of the hip. These researchers have insisted that the iliac blade orientation is similar to that of chimpanzee[89,90]—whereas Lovejoy reconstructs this part to reflect a more human orientation.[91,92] So the degree of lateral flaring in Lucy's hip is contested among paleo-experts, and can shed little light on Naledi's hips.

Moreover, widely flaring ilia are not actually diagnostic of australopiths. Flaring ilia have been observed in both modern humans and fossil humans. This is not unknown to paleo-experts. John Hawks affirms, *"Fossil Homo had broad pelves with widely flaring ilia, a consistent observation across all Pleistocene specimens."*[93] For instance, Hobbit exhibits a marked degree of lateral flaring in the hips. An evolutionary paleo-expert makes note of this in the *Journal of Human Evolution*, stating LB1's (Hobbit's) *"marked degree of lateral iliac flaring recalls that seen in australopithecines such as 'Lucy' (AL 288-1)."*[94] This observation is telling. Hobbit is fully human and was thought to have lived as recent as 12,000 years ago[95] (other

87. VanSickle C., Measuring Lateral Iliac Flare by Different Methods Risks Obscuring Evolutionary Changes in the Pelvis, *The Anatomical Record* 300:956-963, 2017.
88. Tattersall I. and Schwartz J., *Extinct Humans*, Westview Press, New York, 2000.
89. Stern J.T., Susman R.L., The Locomotor Anatomy of *Australopithecus afarensis*, *Am J Phys Anthropol*, 1983. *"...the fact that the anterior portion of the iliac blade faces laterally in humans, but not in chimpanzees, is obvious. The marked resemblance of AL 288-1 [Lucy's half hip bone] to the chimpanzee is equally obvious."*
90. VanSickle C., Measuring Lateral Iliac Flare by Different Methods Risks Obscuring Evolutionary Changes in the Pelvis, *The Anatomical Record* 300:956-963, 2017.
91. Lovejoy O., Evolution of Human Walking, *Scientific American*, 118-125, 1988.
92. Lovejoy C.O, A reconstruction of the pelvis of AL 288 (Hadar Formation, Ethiopia), *Am J Phys Anthropol* (Abstr.) 50:460, 1979.
93. Hawks J., Mrs. Elvis, the *Homo erectus* pelvis, November 15, 2008. http://johnhawks.net/weblog/fossils/lower/gona/gona-pelvis-simpson-2008.html
94. Jungers W.L. *et al.*, Descriptions of the lower limb skeleton of *Homo floresiensis*, *J Hum Evol* 57(5):538-554, 2009 | DOI: 10.1016/j.jhevol.2008.08.014.
95. Brown P. *et al.*, A new small-bodied hominin from the Late Pleistocene of Flores Indonesia, *Nature* 431:1055-1061, 2004.

paleo-experts insisted even younger), until recently re-dated to at least 50,000 years ago.[96] Regardless, with this flaring hip being so recent, it cannot reasonably be considered a "retained" australopithecine trait. Furthermore, widely flaring ilia are also seen in Erectus and Neanderthals specimens.[97,98]

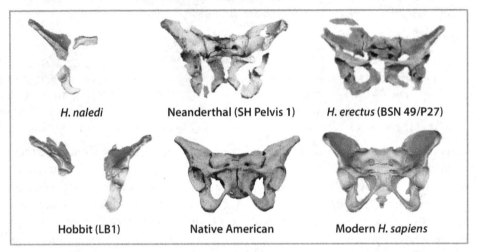

H. naledi   Neanderthal (SH Pelvis 1)   *H. erectus* (BSN 49/P27)

Hobbit (LB1)   Native American   Modern *H. sapiens*

Figure 8. Naledi's pelvis displays a widely flaring iliac blade. Berger *et al.* described this as a "primitive" trait, evidence that Naledi had evolved from an australopith (ape-like) ancestor. However, the same feature is also seen in small-bodied humans from Flores (LB1); Neanderthals from Spain; *H. erectus* from Ethiopia; and modern humans such as 1,000-year-old Native Americans, and those suffering pathologies of growth hormone insensitivity (not pictured). Paleo-experts known as "lumpers" group all of these *Homo* variants into a single species, *H. sapiens*.

One of the most striking examples of this is seen in a Neanderthal from the Pit of Bones site of Sima de los Huesos in Sierra de Atapuerca, Spain. In the journal *Nature*, paleo-experts describe the pelvis as displaying a *"marked iliac flare"*. Several other pelvises confidently attributed to *Homo* display widely flaring ilia, including *H. erectus* (BSN 49/P27), Neanderthal (Kebara 2), and early modern *H. sapiens* pelvis from Cap Blanc, France. Native American pelvises have been shown to exhibit widely flaring ilia (Figure 8). Modern humans diagnosed with Laron syndrome have also been documented with unusually wide flaring iliac blades: *"It is noteworthy that the flaring contour of the lower part of the LS thorax corresponds to the flaring ilia in these patients."*[99] Evolutionary paleo-expert Charles Oxnard has reported in *PLOS ONE* that this feature has been found in patients suffering cretinism.[100] A more recent study published by Maciej Henneberg and colleagues

96. Sutikna T. *et al.*, Revised stratigraphy and chronology for *Homo floresiensis* at Liang Bua in Indonesia, *Nature* 532(7599):366-369, 2016.

97. Churchill S.E. and VanSickle C., Pelvic Morphology in *Homo erectus* and Early *Homo*, *The Anatomical Record* 300:964-977, 2017.

98. Arsuaga J. *et al.*, A complete human pelvis from the Middle Pleistocene of Spain, *Nature* 399:255-258, 1999.

99. Hershkovitz I. *et al.*, Comparative Skeletal Features Between *Homo floresiensis* and Patients With Primary Growth Hormone Insensitivity (Laron Syndrome), *Am J Phys Anthropol* 134:198-208, 2007.

100. Oxnard C. *et al.*, Post-cranial skeletons of hypothyroid cretins show a similar anatomical mosaic as *Homo floresiensis*, *PLOS ONE* 5(9):e13018, p. 1, 2010. DOI: 10.1371/journal.pone.0013018.

in the *Proceedings of the National Academy of Sciences* (2014) has found that people with Down syndrome exhibit flaring ilia to a greater extent than is typically seen in modern humans.[101] If the same traits in the hip can be found in both fossil and modern humans (diseased or not), then flaring hips is not strong evidence for Berger's claim that Naledi was a new species that was "almost human".

The South African Erectus Hypothesis

A number of researchers, including respected paleoanthropologists Chris Stringer and Tim White, have noted the many similarities between Naledi and Erectus. Stringer notes, *"Overall, to my eye the material looks most similar to the small-bodied examples of Homo erectus from Dmanisi in Georgia...."*[102] Tim White, from the University of California, Berkeley, advocates this position more forcefully. In a UC Berkeley article titled, *"Bones of Contention: Cal Paleo Expert Doubts Homo Naledi is New Species"*, White explains that many of the distinctive Naledi characteristics may reflect a non-representative South African form of Erectus. One morphological similarity noted by White was the skull: *"The Homo naledi cranium is similar in conformation and size to the earliest and most primitive Homo erectus representatives."*[103] Berger himself acknowledges, *"...the H. erectus-like aspects of cranial morphology that are found in H. naledi."*[104]

The recognition amongst paleoanthropologists that Naledi shares many features with Erectus is a tacit admission that it is not a new species but a variant of Erectus (and so by extension can be folded into *Homo sapiens*). In view of the overall modern human anatomy, the few distinguishing differences (i.e., slight curvature of finger bones) seem minor, and have been over-emphasized. We need to keep in mind that dog breeds, such as Great Danes and Chihuahuas, are the same species, despite their very different-looking skeletons.

With that picture in mind, consider the variation possible in *Homo sapiens*. Imagine if we lined up human skeletons—including a 7 foot-tall Watusi tribesman, a dwarf, a professional wrestler, a midget, and various modern humans with various growth disorders and pathologies. This would represent a wider range of skeletal morphologies than all the variations seen among the fossils that are described as different species of the genus *Homo*.

Berger regards Naledi's unique traits as justifying its classification as a new species. But as we explained, just because a sample of bones has unique features, it does

---

101. Henneberg M. *et al.*, Evolved developmental homeostasis disturbed in LB1 from Flores, Indonesia, denotes Down syndrome and not diagnostic traits of the invalid species *Homo floresiensis*, *Proc Natl Acad Sci, USA* 111(33):11967-11972, 2014. Table 1 lists the shared traits of LB1 and those with DS, which include flaring ilia.
102. Stringer C., The many mysteries of *Homo naledi*, *eLife* 4:e10627, 2015. DOI: 10.7554/eLife.10627.
103. Martin G., Bones of Contention: Cal paleo expert doubts *Homo naledi* Is new species, 1 October 2015: http://alumni.berkeley.edu/california-magazine/just-in/2015-12-29/bones-contention-cal-paleo-expert-doubts-homo-naledi-new
104. van Wyk E., The science speaks, University of the Witwatersrand, Johannesburg, 2015. Berger is interviewed.

not justify classifying it as a new species. The fully human status of Neanderthals (chapter 3) and the discovery of the Hobbit with its unique features illustrates this. Alternatively, consider a collection of 1,000-year-old Native American Indian skeletons. Evolutionary anatomist Owen Lovejoy made an interesting observation in his study of these remains. Reader explains:

> The Amerindian collection on which Lovejoy works undoubtedly represents a population belonging to the species *Homo sapiens*, yet it includes many unusual bones that probably would have been assigned to a different species, or even a different genus, if they had been discovered as individual fossils…[105]

In this case there was no question that the bones belonged to *Homo sapiens*. However, if the bones were not found within such a clearly defined context, they would have incorrectly been assigned to a new species. Add to this problem, a very strong motivation to find the ever-elusive "missing link" and it is not surprising that some Erectus bones (Naledi) might be misclassified as a new sub-human species.

Evidence for Deliberate Disposal of the Dead

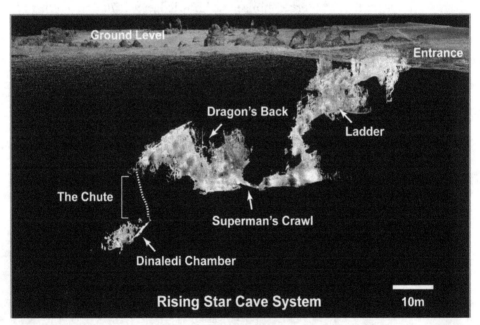

Figure 9. Spatial mapping of the Rising Star cave system produced by three dimensional data collection techniques (i.e., high resolution laser scans). The bones of Naledi were found in a nearly inaccessible region of the cave known as the Dinaledi Chamber. Image from Kruger *et al.*, *South African Journal of Science*, 2016.

Perhaps the most powerful evidence that Naledi was fully human is the cultural evidence. Apparently, Naledi bones were deliberately deposited in the Dinaledi Chamber. This would require great ingenuity, and strongly suggests a belief in an

---

105. Reader J., *Missing Links: The hunt for earliest man*, Little Brown and Company, Boston, p. 232, 1981.

afterlife.

One of the mysteries surrounding Naledi is how the bones ended up deep underground, in a cave that is essentially inaccessible without modern climbing and caving equipment. An *eLife* scientific publication by Dirks *et al.* describes the cave system in detail.[106] The Dinaledi Chamber where the fossils were found was nearly 100 feet below ground and about 300 feet away from the cave entrance. Getting through the cave system into the Dinaledi Chamber is a tortuous ordeal, even with lights, ropes, etc. Two cavers, Steven Tucker and Rick Hunter, found the bones. Even these experienced climbers were dumbfounded in trying to explain how the bones got into the chamber, *How do these quite large bones get into this place in the cave, a place where we as cavers with protective clothing, helmets and especially lights, struggle to get to?*[107] How could these bones be deposited there, if Naledi was indeed a "non-human animal"? The deliberate deposit of these bones requires abstract reasoning, forethought, purpose, extreme commitment, fire, ropes, etc. Only humans use fire to light caves and only humans bury their dead. This problem has been the focus of many popular press articles, and has certainly helped dramatize the discovery.

Soon after Berger heard news of the finding, he made a Facebook post calling for six "underground astronauts" who could handle working in confined spaces. Six, small-framed women who were able to squeeze their way into the cave's most narrow passages, were added to the team to recover the bones. Figure 9 shows a simplified illustration of the cave system in cross-section view. To access the chamber the six brave women had to perform a "superman's crawl" through a 15-foot-long (5-meter) tunnel. The constriction is so narrow (less than 10 inches in diameter), that the only way they could get through was by wriggling along on their belly and extending their arms above their head. From there they had to climb up a rocky structure known as the "Dragon's Back" in order to locate the vertical chute that leads down 40 feet into the Dinaledi Chamber of fossils. The chute is lined with jagged rocks hindering descent. The narrowest point is only 7.5 inches wide (Figure 10). The cavers and the six women who assisted the excavation were barely able to squeeze through. What is more, the cave is pitch black. It would have been virtually impossible for them to access the Dinaledi Chamber without headlamps. As Jamie Shreeve writes in the Naledi cover story in *National Geographic*:

> Deliberate disposal of bodies would still have required hominins to find their way to the top of the chute through pitch-black darkness and back again, which almost surely would have required light-torch, or fires lit at intervals. The notion of such a small-brained creature exhibiting such complex behavior seems so

---

106. Dirks P., Geological and taphonomic context for the new hominin species *Homo naledi* from the Dinaledi Chamber, South Africa, *eLife*, 2015. DOI: 10.7554/eLife.09561.001

107. http://www.rdm.co.za/lifestyle/2015/09/10/steven-tucker-the-man-who-found-the-homo-naledi-fossil

unlikely that many other researchers have simply refused to credit it.[108]

Leading evolutionary paleo-expert Chris Stringer observes, *"This cave chamber lies some 80 meters into the Rising Star system, and must have always been in constant darkness."*[109] Naledi must have needed torches. As Berger states:

> How did the hominins find their way into the Dinaledi Chamber? This is a very puzzling question. Our geological investigation indicates that the Dinaledi Chamber was always in the dark zone, and the route to get there was probably very complex, involving navigating difficult terrain. This suggests that they may have used fire to guide them into the cave.[110]

Constructing a torch that can burn long enough to navigate the cave system would certainly require great sophistication. Exiting the cave system is a huge feat by itself, especially climbing up the chute. It seems unlikely that Naledi tossed their dead down the chute into the chamber, because the bones were found throughout the cave floor and not just directly below the vertical chute, where they would have landed if dropped from above.[111] The presence of well-articulated skeletal parts far from the chute's opening suggests Naledi actually entered the chamber.[112,113] To exit the chamber the excavation team used rope and climbing gear. Tucker (an experienced caver) said, *"It is very exhausting. Going down is relatively easy—gravity pulls you down—but going up it is a real mission. It takes 15 minutes just to traverse this 12m space* [approximately 40 feet]. *It's very hard to do that."*[114] The evidence further indicates Naledi had ritualistically buried their dead over several generations.[115] This would have required a collective effort and an advanced social structure, which suggests a level of complex behavior never observed in animals. Berger himself acknowledges this behavior is exclusive to cognitively modern humans:

> Until the moment of discovery of 'naledi,' I would have probably said to you that it was our defining character. The idea of burial of the dead or ritualized body disposal is something utterly uniquely human.[116]

108. Shreeve J., This face changes the human story. But how? http://news.nationalgeographic.com/2015/09/150910-human-evolution-change/
109. Stringer C., The many mysteries of *Homo naledi*, eLife 4:e10627, 2015. DOI: 10.7554/eLife.10627
110. van Wyk E., The science speaks, 2015; https://www.wits.ac.za/news/latest-news/research-news/2015/2015-09/homo-naledi/the-science-speaks/the-science-speaks.html
111. Though it is possible low-level water flow dispersed the remains as sediment drained into crevices in the chamber floor: van Wyk E., The science speaks, 2015.
112. Dirks P. *et al.*, The age of *Homo naledi* and associated sediments in the Rising Star Cave, South Africa, 2017. https://doi.org/10.7554/eLife.24231.001
113. Bower B., Pieces of *Homo naledi* story continue to puzzle, *Science News*, April 19, 2016; https://www.sciencenews.org/article/pieces-homo-naledi-story-continue-puzzle
114. Hartley R., Steven Tucker: The man who found the *Homo Naledi* fossils, *Rand Daily Mail* September 18, 2015.
115. Berger states, *"Fossil parts are found in different parts of the stratigraphy, suggesting that the fossils entered the cave over an extended period of time, and therefore we think that they did not die during a single catastrophic event."*—Wits, The Science Speaks
116. Berger in CNN article: *Homo naledi*: New species of human ancestor discovered in South Africa, David McKenzie. http://www.cnn.com/2015/09/10/africa/homo-naledi-human-relative-species/

Figure 10. The vertical chute leading down into the Dinaledi Chamber is 40 feet deep and 7.5 inches wide at its narrowest parts. Image from Kruger *et al.*, SAJS, 2016.

Berger and others found it very hard to believe that the small-brained Naledi were capable of navigating tight passageways in complete darkness while carrying their dead to dispose of them in a ritualistic manner. Yet this appears to be the most plausible explanation, given the facts. The researchers in the journal *eLife* ruled out all other possibilities (separate entryways, predators, etc.) as have been raised.

All of their observations consistently suggest a burial site. These facts have led the researchers to the very logical conclusion that Naledi *"deliberately disposed of its dead inside of the chamber...*"[117] This is not consistent with Berger's claim that Naledi was a "non-human animal." Berger himself makes this point in *National Geographic*:

> Disposal of the dead brings closure for the living, confers respect on the departed, or abets their transition to the next life. Such sentiments are a hallmark of humanity. But *H. naledi*, Berger emphatically stresses, was not human—which makes the behavior all the more intriguing. 'It's an animal that appears to have had the cognitive ability to recognize its separation from nature,' he said.[118]

Notice his strong commitment to the idea that Naledi must be less than human. Naledi can even be "almost human", as long as its not *fully* human. In the field of paleoanthropology, it is widely known that interpreter bias plays a major role in the assignment of fossils to a particular place in a lineage. The bottom line is, if Naledi is fully human then it makes a lot of sense that they buried their dead.

How Old is Naledi?

Following the discovery of Naledi, Ed Yong wrote in *The Atlantic*:

> ...But one significant problem clouded the excitement over the discovery: the team doesn't know how old the fossils are. And without that age, it's hard to know how *Homo naledi* fits into the story of human evolution, or how to interpret its apparent habit of deliberately burying its own kind. Everyone from professional paleontologists to interested members of the public raised the same question: Why hadn't the team dated the fossils yet?[119]

What is unusual about this particular discovery is that the bones were not officially dated at the time of publication or release to the media. Media headlines regarding the identity of a putative new hominin species are always reported after a date is published—not beforehand. Logically this makes sense. Without a date, the researchers have no clear way of determining its presumed place in the hominin family tree. The researchers involved with Naledi did not follow this widely accepted convention.

Due to the nature of the remains and their geological setting, it was not immediately obvious to the researchers which dating methods could be used. Even though the researchers had no idea of how old the bones were, Berger was already claiming a date of around 2–3 million years old, as required to support his claim that Naledi marked the beginning of the genus *Homo*.[120]

The bones themselves certainly did not appear to be millions of years old. Photos

---

117. Knapton S., *Homo naledi* a new species of human discovered in a cave in South Africa, *Telegraph* 10 September 2015. http://www.telegraph.co.uk/news/science/science-news/11855405/Ho...a-new-species-of-discovered-in-a-cave-in-South-Africa.html
118. Shreeve J., Mystery Man, *National Geographic*, October pp. 30-57, 2015.
119. Yong E., Why Don't We Know the Age of the New Ancient Human, *The Atlantic*, 14 September 2015.
120. https://www.thequint.com/news/world/introducing-homo-naledi-our-ancient-human-relative; New Human Ancestor Discovered: *Homo naledi* (EXCLUSIVE VIDEO) | National Geographic: https://www.youtube.com/watch?time_continue=161&v=oxgnlSbYLSc

taken of the find at the time of discovery demonstrated to paleo-expert Tim White that many of the fossils were not found *in situ* but appeared *"very disturbed, perhaps by earlier cavers, in the geologically recent past."*[121] The bones were buried in mud less than eight inches deep. Many were found lying exposed on the surface of the chamber floor, with some that looked freshly broken as if recently tampered with. According to the researchers own evaluation, the bones were *"exceptionally well preserved"*—light in weight and un-mineralized. Articles and published reports noted that the bones were lying in *"wet sediment."* Dirks *et al.* write:

> ...the Dinaledi Chamber occurs deep inside the cave, very close to the water table, where sediments [containing the fossils] are expected to have always been closer to water saturated.[122]

How could the remains have stayed in pristine condition over millions of years in perpetually wet conditions? Hobbit, from Liang Bua cave, was initially believed to be less than 18,000 years old (based on carbon-14 analysis), yet its remains were complete mush, and crumbled at the slightest touch. In the case of Hobbit, it was obvious to the researchers that it should be carbon dated. Naledi's age was tested using carbon-14 analysis. Given the expectation that Naledi was at least 1 million years old, this is surprising because carbon-14 cannot yield dates much beyond 50,000 years old[123] (i.e., no measurable carbon-14 should remain after so many half-lives). Nevertheless, carbon-14 was surprisingly detected, suggesting an age for Naledi of about 30,000 years old. However, this "anomalously" young age was promptly rejected by Dirks *et al.*, who claimed that the samples must have been contaminated with modern carbon. No further samples were subjected to carbon-14 analysis. Berger commented on the difficulties with dating Naledi:

> Unlike other cave deposits in the Cradle [of Mankind in South Africa] the fossils are not found in direct association with fossils from other animals making it impossible to provide a faunal age. There are also few flowstones that can be directly linked to the fossils, and those that exist are contaminated with clays making them hard to date. On top of that, the fossils are contained in soft sediments and they are partly re-worked and re-deposited making it difficult to establish their primary stratigraphic position. Taken together, this makes it hard to obtain a definitive date for the fossils.[124]

Berger and colleagues had originally thought that it might not be informative to date the flowstones in the Rising Star cave (where Naledi was found) because the bones may have been deposited long after the flowstone formed. It did not help that Naledi's bones were found lying on or near the surface of cave floor

---

121. Martin G., Bones of Contention: Cal Paleo Expert Doubts *Homo Naledi* is New Species, UC Berkely Magazine: http://alumni.berkeley.edu/california-magazine/just-in/2015-12-29/bones-contention-cal-paleo-expert-doubts-homo-naledi-new
122. Dirks P. *et al.*, The age of *Homo naledi* and associated sediments in the Rising Star Cave, South Africa, *eLife*, 2017. DOI: 10.7554/eLife.24231
123. Dirks P. *et al.*, The age of *Homo naledi* and associated sediments in the Rising Star Cave, South Africa, *eLife*, 2017. DOI: 10.7554/eLife.24231
124. van Wyk E., The Science Speaks, University of the Witwatersrand, Johannesburg, 16 September 2015.

sediments. The researchers noted that the flowstones were rich in clay, which is known to contribute to open system behavior (resulting in erroneous ages). It is for this reason that uranium-lead dating was deemed unsuccessful, again because of presumed contamination (it gave dates that were far "too old"). Electron spin resonance (ESR) also proved problematic. For that method to work properly, the natural radiation level in the cave chamber where Naledi was found needs to be accurately measured. Hawks confesses that this is *"sort of nightmarish."* Yong writes, *"It involves, for example, installing actual radiation dosimeters and taking out vertical cores of sediment. And even then, the results from ESR typically needs to be cross-checked against other sources of data."*[125] In short, ESR involves a complicated process that is infused with layers of questionable assumptions. And so, their options were increasingly limited.

A later interview with Berger in a news article posted by the University of the Witwatersrand discussed their early attempts to date the bones and surrounding deposits using a number of different techniques (e.g., ESR, carbon-14, U-series techniques, and optically stimulated luminescence (OSL)).[126] Berger admitted that the various trial attempts failed and that *"they [were] working on further attempts... we only want to publish age limits for them when we are absolutely sure they are right. We do not want to cause confusion over the age."*[127] It appears that the dating methods gave extremely contradicting dates—none of which were acceptable to the discovery team's hopes. Science writer, Ed Yong wrote an excellent article on the problems associated with dating Naledi. In it, Yong talks with John Hawks, a lead researcher on the Naledi team who described the problems of dating a different set of bones (*Australopithecus prometheus*):

> People want to know why this [dating Naledi] is a problem? Little Foot is the best example." He's talking about an *Australopithecus* skeleton that was found in South Africa's Sterkfontein cave in the 1990s. Over the last decade, many people have tried to date those bones using animal remains, paleomagnetism, flowstones [U-series], and more, but their estimates differ by around 2 million years depending on the technique they use. "The different lines of evidence just don't agree," says Hawks. "We're really hoping to avoid that scenario. We're committed, as a team, to not publish a date estimate until we have multiple estimates that arrive at the same result."[128]

Here Hawks hits on the real reason for why they took so long (two years after the announcement paper) before they reported how old Naledi is. The various dating methods all produced conflicting ages. If the dating methods used are reliable then they should all agree when applied to the same specimens. On the other hand, if each dating method yields significantly different ages, then that would suggest they cannot be trusted (see chapter 12). In the case of Naledi, none of the

---

125. Yong E., Why don't we know the age of the New Ancient Human, *The Atlantic*, 14 September 2015.
126. van Wyk E., The Science Speaks, University of the Witwatersrand, Johannesburg, 15 September 2015.
127. van Wyk E., The Science Speaks, University of the Witwatersrand, Johannesburg, 15 September 2015.
128. Yong E., Why don't we know the age of the New Ancient Human, *The Atlantic*, 14 September 2015.

dating methods agreed, and so the researchers decided not to publish a date in the announcement paper.

Newest Data Confirm Naledi is not a Transitional "Bridge" Species

Figure 11. Berger *et al.* had originally proposed that they expected Naledi to represent the inception of the genus *Homo*, living sometime between 2–3 million years ago (based on morphology of the bones). New dates published in 2017 contradicted these expectations. The *Nature* news article shown above tells of the latest findings reported in the journal *eLife* that suggests Naledi lived far more recently than thought. This update is consistent with our alternative model—Naledi coexisted with modern *H. sapiens* and is therefore not a credible evolutionary precursor to man.

Two years after the discovery paper was published, a date was finally assigned to Naledi (Figure 11). In 2017 the Naledi fossils were dated in the range of 236,000–335,000 years old (how this date was chosen is discussed further in chapter 12).[129] This was a game-changer. Naledi had to be around 2–3 million years old in order to serve as a transitional "bridge" species linking the australopiths to the genus *Homo,* as Berger had hoped. The new date falsifies the "almost human" status of Naledi claimed by Berger, because Naledi would have lived long after the species it is claimed to have given rise to (such as Erectus and Neanderthal). The currently published age now suggests Naledi coexisted with multiple reputed *Homo* species, including early modern humans in Africa (*H. sapiens*), Neanderthals, Denisovans, Hobbit, and Erectus. This suggests that all of these putative species, including Naledi, are simply variants of *Homo sapiens* (see chapters 3-5 and 11).

In light of the unexpectedly young date, the paleo-community now acknowledges that Naledi is *not* our ancestor, and is *not* the precursor to all later *Homo* species. Berger himself now warns that primitive-looking traits don't necessarily mean a primitive evolutionary origin/age, and that such traits can be misleading. The *eLife*

129. Dirks P. *et al.*, The age of *Homo naledi* and associated sediments in the Rising Star Cave, South Africa, *eLife*, 2017. DOI: 10.7554/eLife.24231

digest summary emphasizes this very point: *"These new findings demonstrate why it can be unwise to try to predict the age of a fossil based on its appearance..."*[130] Instead, the "surprisingly young age" means that these so-called "primitive" traits are better explained by our model—which is extreme isolation, inbreeding, and subsequent genetic degeneration (see chapter 14). In other words, Naledi is fully human.

Conclusion—Naledi was Fully Human

A careful analysis of the bones in question supports that Naledi was fully human. Naledi is not a new species, nor does it have features *"retained from a more ape-like ancestor."*[131] Naledi's distinctive features are better explained in terms of inbreeding and physiological changes. Physiological changes involve non-genetic, non-heritable modifications due to environment (i.e., curved finger bones can be caused by mechanical stress from either tool use or climbing).

The discovery of the Naledi bones made a huge media splash. A flood of popular press articles and news outlets, including the front page of the *New York Times*, showcased Naledi as conclusive proof of human evolution. The front cover of *National Geographic* offered a catchy headline: *"Almost Human."*[132] Was the media hype consistent with the science? The paleo-community was clearly more skeptical than the media. Just as they largely rejected Berger's claims about Sediba, leading experts in the field did not take Berger's Naledi claims seriously. A UC Berkeley article reports:

> White is not alone in his uneasiness over *H. naledi*. Reviewers at top scientific journals also found evidence for the new hominin species to be suspect. Berger and his team originally submitted multiple papers on *H. naledi* to the prestigious journal *Nature*, which rejected them.[133]

Preeminent scientific authorities, including leading evolutionary paleo-experts, have dismissed the claims made by Berger and colleagues regarding Naledi. The paleo-community as a whole now rejects Naledi as a possible "missing link." So why is the public still being led to believe that the Naledi discovery is conclusive proof of human evolution?

The failure of paleo-experts to find a legitimate "ape-like" ancestor to man after over 150 years of fossil hunting is remarkable. This flies directly in the face of the claim that human evolution is an uncontested fact. It is clear that neither Habilis, nor Sediba, nor Naledi bridge the vast evolutionary gap between the ape-like

130. Dirks P. *et al.*, The age of *Homo naledi* and associated sediments in the Rising Star Cave, South Africa, *eLife*, 2017. DOI: 10.7554/eLife.24231

131. Shreeve J., This Face Changes the Human Story. But How? *National Geographic*, 10 September 2015. "*Homo* Features" Image.

132. Shreeve J., Mystery Man, *National Geographic*, October pp. 30-57, 2015. Issue title: Almost Human.

133. Martin G., Bones of Contention: Cal paleo expert doubts *Homo naledi* Is new species, 1 October 2015: http://alumni.berkeley.edu/california-magazine/just-in/2015-12-29/bones-contention-cal-paleo-expert-doubts-homo-naledi-new

australopiths and man. Naledi is the latest and greatest claim of a bridge species between australopith and man. The date now assigned to Naledi shows it is not a pre-human species but appears to be a degenerant human population that lived in isolation. The missing link is still missing. The failure of Naledi as a transitional bridge species seems like the final "nail in the coffin" of the ape-to-man paradigm. However, the origin of mankind is not just a scientific issue. There are deep moral and philosophical implications tied to this very important topic. Regardless of the evidence, the ape-to-man paradigm is not likely to go away soon.

**Latest Developments

The latest endocast scans of the braincase further support the fully human status of Naledi. It is well established that certain sulci patterns are only seen in apes (including australopiths), while others are only seen in humans. For example, the fronto-orbital sulcus (*fo*) is a feature common to all apes, but is not seen in human brains. In place of the ape *fo*, humans have two smaller groves that make up a triangular region (pars triangularis), called Broca's area. Broca's area plays an essential role in speech and language (see chapter 9). When these features are well-preserved in endocast scans, the results are clear. In the *Proceedings of the National Academy of Sciences* (2018) paleo-experts Ralph Holloway *et al.* report *"The DH3 endocast of H. naledi has no fronto-orbital sulcus, similar to Homo and different from apes and Australopithecus."*[134] The Naledi endocast scans reveal a modern human brain configuration, including Broca's area.

The Naledi story is far from over. To keep up with the latest developments visit ContestedBones.org.

---

134. Holloway R.L. *et al.*, Endocast morphology of *Homo naledi* from the Dinaledi Chamber, South Africa, *Proc Natl Acad Sci*, USA, 2018. See also *Supplementary Information*: http://www.pnas.org/content/pnas/suppl/2018/05/08/1720842115.DCSupplemental/pnas.1720842115.sapp.pdf

CHAPTER 11

Coexistence
Australopith & Man

...I would expect that the genus Homo will eventually be traced into the Pliocene at an age of between 4 and 6 million years, together with Australopithecus.[1]

Paleoanthropologist Richard Leakey, Former Director of the National Museums of Kenya and Former Head of the East Turkana Research Project

Extensive Coexistence of Man and His Presumed Ancestors

The central premise of human evolutionary theory is that over a period of several million years, the ape-ish australopiths gradually evolved into modern human beings, through a series of transitional forms. Intuitively we understand that ancestors should exist before their descendants; so australopiths should have lived long before the first humans. So what if human bones and artifacts were consistently being found alongside the earliest australopiths bones? The idea that bones of australopiths and man would be found in the same bone bed should seem incredible. Yet this is routinely what has been seen. Certainly we should not expect to find evidence of humans coexisting with their australopithecine ancestors through deep time. Still more certainly we should not expect to find humans and australopiths buried together in the very same bone beds, in locations where they would be competing for the same habitat. Most certainly, we should not see evidence of modern man existing simultaneously with (or prior to) the earliest australopiths. Yet the evidence indicates all of these things.

Most of the major hominin sites consist of jumbled bone beds containing diverse taxa, including: 1) bones described as distinctly ape-like; 2) bones described as being indistinguishable from those of modern humans; and 3) bones of many other African life forms. For instance, in the shallow "miner's pit," where paleo-expert Lee Berger discovered the Sediba bones, there were *thousands* of bones from many diverse African species. These included bones that appeared to be fully human, bones that appeared to be australopith, and bones of other animals

---

1. Leakey R.E., Hominids in Africa, *American Scientist* 64(2):174-178, 1976.

such as zebra, antelope, and even baboon.[2] Berger described the situation as being *"the most taxing jigsaw puzzle."* Piecing together hominin skeletons from a pile of mixed bones would not be a straightforward task—especially if the bones were just fragments, and when there is no way to know ahead of time what a putative new species might look like.

Given that bones of multiple species including *Homo, Australopithecus*, monkey, baboon, and other primates are frequently found buried together, it is not surprising that paleo-experts have often mistakenly assembled partial skeletons that actually include bones that don't even belong within the same species. Such skeletons are actually anatomical chimeras (made up of bones from different species). In previous chapters we have briefly summarized several important instances of this (see the chapters on Afarensis, Habilis, and Sediba). Mixed bone beds can lead to artificial "ape-man" reconstructions. More than this, such beds demonstrate the intimate coexistence of the different hominin types.

It is true that, on rare occasions, an ancestor species might split to give rise to two descendant species—one remaining nearly unchanged from the original, the other changing greatly. This is called "cladogenesis" (as opposed to the traditional straight-line evolution called "anagenesis"). When this occurs it is possible for the ancestral population to coexist in time and space with the descendant species. This is easy to understand—dogs came from wolves, yet wolves are still around. However, the duration of overlap would usually be short. In deep time, such "sister species" will not both survive if they remain in the same territory and in the same niche—one will always eventually win out over the other. Paleo-experts understand this can be problematic for ancestor/descendant theories, particularly when the overlap is extensive. It is for this reason Berger and other experts in the field cast doubt on Habilis as an ancestral species to Erectus[3] and why Carl Swisher *et al.* at one time rejected Erectus as the ancestor to *Homo sapiens*.[4]

Coexistence of ancestors/descendants can be more than just "problematic." At a certain point, coexistence can falsify a claimed ancestor/descendant relationship (Figure 1). For instance, suppose human bones and sophisticated stone tools are found dating to the time of Lucy. In such a scenario, cladogenesis cannot be invoked. This is because a descendant species cannot possibly live at the same time as its earliest ancestors. In more familiar terms, we all know that grandparents can coexist with their grandchildren (think cladogenesis), but we also know that grandchildren cannot possibly be as old as (or older than) their grandparents. Likewise, grandchildren should not commonly coexist with ancestors who were born many generations earlier.

In this chapter, we will show examples of two categories of difficulty: 1) extensive

2. https://www.wits.ac.za/news/latest-news/general-news/2015/2015-08/earliest-baboon-found-in-cradle.html

3. Berger L.R. *et al.*, *Australopithecus sediba*: a new species of *Homo*-like Australopith from South Africa, *Science* 328:195-204, 2010.

4. Swisher C.C. *et al.*, *Java Man*, Scribner, New York, 256 pp., 2000.

coexistence of ancestors/descendants in time and space, which greatly reduces the likelihood of cladogenesis as a satisfactory explanation; and 2) bones and artifacts of descendant species (*Homo sapiens*/Erectus) that are just as old as their presumed ancestors (australopiths). The paleo-community accepts many examples that fall under category 1. Typically their solution is to invoke cladogenesis. Examples that fall under category 2 are much more interesting, because they could potentially falsify reputed ancestor/descendant relationships (cladogenesis cannot realistically be invoked).

Burial in the same bone bed most clearly demonstrates intimate coexistence. This consistent pattern of ancestor/descendant mixed bone beds argues against the ape-to-man story. Extensive coexistence greatly confounds the evolutionary

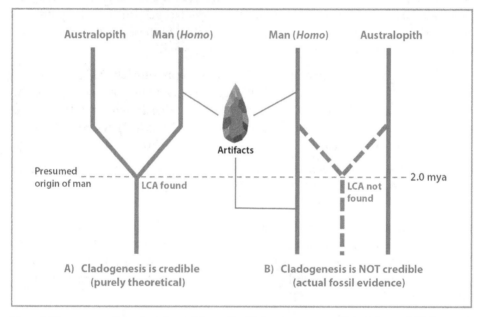

Figure 1. When one species evolves cleanly into another it is known as anagenesis (not pictured). Cladogenesis is when an ancestral species diverges or branches to form two separate lineages (i.e., australopith and man). Traditionally it was assumed that the australopiths evolved cleanly into man (anagenesis). However, with the discovery of human bones and human artifacts together with australopith fossils, anagenesis was shown to be false. The coexistence of these two genera seemed to suggest australopiths did not evolve into man. To rescue the theory, cladogenesis is now invoked to explain why these presumed ancestor descendant species (australopith and man) coexisted so extensively. Yet cladogenesis is not always a satisfactory explanation. Two hypothetical cladogenetic relationships are pictured above, one is credible the other is not. When human bones and/or human artifacts are found *prior* to the presumed origin of cognitively modern humans, it poses a problem for the ape-to-man story (shown in B). This is because anatomically modern human bones and sophisticated stone tools should not appear before the proposed origin of man. Alternatively, when human bones and/or artifacts are found *after* the presumed origin of man (shown in A), cladogenesis may *potentially* be a credible explanation given two conditions: 1) the bones of the hypothetical Last Common Ancestor (LCA) of australopith and man have been found, and 2) macroevolution from australopith-to-man can be shown to be genetically feasible. Neither of these two conditions have been met/validated (see chapter 13). Consequently, the many cladogenetic examples cited in this chapter (both A and B scenarios) are problematic for the ape-to-man story. The actual fossil evidence (shown in B) reveals the extensive coexistence of australopith and man, which is consistent with our alternative model (chapter 14).

model, while coexistence is a straightforward prediction in our alternative model (see chapter 14)

Extensive Coexistence of All Major *Homo* Types Outside of Africa

Before we examine the overlap in time of australopiths and man, it is useful to examine the extensive overlap of all the *Homo* species. All of the major reputed *Homo* species coexisted, and apparently interbred. This includes modern man, Neanderthal, Denisovans, Erectus, Hobbit, and Naledi. In the previous eight chapters we have shown that all these groups coexisted extensively. They clearly interacted and interbred. The interbreeding of modern man, Neanderthal, and the Denisovans has been proven based on DNA sequences. So modern man coexisted with his supposed human precursors. Experts describe this interconnected web of *Homo* types as a large interbreeding "metapopulation." This is in keeping with the Biological Species Concept and confirms that all of these reputed *Homo* types really belong to a single variable species, *Homo sapiens*.

In the last chapter we showed that Naledi lived approximately 236,000–335,000 years ago.[5] This corresponds with the emergence of *Homo sapiens* in Africa some 300,000 years ago.[6] Naledi overlaps in time with all other *Homo* variants (Erectus, Hobbit, Denisovans, and Neanderthals). Paleo-expert John Hawks offers insight into the latest dating of Naledi in a BBC Inside Science broadcast:

> They're the age of Neanderthals in Europe, they're the age of Denisovans in Asia, they're the age of early modern humans in Africa. They're part of this diversity in the world that's there as our species was originating.[7]

This means there is no clear evolutionary progression of the *Homo* variants. Naledi did not become Erectus, which became Neanderthals and archaic humans, which became modern man. The extensive coexistence of all the various *Homo* types is not consistent with the standard evolutionary model, but it is consistent with our alternative model (see chapter 14).

The rest of this chapter is devoted to examining evidence supporting the coexistence of *Homo sapiens* with our reputed non-human ancestors (the australopiths). This is seen at all of the three major East African hominin sites: 1) Tanzania, 2) Ethiopia, and 3) Kenya.

1) Tanzania—Coexistence of Australopith and Man at Olduvai and Laetoli

Olduvai Gorge is arguably the most important hominin site of all: *"It contains one of the richest and best preserved archaeological and paleontological records for*

5. Dirks P. *et al.*, The age of *Homo naledi* and associated sediments in the Rising Star Cave, South Africa, *eLife*, 2017. DOI: 10.7554/elife.24231

6. Hublin J. *et al.*, New fossils from Jebel Iroud, Morocco and the pan-African origin of *Homo sapiens*, *Nature* 546:289-292, 2017. DOI:10.1038/nature22336

7. Rincon P., Primitive human 'lived much more recently', BBC April 25, 2017. http://www.bbc.com/news/science-environment-39710315

the study of human evolution.[8] The first scientifically rigorous paleoanthropology research began at this site. Olduvai Gorge is where highly esteemed paleo-experts Louis and Mary Leakey laid down the conceptual framework of the field. They have been credited with documenting the early evolution of man in east Africa, shifting the focus away from eastern Asia (where man was previously believed to have originated). During excavations in the 50s, 60s, and 70s, the Leakeys discovered numerous fossils. These include *Zinjanthropus boisei* (an extinct ape later re-named *Australopithecus boisei*) and other australopithecine species. At the same site they found human bones (including Erectus), and even witnessed the excavation of a complete modern human skeleton. In the same stratum they also found archaeological evidence for human "living sites" which contained an abundance of stone tools, butchered bones, and a windbreak shelter. These archaeologically rich layers were described as "living floors" or "communal centers." The ape bones (including *Au. boisei* and the non-human Habilis bones) on this site appear to represent creatures that were hunted, butchered, and eaten by those humans responsible for making the campsites and stone tools. Indeed this is exactly how the Leakey's described it. Richard Leakey, son of Mary and Louis Leakey, wrote, "*I see no reason that bands of Homo would not have killed and eaten robust australopithecines when they could, just as they killed and ate antelopes and other prey animals.*"[9] We agree with the Leakey's observations, but add one key point for clarity. There is compelling evidence those "bands of *Homo*" were simply nomadic tribes of *Homo sapiens*/Erectus (not transitional hominin species). The recovered bones at Olduvai Gorge do not reflect an ape-to-man progression, but rather, they show extensive coexistence of australopiths and man.

The exposure at Olduvai Gorge is made up of five main series of deposits designated Beds I-V. The two lowermost in the series, Bed I and Bed II, are most relevant to this discussion, because they are believed to mark the evolutionary transition from *Australopithecus* to *Homo*. Volcanic ash layers found within these deposits were potassium-argon dated. The conventionally accepted age of Bed I is 1.7–2.0 million years old.[10] It is overlain by Bed II, which is dated 1.15–1.7 million years old. What is most remarkable about the diverse hominin species identified at Olduvai Gorge is their extensive overlap in time. For instance, ape bones (*Au. boisei*) and other australopithecine bones (e.g., OH 62 and OH 3) were dispersed widely throughout both beds. Erectus bones were also found in Bed II. "Habilis" bones were also found in both beds. This means that in Bed II, all three major hominin taxa (*Australopithecus*, Habilis, and Erectus) were contemporaries—all being buried in strata of roughly equivalent age. This is fascinating because all three species have

8. http://www.olduvaiproject.org/what-is-olduvai-gorge/

9. Leakey R. and Lewin R., *Origins Reconsidered: In Search of What Makes Us Human*, Anchor Books (Doubleday), New York, p.171, 1992.

10. For the latest age estimates for Bed I and Lower Bed II see: Deino, A.L., [40]Ar/[39]Ar dating of Bed I, Olduvai Gorge, Tanzania, and the chronology of early Pleistocene climate change. In: Blumenschine R.J., Masao F.T., Stanistreet I.G., Swisher C.C. (Eds.), Five decades after *Zinjanthropus* and *Homo habilis*: Landscape Paleoanthropology of Plio-Pleistocene Olduvai Gorge, Tanzania, *J Hum Evol* 63(2):252-273, 2012.

been thought to represent different phases of a single evolving lineage. Thus if they had evolved one into the other, we should not expect all three species to be in the same strata. It is here that "cladogenesis" is conveniently invoked.

Is Erectus absent from Bed I? The Leakeys identified isolated human bones in Bed I, but they mistakenly attributed the anatomically human bones in Bed I to the pseudo-species they named *Homo habilis*. As we showed in chapter 8, Habilis is a "wastebasket taxon," consisting of scattered and fragmentary remains, which are mostly australopith, but with some human bones mixed in. Mary Leakey concluded, *"It seems clear from the evidence at Olduvai that Homo habilis and Homo erectus did not overlap chronologically, and it is possible that they represent two stages in human evolution."*[11] Her opinion eventually took hold, and the "Habilis-evolved-into-Erectus" narrative became a widely accepted "fact" (and is still taught in textbooks and in the popular press). But a lot has changed since she expressed that opinion. In light of new findings, such as evidence published in *Nature* in 2007, we now know Erectus also lived just north of Olduvai in Kenya, presumably 1.9 million years ago.[12] Earlier findings from Kenya dating to the same age are now also attributed to Erectus. This includes an anatomically human leg bone designated KNM-ER 1481. These findings coincide with the age of Bed I at Olduvai. Therefore the anatomically human bones in Bed I are best understood as Erectus (not the false taxon Habilis). So Erectus clearly existed in the time frame of both Bed I and Bed II in East Africa—coexisting intimately and extensively (for at least half a million years) with its supposed australopithecine ancestors.

When Louis and Mary Leakey discovered stone tools and artifacts consistent with human activities in Bed I, they initially assumed that the toolmaker was the ape-ish "Zinj" (*Australopithecus boisei*). A year later they realized their error and decided that the real toolmaker was the artificial taxon "Habilis" (a mixture of ape and human bones). In their assessment at that time, Erectus did not appear until later, in Bed II, and so they felt justified in designating Habilis as the toolmaker at Olduvai (hence his nickname, "Handy Man"). However, we now know that this was their second mistake. The more human-looking bones attributed to Habilis were due to the accidental commingling of australopith and human bones. The Leakeys had presupposed that Erectus had not yet evolved when Bed I was deposited, which influenced their interpretation. Consequently, numerous anatomically modern human bones from Bed I were first erroneously assigned to Zinj, and shortly after were reassigned to Habilis. In reality, all of those human-looking bones should have been attributed to Erectus, just as many other paleo-experts have insisted since the announcement of Habilis in 1964. As noted previously, there is now clear fossil evidence that Erectus/*H. sapiens* did in fact live during the time of Bed I, in nearby Kenya. In fact, Bed I of Olduvai Gorge clearly contains the bones of

---

11. Leakey M.D., *Olduvai Gorge: My Search for Early Man*, Collins, London, p. 74, 1979.
12. Spoor F., Leakey M.G. *et al.*, Implication of new early *Homo* fossils from Ileret, east of Lake Turkana, Kenya, *Nature* 448:688-691, 2007.

Erectus/*H. sapiens*. Those evidences are discussed next.

In 1960 the Leakeys discovered specimens OH 8 and OH 35 that they initially attributed to Zinj and soon after reassigned to Habilis. OH 8 is a partial foot (a nearly complete set of tarsals and metatarsals) which was excavated from FLKNN site in Bed I, dating to 1.7 million years old. The anatomy of OH 8 is unmistakably human and displays an adducted hallux, which means the big toe is in line with the other four, just like in modern humans. Michael Day, in the standard reference work on hominin fossils, *Guide to Fossil Man*, writes:

> The presence of an articular facet between the bases of the first and second metatarsals demonstrated unequivocally the absence of hallucial divergence [opposable great toe], which characterizes non-human primate feet.[13]

This feature is unique to modern humans. Evolutionary anatomists Lovejoy and Latimer, rightly consider the adducted hallux to be a defining characteristic of human morphology.[14] There is no other species on the planet that has a foot like ours. Some have tried to dismiss the inherent humanness in the anatomy of the OH 8 foot, but these attempts have been shown to be misguided. Randall Susman, expert on primate and human foot anatomy, corrects this mistake in the *American Journal of Physical Anthropology*: *"The suggestion of ape-like, arboreal adaptations in the OH 8 foot including among them an abductable hallux* [opposable great toe], *(Lewis, 1980; Oxnard and Lisowski, 1980; Kidd et al., 1996) is at odds with the morphology (and total morphological pattern) of OH 8."*[15] Susman goes on to point out key features that OH 8 shares with modern humans, including a longer midfoot, an adducted hallux, longitudinal and transverse arches, and a "spring" ligament for propulsion during a free striding gait.[16] Susman writes in a separate publication that the OH 8 foot bones are *"remarkably like those of modern humans."*[17] Later publications provide further confirmation of the modern human anatomy of the OH 8 partial foot.[18,19] Reconstructions of the foot often include one additional bone that was found a year later in 1961. Specimen OH 10 is a distal phalange, the tip of a great toe. It was excavated from FLK North site at the top of Bed I, which dates to 1.8 million years old.[20] The toe bone matches the modern human anatomy displayed in the partial foot (OH 8). The anatomy of OH 10 indicates it functioned in a recognizably human bipedal gait. Together OH 8 and OH 10 provide strong

13. Day M.H., *Guide to Fossil Man*, Univ. of Chicago Press, Chicago, p. 169, 1986.

14. Latimer B. and Lovejoy C.O., Hallucal tarsometatarsal joint in *Australopithecus afarensis. Am J Phys Anthropol* 82:125-133, 1990.

15. Susman R.L., Brief communication: evidence bearing on the status of *Homo habilis* at Olduvai Gorge, *Am J Phys Anthropol* 137:356-361, 2008.

16. Susman R.L., Brief communication: evidence bearing on the status of *Homo habilis* at Olduvai Gorge, *Am J Phys Anthropol* 137:356-361, 2008.

17. Susman R.L., Evolution of the human foot: Evidence from Plio-Pleistocene hominids, *Foot and Ankle* 3(6):365-376, 1983.

18. DeSilva J.M., Revisiting the "Midtarsal Break," *Am J Phys Anthropol* 141:245-258, 2010.

19. Ward C.V., Kimbel WH, Johanson DC., Completed Fourth Metatarsal and Arches in the Foot of *Australopithecus afarensis, Science* 2011: 750-753, 2001.

20. Day M.H., *Guide to Fossil Man*, Univ. of Chicago Press, Chicago, p. 169, 1986.

evidence for the presence of anatomically modern man at Olduvai. This extends the coexistence of australopiths and humans deeper into Bed I at Olduvai Gorge, much earlier than was thought possible.

Specimen OH 35 consists of the two bones of the lower leg, the tibia and fibula. Potassium-argon dating suggested a date of 1.8 million years old. Like OH 8, the leg bones were initially mistakenly attributed to Zinj because of their close proximity to the skull (OH 5). The Leakeys later reassigned OH 35 to Habilis, even though the bones closely resembled Erectus/*Homo sapiens*. Evolutionary experts in comparative anatomy, Randall Susman and Jack Stern, reexamined the morphology of the leg bones.[21] They agree with an earlier assessment published in *Nature,* which noted that the specimen, *"in many ways resembles that of H. sapiens; indeed there are fibulae from modern human beings which resemble it almost exactly."*[22]—clearly indicating the bones functioned in upright walking.[23] In a separate publication in the *American Journal of Physical Anthropology*, Susman describes OH 35 as an *"essentially human leg."*[24] Both of these experts can agree that the anatomy is consistent with modern man. However, this interpretation was largely ignored, because it did not fit with the ape-to-man story.

The most recent finding of an anatomically modern human bone from Olduvai Gorge was in 2015. Manuel Dominguez-Rodrigo *et al.* discovered a proximal finger bone (OH 86) excavated from Bed I, the oldest bed in the gorge, and the same deposit where Zinj and Habilis were found. The researchers report in *Nature: "The discovery of OH 86 suggests that a hominin with a more MHL* [modern-human-like] *postcranium co-existed with Paranthropus boisei and Homo habilis at Olduvai during Bed I times."*[25] The researchers noted that OH 86 is different from the OH 7 hand, the defining specimen of Habilis. Recently, paleo-experts have challenged the traditional human-like interpretation of the OH 7 (it might actually belong to the extinct ape *Au. boisei*).[26,27] On the basis of several morphological features, OH 86 is said to align best with *Homo sapiens.* The researchers openly confess this, but quickly clarify that this is not possible. According to theory (as opposed to a straightforward observation), *Homo sapiens* are not supposed to have yet evolved. Consequently, they decided the new bone must have belonged to something else, possibly Erectus:

---

21. Susman R.L. and Stern J.T., Functional morphology of *Homo habilis*, Science 217(4563):931-934, 1982.

22. Davis P.R., Hominid fossils from Bed I, Olduvai Gorge, Tanganyika: A tibia and fibula, *Nature* 201:967–968, 1964.

23. Cartmill M. and Smith F.H., *The Human Lineage*, Wiley-Blackwell, Hoboken, NJ, p. 228, 2009.

24. Susman R.L., Brief communication: evidence bearing on the status of *Homo habilis* at Olduvai Gorge, *Am J Phys Anthropol* 137:356-361, 2008.

25. Dominguez-Rodrigo M. *et al.*, Earliest modern human-like hand bone from a new >1.84-million-year-old site at Olduvai in Tanzania, *Nature Comm*, 6:7987, 2015.

26. Almécija S., Moya-Sola S., and Alba D.M., Early Origin for Human-Like Precision Grasping: A Comparative Study of Pollical Distal Phalanges in Fossil Hominins, *PLOS ONE* 5:e11727, 2010.

27. Dominguez-Rodrigo M. *et al.*, Earliest modern human-like hand bone from a new >1.84-million-year-old site at Olduvai in Tanzania, *Nature Commun*, 6:7987, 2015. *"OH 7 does not conform to the modern human characterization."*

Collectively, these results lead to the conclusion that OH 86 represents a hominin species different from the taxon represented by OH 7, and whose closest form affinities are to modern *H. sapiens* (Fig. 3). However, the geological age of OH 86 obviously precludes its assignment to *H. sapiens*, and ambiguity surrounding the existing potential sample of African *H. erectus* (*sensu lato*) hand bones also prohibits its confident assignment to that species at this time.[28]

Dominguez-Rodrigo *et al.* were forthright in defining their presuppositions. They hold an *a priori* commitment to the ape-to-man narrative, which constrained their interpretation of the evidence. Instead of interpreting the evidence in light of anatomy, they interpreted it in light of evolutionary preconceptions. OH 86 is just one of many instances where paleo-experts have assigned anatomically modern human bones to a non-human species, because those human bones rudely appear in the fossil record where theory demands they should not be.

Human Artifacts at Olduvai—In the Same Bed with Australopith Bones

We have already discussed in the previous section the presence of anatomically human bones at Olduvai Gorge in the oldest deposit (Bed I). In this section we will focus on the evidence from archaeology that corroborates the presence of cognitively modern humans at Olduvai Gorge, long before they are thought to have evolved. There are at least two key pieces of archeological evidence which support this conclusion.

Evidence 1—Living Sites: Expeditions headed by the Leakeys in the 1950s, 60s, and 70s, as well as recent excavations, have produced a wealth of evidence indicating cognitively modern human activity at Olduvai Gorge. Many thousands of stone tools and butchered animal carcasses have been found within these deposits. For instance, a total of 2,500 stone artifacts and 3,500 large animal fossils were identified in Bed I—the same strata where australopithecines and Erectus/*Homo sapiens* (wrongly attributed to Habilis) were excavated (FLK Zinj layer). Further evidence demonstrating the presence of modern humans came from the lowermost sequence of Bed I (DK layer), dating nearly 2.0 million years old. Mary Leakey discovered something that she was initially very reluctant to accept—the world's oldest man-made structure. She found a circle of stones forming a windbreak shelter. Mary Leakey tells of her reaction in her book, *Olduvai Gorge: My Search for Early Man*, saying:

> At DK there is a stone circle which is the earliest manmade structure known. It is built of loosely piled blocks of lava and measures three and a half to four metres in diameter. It bears a striking similarity to crude stone circles constructed for temporary shelter by present-day nomadic peoples such as the Turkana in Kenya … The Olduvai structure was a most surprising discovery in view of its age and for a while I was reluctant to believe that the blocks of lava had been artificially

---

28. Dominguez-Rodrigo M. *et al.*, Earliest modern human-like hand bone from a new >1.84-million-year-old site at Olduvai in Tanzania, *Nature Commun* 6:7987, 2015.

arranged into a circle. However, the geologists and prehistorians who have since seen the circle are almost unanimous in considering that it is likely to be the work of the early hominids and not a natural feature.[29]

To Mary Leakey, findings like this *"proved conclusively"* that *"nearly two million years ago, man had already reached a stage of social structure which included communal centres where groups gathered together, built shelters and ate food."*[30]

Henry Bunn is a professor of anthropology at the University of Wisconsin and head of archaeological excavations currently taking place at Olduvai Gorge. His research team is continuing work at the site where the Leakey's excavated decades earlier. In light of the slice marks on many of the bones found there, Bunn concludes that the hominins transported the carcasses to the living site at Olduvai, skinned them, butchered them down to sizeable portions, cut the meat off the bones to cook, and smashed marrow-rich bones for consumption.[31,32] Bunn describes the living floors originally excavated by the Leakeys as virtual "campsites." He considers the high density of stone tools and large collections of processed bones to be clear evidence that the hominins there lived in communal centers. They cooperated in social groups, shared food, and ate together in what he considers to be a *"recognizably human, rather than ape-like, form of behavior."*[33,34]

Another research team at Olduvai, which founded the Olduvai Paleoanthropology and Paleoecology Project (TOPP) in 2006,[35] cited evidence from Bed I that indicates that the occupants at Olduvai acquired large prey by active hunting, and not merely as *"passive scavengers."*[36] High-density bone assemblages reveal repeated carcass transport to the same location where they were butchered.[37] The transported carcasses included large mammals such as hippo, wildebeest,

29. Leakey M.D., *Olduvai Gorge: My Search for Early Man*, Collins, London, p. 55, 1979.

30. Leakey M.D., *Olduvai Gorge: My Search for Early Man*, Collins, London, p. 51, 1979.

31. Henry Bunn, paleoanthropologist at the University of Wisconsin. Documentary shown on YouTube: https://www.youtube.com/watch?v=B3Lw40BRHjc; roughly 14 minutes and 55 seconds into video. He states, *"One approach is to look at bone damage produced by humans using stone tools. So cut marks or butchery marks from slicing up the animals, cutting meat off the bones, skinning the animals, cutting the joints apart, which show up on the bones like they would on your wooden cutting board at home; things you can hold up and see with your naked eye."*

32. Dominguez-Rodrigo M. *et al.*, Deconstructing Olduvai—A Taphonomic Study of Bed I Sites, Springer, Dordrecht, Netherlands, 2007. *"Cut mark frequencies show that evisceration, disarticulation, and defleshing were all systematically carried out on both small and medium carcasses at FLK Zinj."*

33. Henry Bunn, paleoanthropologist at the University of Wisconsin. Documentary shown on YouTube (8:41 time code): https://www.youtube.com/watch?v=B3Lw40BRHjc

34. Dominguez-Rodrigo M. *et al.*, Deconstructing Olduvai—A Taphonomic Study of Bed I Sites, Springer, Dordrecht, Netherlands, 2007. *"The site thus seems to have been a sort of primitive version of a home base that the ancestors of our genus used repeatedly over time and in which some basic features of human behavior, such as intentional food-sharing, seem to have taken place."*

35. OlduvaiProject.org

36. Bunn H. T. and Pickering T.R., Bovid mortality profiles in paleoecological context falsify hypotheses of endurance running-hunting and passive scavenging by early Pleistocene hominins, *Quaternary Research* 74:395–404, 2010.

37. Dominguez-Rodrigo M. *et al.*, Deconstructing Olduvai—A Taphonomic Study of Bed I Sites, Springer, Dordrecht, Netherlands, 2007.

and antelope.[38] The researchers described the manner by which the carcasses were acquired, transported, and processed as undeniably human. The primary occupants at Olduvai lived in a manner typical of modern, semi-nomadic people groups. All of this is further confirmation that the occupants of Olduvai were fully human, even in the oldest strata.

Evidence 2—Manufactured Stone Tools: The existence of stone tools alone unequivocally demonstrates humans must have been around at the time Bed I and Bed II were deposited (1.15–2 million years ago, according to standard dating methods). The Leakeys mistakenly attributed these stone tools first to the extinct ape Zinj (*Australopithecus boisei*), and then, a few years later, to Habilis. However, it now appears they were made by man.

The types of stone tools found at Olduvai are diverse, indicating that they were made for specific purposes (chopping, pounding, scraping, punching holes, etc.). Mary Leakey has noted that the different tools indicate *"diverse occupations,"* with some meant for hunting and others *"purely [for] domestic activities."* A common tool found in Bed II is a small quartzite awl with sharpened point. Leakey notes, *"In more recent pre-historic times, such tools have been used for working leather."*[39] Anvils with depressions have also been found in Bed I and Bed II. It has been suspected that these pitted anvils were used together with the awls to punch holes into hides.[40] Many other types of stone tools have been found at Olduvai.[41]

The level of cognition needed to carefully select a specific rock type that can be shaped through a flaking process to serve a specific purpose has never been seen in apes. An article published in *Nature* (2015), Sonia Harmand *et al.* explain that the manufacture of the stone tools at Olduvai requires *"understanding of the stone's fracture properties ... planning, manual dexterity and raw material selectivity."*[42] Material selectivity is crucial, as not just any rock will flake to a point. Mary Leakey explains they must be fine-grained and homogeneous, which are *"essential criteria for obtaining sharp-edge cutting or chopping tools; really sharp edges cannot be obtained with course-grained material and flaws make accurate flaking impossible."*[43] The toolmaker must locate the exact type of rock needed, oftentimes many miles from the location where it is used. The tools used at Olduvai during the time of Bed I and Bed II were made from source rocks located impressive distances away from the living sites. For instance, the basalt-trachyte stone tools come from Olmoti Crater in Tanzania, 10 miles (nearly 15 km) away from the living site. Leakey suggests this may indicate *"some form of exchange or barter of rocks among the groups of hominids living in the areas where they occurred, rather than*

38. Ungar P. (ed.), *Evolution of the Human Diet*, Oxford University Press New York, 2007.
39. Leakey M.D., *Olduvai Gorge: My Search for Early Man*, Collins, London UK, p. 111, 1979.
40. Leakey M.D., *Olduvai Gorge: My Search for Early Man*, Collins, London UK, 187 pp., 1979.
41. Leakey M.D., *Olduvai Gorge: My Search for Early Man*, Collins, London UK, 187 pp., 1979.
42. Harmand S. *et al.*, 3.3-million-year-old stone tools from Lomekwi 3, West Turkana, Kenya, *Nature* 521:310-315, 2015.
43. Leakey M.D., *Olduvai Gorge: My Search for Early Man*, Collins, London UK, 187 pp., 1979.

transportation over the entire distance by members of a single group." All of these evidences suggest the real toolmakers at Olduvai were fully human.

Modern Human Skeleton in Bed II at Olduvai Gorge

Figure 2. German paleontologist Hans Reck is credited with describing the geology at Olduvai Gorge. In 1913, Reck discovered the first hominin specimen at Olduvai Gorge, dubbed "Oldoway Man" (OH 1) and thousands of Pleistocene fossils. In 1931 he returned to the site with Louis Leakey where they collaborated and defended the authenticity of Oldoway Man.

In the sections above, we have shown that three major hominin taxa, traditionally believed to represent ancestor-descendant relationships, coexisted in the fossil record in the oldest strata of the Olduvai Gorge. Australopiths, the chimeric "Habilis," and Erectus have all been found buried together in the very same strata (Beds I and II). Yet there is one particular finding at Olduvai Gorge that is even more surprising. That find is specimen OH 1, which was the very first fossil hominin discovered at Olduvai Gorge. It is universally agreed to be an anatomically modern human (*Homo sapiens*), but was excavated from Bed II, where *Australopithecus* and Erectus bones were also found.

German paleontologist Hans Reck was the first scientist to study the geology at Olduvai. He embarked on his first expedition in 1913 where he conducted extensive research, cataloguing numerous fossils and meticulously detailing the geology. Reck identified the five main depositional sequences that make up Olduvai Gorge (Beds I-V), a system that is still used by geologists today. He is also credited with finding the first fossil hominin, designated Olduvai Hominin 1 (OH 1), a nearly complete modern human skeleton (Figure 3). The provocative finding stirred up immense controversy among the paleoanthropology community of his time. Today, Reck's finding has been swept aside and ignored, but not for any sound scientific reason (apart from the commitment to the ape-to-man paradigm). Yet Reck and this skeleton very literally represent the beginning of modern paleoanthropology!

It was many years prior to the discovery of Zinj and Habilis when Reck found the first human bones from Olduvai Gorge (OH 1), nicknamed "Oldoway Man." The skeleton was nearly complete and unquestionably modern in its anatomy. It was excavated from Bed II making it the oldest discovery of a modern *Homo sapiens*. Reck reported his find, and invited Louis Leakey to visit the Olduvai site. At first, Leakey was skeptical about Reck's find, until 1931 when he collaborated with him in Tanzania and examined the finding firsthand. Leakey was then convinced that Oldoway Man was authentic. But this was an unwelcome find for most paleoanthropologists who did not accept the possibility of such an early date for the origin of man (1.15–1.7 million years old, according to current potassium-argon dates for Bed II). This is significantly older than the oldest currently accepted *Homo sapiens* fossil; a jawbone that dates 315,000 years old was recently found in Jebel Irhoud, Morocco of northern Africa.[44]

Figure 3. Olduvai Hominind 1 (OH 1) was discovered by Hans Reck in 1913. The complete human skeleton was described as distinctly modern in its anatomy. Yet it was excavated from Bed II which significantly pre-dated the presumed origin of *Homo sapiens*. This did not agree with the ape-to-man timeline and created quite the controversy among the paleo-community. Some argued that Oldoway Man was an intrusive burial, a recent grave dug into the top of Bed II. However, Hans Reck and Louis Leakey enthusiastically defended their claim that the skeleton was excavated from a genuine Bed II *in situ* deposit.

Many who had never directly examined the excavation site, put heavy pressure on Leakey to recant his position. They argued that it must have been an intrusive grave dug into Bed II in recent history, rather than an *in situ* burial at the time of deposition. Leakey, Reck, and a number of other researchers adamantly disagreed and expertly defended the find.[45] Those who had actually seen and carefully analyzed the site first-hand made numerous observations demonstrating that Oldoway Man could not have been an intrusive burial. Reck, who understood the geology at Olduvai better than anyone noted, *"The bed in which the human*

44. Hublin J. *et al.*, New fossils from Jebel Iroud, Morocco and the pan-African origin of *Homo sapiens*, *Nature* 546:289-292, 2017. DOI:10.1038/nature22336
45. Reck H., Boswell P.G.H., Hopwood A.T., and Solomon J.D., The Oldoway human skeleton, *Nature* 131:397-398, 1933.

remains were found ... showed no signs of disturbance. The spot appeared exactly like any other in the horizon. There was no evidence of any refilled hole or grave."[46] He further stated:

> The sediment... is so constituted that the artificial breaking of the bed with its visible layering by digging of a grave would necessarily be recognizable. The wall of the grave would show in profile a division from the undisturbed stone. The grave filling would show an abnormal structure and heterogeneous mixture of excavated material, including easily recognizable pieces of calcrete. Neither of these signs were to be found despite the most attentive inspection. Rather the stone directly around the skeleton was not distinguishable from the neighboring stone in terms of color, hardness, thickness of layers, structure, or order.

Among the many scientists who accepted the legitimacy of their findings was American anthropologist George Grant MacCurdy of Yale University. He wrote in *Science* saying:

> The skeleton was found some three or four meters below the rim of the Oldoway gorge, which here is about fifty meters deep. The skeleton bore the same relation to the stratified bed as did the other mammalian remains and was dug out of the hard clay tuff with hammer and chisel just as these were. In other words the conditions of the find were such as to exclude the possibility of an interment [a recent grave burial]. The human bones are therefore as old as the deposit (No. 2).[47]

Although there was no valid evidence against its authenticity, scientific politics won the day. Louis Leakey eventually yielded to the demands of the senior members of the paleo-community to dismiss the finding, as those hostile to his position were reviewing his latest submitted papers. Since then, Oldoway Man has been largely forgotten. If mentioned at all, Oldoway Man is listed as an *"intrusive burial."*[48] But the early debate about Oldoway Man is well documented in a series of *Science* papers.[49] This is just one more example of fiercely contested bones and the unceasing effort to force the data to conform to the ape-to-man narrative. We will review this history and its implications elsewhere.

Homo Bones from Laetoli Predate the Oldest *Homo* Bones from Olduvai

In Laetoli, Tanzania, just 30 miles away from Olduvai Gorge, Mary Leakey discovered jawbones and teeth from at least 13 individuals. The specimens were situated in volcanic ash tuffs that were potassium-argon dated as 3.7 million years old. Remarkably, her samples predate the earliest occurrence of *Homo* bones from Olduvai Gorge (or anywhere else) by nearly two million years. She, along with Tim White and other colleagues, published their findings in *Nature* in 1976.[50] In their paper all of the bones were attributed to the genus *Homo* without any qualification.

46. Hopwood A., The age of "Oldoway Man," *Man* 32:193 (192-195), 1932.
47. MacCurdy G.G., A fossil skeleton from German East Africa, *Science* 40(1018): 19-20, July 3, 1914.
48. Day M.H., *Guide to Fossil Man*, Univ. of Chicago Press, Chicago, p. 177, 1986.
49. *Science* Classic, archives: http://science.sciencemag.org/content/by/year
50. Leakey M.D. *et al.*, Fossil hominids from the Laetoli Beds, *Nature* 262(5568):460-466, 1976.

One of those specimens was a jawbone (LH-4) that would later be reclassified, and used as the defining specimen for Johanson's new species *Australopithecus afarensis* (Lucy's kind). Mary was vehemently opposed to Johanson and White's decision to reclassify her bones; she was convinced her Laetoli sample belonged in the human genus (more later).

During the same year of her publication in *Nature*, Mary made another remarkable discovery that further confirmed the presence of humans at the Laetoli site. A heel impression of a "hominin" foot was fossilized in ash just a short distance from where one of her *Homo* specimens (LH-5 upper jawbone) was found.[51] Excavations continued over the next two field seasons to reveal an entire bipedal footprint trail (labeled site G). A total of nearly 70 footprints were uncovered, with the trail continuing for 88 feet. The Laetoli G footprints appear to have been made by three individuals (one of whom was smaller, walking in the footprints of another) traveling in the same direction in close proximity. The fossilized footprints were dated as being 3.7 million years old, the same age as the *Homo* bones. The findings were published in *Nature* in 1979.[52]

We have already discussed in chapter 7 the observations from a number of paleo-experts who acknowledged what is already self-evident to any casual observer: the morphology of the Laetoli footprints is unmistakably human. Mary, Tim White, Owen Lovejoy, Russell Tuttle, among others, describe them as looking *"indistinguishable from those of habitually barefoot Homo sapiens."* (see chapter 7). Yet their radioisotopic age approaches 4 million years old! According to the standard ape-to-man story, that should be utterly impossible. How can upright-walking anatomically modern humans exist at the time of Lucy, well over a million years before the first humans (Erectus) are said to have evolved? In this case, it is impossible to resort to a cladogenesis explanation.

The Laetoli footprints would have resulted in a comprehensive re-examination of the ape-to-man story, if it had not been for Donald Johanson and Tim White. They subsequently reclassified all of Mary Leakey's *Homo* fossils, assigning them to Johanson's reputed new species *Australopithecus afarensis* (Lucy's kind) from Hadar, Ethiopia. The human-looking footprints were also credited to Afarensis. This is extraordinary because no australopith skeleton has ever been found clearly associated with anatomically modern human feet (see chapter 7). This largely untold history of intrigue and politics is discussed further in the next section on the Ethiopia findings. This single event (assigning the Laetoli *Homo* bones and the Laetoli footprints to Lucy's kind) is remarkable in that it reflects a major turning point in the field of paleoanthropology. It also reflects what looks to be an unprecedented example of showmanship, manipulation, and scientific politics.

---

51. White T. and Suwa G., Hominid Footprints at Laetoli: Facts and Interpretations, *Nature* 72:485-514, 1987.
52. Leakey M.D. and Hay R.L., Pliocene footprints in the Laetolil Beds at Laetoli, northern Tanzania, *Nature* 278:317-323, 1979.

Latest Findings Confirm Coexistence of Australopith and Man in Tanzania

In 2015, a dozen additional footprints were found less that 500 feet south of site G.[53] The newly found trackway is designated site S. The footprints belonged to two individuals who walked on the same surface and in the same direction as the G footprints discovered 40 years earlier by Mary Leakey. The average foot length of the larger individual (SI) was 10.28 inches (261 mm). Had the individual lived today, he could have worn a size 11 shoe size and stood over 6 feet tall. Paleo-experts have nicknamed the larger individual "Chewie," after the *Star Wars* character. Chewie's footprints are human in shape, size, and gait. The new finding makes it even more incredible to claim that they were formed by Lucy's kind, Afarensis. To justify their claim, Johanson and colleagues would now have to insist an extreme level of sexual dimorphism, such that the adult females would be the size of a chimp, around 3 feet tall, and with a very ape-ish anatomy, while the males would be 6 feet tall, with a strikingly modern free-striding human gait and perfect human feet.

Not surprisingly, many paleo-experts have found this interpretation to be unconvincing. Since Johanson and White's *Science* announcement of their reputed new species *Australopithecus afarensis* in 1979, numerous paleo-experts have contested Johanson's sexual dimorphism hypothesis. To these paleo-experts the highly variable bones (in size, anatomy, and inferred locomotory function) attributed to Lucy's kind Afarensis, belong to two or more species (not a single, sexually dimorphic species). For instance, Peter Schmid of Wits University, Johannesburg and his colleague Martin Häusler from the Anthropological Institute in Zurich, published a revised reconstruction of Lucy's pelvis in the *Journal of Human Evolution*.[54] Schmid and Häusler concluded, based on the pelvic inlet (birth canal) and related pelvic features, that Lucy was not a female (they suggested renaming Lucy's skeleton "Lucifer"). In their assessment, the males (Lucy's skeleton) were not significantly larger than the females, contrary to what Johanson *et al.* have claimed. Both genders were of about the same size. Therefore Afarensis cannot be accepted as a sexually dimorphic species. The larger, anatomically distinct bones apparently belonged to an entirely separate species, and likely a separate genus. This is actually what Johanson had originally reported in *Nature*. He was convinced that there were two or more species from separate genera (*Homo* and *Australopithecus*) represented in his Hadar collection of bones (see next section on Ethiopia). Häusler and Schmid argue that Johanson's original interpretation was not far from correct. In fact, they insist that is precisely what Afarensis is—an artificial taxon consisting of a jumble of bones from multiple species. They make this observation in the *Journal of Human Evolution*: *"...the Hadar (and by inference the Sterkfontein) material consists of several distinct species*

53. Masao F. *et al.*, New footprints from Laetoli (Tanzania) provide evidence for marked body size variation in early hominins, *eLife*, 2016. DOI: 10.7554/eLife.19568.001

54. Häusler M. and Schmid P., Comparison of the pelves of Sts 14 and AL 288-1: implications for birth and sexual dimorphism in australopithecines, *J Hum Evol* 29:363-383, 1995.

which were previously jumbled together."[55]

This is the "Third Competing View" regarding Lucy's kind Afarensis, which we discussed in chapter 7. Why do education systems and the media rarely expose the weakness of Johanson's interpretation of Afarensis? Why is the hotly contested sexual dimorphism hypothesis the only view widely promoted to the public, even while a significant portion of the paleo-community (including leading paleo-experts, reporting in prestigious scientific journals) reject this interpretation? Remarkably, Lucy and her kind are just as contested as the other reputed hominin species.

2) Ethiopia—Extensive Coexistence of Australopith and Man at Afar Region

The famous Lucy "ape-man" shown in museums and textbooks consists of what is said to be a single skeleton that belongs to the reputed species *Australopithecus afarensis*. As discussed in depth in chapter 7, Donald Johanson discovered the 3.2 million-year-old partial skeleton in 1974 in the Afar region of Ethiopia. While most of us have heard of Lucy, few people know that Donald Johanson found far more than Lucy during his expeditions in the 70s. His team found roughly 300 additional bones across the Afar landscape, mostly isolated, fragmentary remains. All of those bones are now described as Lucy's kind, but this was not what Johanson initially claimed.

The site where Lucy and her kind were discovered (the Hadar region of Ethiopia) contained many bones that were initially classified as *Homo* (human) by none other than the discoverer of Lucy—Donald Johanson.

Donald Johanson and Mary Leakey originally agreed that the Laetoli collection consisted of *Homo* bones, and that the Hadar sample contained a mixture of *Homo* and *Australopithecus*. In Laetoli, Mary Leakey found *Homo* jawbones and modern human-looking fossilized footprints. She reported her findings in *Nature* (1976, 1979) and assigned her bones to the genus *Homo* (discussed in previous section).[56,57] Meanwhile, Johanson's growing collection of bones from various sites in Hadar displayed mixed anatomies. Some of his bones looked very ape-like and fit neatly within the genus *Australopithecus*. Paleo-expert Philip Tobias observed that they closely resembled the bones of the already discovered species *Au. africanus*. Still other bones included within the Hadar collection, particularly the larger ones, looked remarkably human. Johanson himself (and his colleague) originally reported in his announcement paper in *Nature* (1976) that his Hadar sample consisted of both *Homo* and *Australopithecus* bones: *"The collection suggests that Homo and*

---

55. Häusler M. and Schmid P., Comparison of the pelves of Sts 14 and AL 288-1: implications for birth and sexual dimorphism in australopithecines, *J Hum Evol* 29:363-383, 1995.
56. Leakey M.D., Hay R.L., Curtis G.H., Drake R.E., Jackes M.K., and White T.D., Fossil hominids from the Laetoli Beds, *Nature* 262:460-466,1976.
57. Leakey M.D., Hay R.L., Pliocene footprints in the Laetolil Beds at Laetoli, northern Tanzania, *Nature* 278:317-323, 1979.

Australopithecus coexisted as early as 3.0 Myr ago."[58] They noted that some of the recovered bones closely resembled *Homo erectus* from East Rudolf (Turkana), Kenya. At that time in an article in *National Geographic* Johanson described a nearly complete hand as being anatomically modern, indistinguishable from *H. sapiens*. In describing the hand bones from Hadar, Johanson observed they *"bear an uncanny resemblance to our own—in size, shape, and function. ... the thumb rotates, making it possible to manipulate tools with finesse."*[59] Johanson recounts, *"I was convinced that there were two species at Hadar."*[60] The bones (human and australopith) found in Hadar all dated between 3 and 4 million years old—the oldest *Homo* bones ever found.

Despite multiple confirmations of *Homo* bones at both sites, Johanson later decided to reclassify the entire Hadar/Laetoli collection of bones (including Mary Leakey's bones, which she had already reported in *Nature* as *Homo*) as a single, highly variable species—*Australopithecus afarensis*. Conveniently, Johanson swept his famous Lucy skeleton into this newly named species. He simultaneously swept in all the other *Homo* and *Australopithecus* bones that he himself had found and all the *Homo* bones and fossilized footprints, which Mary Leakey had discovered. In a single stroke, all of those anatomically human looking fossils from Hadar and Laetoli, which were originally classified as *Homo*, were arbitrarily reassigned to Lucy's kind, *Au. afarensis*. The larger bones originally assigned to the human genus were explained away as being merely due to physical differences between the males and the females of the same species (sexual dimorphism). Johanson's unwarranted claim, that the males looked more human, and the females looked more ape-ish, is still hotly contested today.

Arguably, Johanson wanted to place his discovery (Lucy and all her contemporaries) on the paleoanthropological throne, as the earliest and primary human ancestors. Otherwise, Lucy and her kind would have been regarded as just another extinct australopithecine ape, among the many branches of the messy bush of human evolution. We believe that the reason the media and textbook-writers jumped on Johanson's bandwagon was because it was an evolutionary story they could effectively promote and defend. But if *Homo* bones/footprints reached all the way back to the time of the earliest australopiths, the ape-to-man story would not be credible.

Mary Leakey and Johanson had agreed that at each of their sites they were seeing mixed bone beds with both australopith and human bones. When Johanson changed his story to put "his" Lucy as the center, Mary Leakey expressed very

---

58. Johanson D.C. and Taieb M., Plio-Pleistocene hominid discoveries in Hadar, Ethiopia, *Nature* 260(5549):293-297, 1976.

59. Johanson D.C., Ethiopia yields first "family" of early man, *National Geographic* 150(6):808, December 1976.

60. Johanson D. and Edey M., *Lucy – The Beginnings of Humankind*, Simon & Schuster Paperbacks, New York, p. 257, 1981. On page 293 Johanson states again, *"I'd already published that there were two species. Was I now going to publish again and say there was only one?"*

strong scientific opposition, and even personal anger, for having her *Homo* fossils assigned to his new species.

Johanson, Mary Leakey, and Tim White (who was working with Mary in Laetoli) had originally agreed to publish a joint paper in *Science* describing their findings. They planned to publish how they had found *Homo* and australopith bones at Hadar and Laetoli dating to 3–4 million years ago. However, this is not what happened. Little did Mary know that behind the scenes, Johanson and White had decided to rename all of the aforementioned fossils from Hadar and Laetoli to a single new species, *Au. afarensis* (Lucy's kind). Johanson even reclassified a *Homo* jawbone (LH-4) found by Mary in Laetoli as the defining specimen for his new species, *Au. afarensis*. The joint paper published in *Kirtlandia* (1978) was just coming out when Johanson announced at a paleoanthropology meeting—the Nobel Symposium in Sweden on the Current Argument on Early Man—that he had discovered a new hominin species.

Johanson didn't seem to realize that Mary was sitting in the audience to hear his unexpected announcement (betrayal). She was livid and demanded that Johanson and White remove her name from the joint paper. She adamantly disagreed with Johanson and White's decision to combine the Hadar/Laetoli sample into a single new australopithecine species. To Mary, her Laetoli sample (as well as Johanson's Hadar collection) certainly included *Homo* bones, as they had all initially agreed, and as they had all separately reported in *Nature*. Renaming all of the bones from Hadar and Laetoli, including the bones that Johanson originally insisted were clearly human, was undoubtedly a strategic move. Johanson and White understood that by reassigning all of the human bones to their new species, *Au. afarensis*, they could then promote their finding as an early human ancestor, and the ancestor to all later hominins. This was just what they reported in their *Kirtlandia* paper that was reprinted without Mary's name.[61] This very strategic move instantly catapulted Johanson into the limelight, along with his newly famous Lucy skeleton as the reputed ancestor of us all.

To this day the paleo-community remains divided. Some have sided with Johanson but others remain convinced that the Hadar/Laetoli sample includes bones of two or more species, belonging in separate genera—*Homo* and *Australopithecus* (effectively refuting the ancestral status of Lucy's kind, Afarensis). Although there are at least three competing views, only one of those views has been widely publicized. Johanson won over the media, manipulated the field, and effectively marketed the significance of his own discovery. This put him on top of the field and made his Lucy discovery the most famous hominin fossil of all time.

Richard Leakey, renowned paleoanthropologist and son of Louis and Mary Leakey, tells the story of these contested bones:

---

61. Johanson D.C., White T.D., Coppens Y., A New Species of the Genus *Australopithecus* (Primates: Hominidae) From the Pliocene of Eastern Africa, *Kirtlandia*, 28:1-14, 1978.

When I had seen many of the Ethiopian fossils in Nairobi, during those trips Don made on his way back to the States in the mid-1970s, I was impressed by the range of size. Some individuals had clearly been more than five feet tall; others, particularly Lucy, were not much more than three feet. There was also a great deal of anatomical variability. These were the reasons Don initially considered that three different species were represented among the fossils, a large and small *Australopithecus* and an early *Homo*. He had announced this in his March 1976 *Nature* paper, with his French colleague Maurice Taieb. I agree with him.

Now, Don had changed his mind, the results of the reassessment of the fossils with Tim White, an anthropologist of Berkeley. They concluded that the Hadar fossils represented just one variable species, not three separate species. Furthermore, they said that fossil teeth and jaws from my mother's footprint site at Laetoli were from exactly the same species as at Hadar. The fact that the Laetoli fossils were located a thousand miles to the south and were half a million years older apparently did not worry Don and Tim. Theirs was an audacious move that raised many eyebrows among evolutionary biologists.

Don and Tim said that the Hadar and Laetoli samples were all from the newly named *Australopithecus afarensis*. Furthermore, they argued that afarensis was the ancestral stock from which all hominid species evolved... The anthropological community threw itself into turmoil over Don and Tim's *Science* paper, some supporting the validity of afarensis, some challenging it.[62]

Textbooks and science programs never mention any of this fascinating history, or any of the controversy among paleo-experts regarding Johanson, Lucy, and the early reports of human bones being found at all the key australopith sites. This is not because the controversy has been resolved, it is because the priority is marketing the paradigm. To this day, paleo-experts remain divided over the legitimacy of Lucy's kind, questioning it as a sexually dimorphic species and as our ancestor. Some have sided with Johanson's reassessment whereas others remain convinced that the species' hypodigm (total collection of bones) includes both australopith and *Homo* bones.

The coexistence of these two genera, as evidenced by their burial together in layers of equivalent age, is obviously very problematic for Johanson and colleagues who have built their careers on proclaiming to the world that Lucy and its kind are a pivotal hominin precursor to man. Human bones buried together with Lucy's kind, is obviously a problem for the paradigm. The coexistence of Lucy and humans that dates back to the Laetoli footprints, means that Lucy and man are both the same age. So man is not the descendant of Lucy. The first anatomical members of the genus *Homo* are not supposed to have evolved until nearly a million years *after* the last Afarensis survivors. Something is clearly wrong. In this light it is easy to understand why Johanson *et al.* felt they needed to attribute the extensive morphological variation found within the Hadar-Laetoli bone collection

62. Leakey R. and Lewin R., *Origins Reconsidered: In Search of What Makes Us Human*, Anchor Books (Double-day), New York, p.114-116, 1992.

to extreme sexual dimorphism. We are told that the smaller ape-like bones were females, while the larger human-like bones were males.

Stern and Susman in the *American Journal of Physical Anthropology* noticed the anatomical differences in Afarensis and reasoned that the more ape-like females must have spent most of their time in the trees, whereas the larger males with more human-looking bones walked habitually upright on the ground. They write:

> A comparison of the specimens representing small individuals, presumably female, to those of larger individuals, presumably male, suggests sexual differences in locomotor behavior linked to marked size dimorphism. The males were probably less arboreal and engaged more frequently in terrestrial bipedalism.[63]

Just think how absurd this is! To make the story work we have to make the females look and act like apes, while the males look and act like humans. The more reasonable interpretation of the mixed bone types is precisely what Johanson and Mary Leakey originally concluded—that the smaller bones belonged to ape-like australopiths, and the larger human-looking bones were of the genus *Homo*. This would explain and resolve the dilemma of the species having a *"combination of arboreal and bipedal traits."*[64] This is consistent with the findings of numerous paleo-experts who have argued that Afarensis is not a valid taxon, but rather consists of two or more distinct hominin species (just like Habilis and Sediba). For instance, Senut and Tardieu[65] and Deloison[66] have insisted that Afarensis is *"two separate species of hominin with two very different locomotor repertoires."*[67] Many other paleo-experts have come to similar conclusions. Their findings have been reported in several publications over the years (unfortunately what we call the "Third Competing View" is not widely known to those outside the paleo-community).[68,69]

This Third Competing View maintains that the Hadar-Laetoli bone collection does not represent one highly variable species, but rather represented two distinct genera. This best explains why, even after Johanson reassigned all the bones to *Au. afarensis,* researchers have unwittingly noticed how strikingly similar some of the

---

63. Stern J.J.T. and Susman R.L., The locomotor anatomy of *Australopithecus afarensis., Am J Phys Anthropol* 60:279-317, 1983.

64. Stern J.J.T. and Susman R.L., The locomotor anatomy of *Australopithecus afarensis., Am J Phys Anthropol* 60:279-317, 1983.

65. Senut B. and Tardieu C., Functional aspects of Plio-Pleistocene hominid limb bones: implications for taxonomy and phylogeny. In *Ancestors: the Hard Evidence* (ed. Delson E), pp. 193-201, Alan R. Liss, Inc., New York, 1985.

66. Deloison Y., L'Homme ne descend pas d'un Primate arboricole! une evidence meconnue, *Biom Hum Anthropol.,* 14:147-150, 1999.

67. Harcourt-Smith W.E.H. and Aiello L.C., Fossils, feet and the evolution of human bipedal locomotion, *J Anat* 204(5):403-416, p. 409, 2004.

68. Leakey R.E., *The Making of Mankind,* E.P. Dutton, New York, 256 pp., 1981.

69. Ferguson W.W., An Alternative Interpretation of *Australopithecus* Fossil Material, *Primates* 24(3):397-409, 1983.

bones are to modern *Homo sapiens*.[70] For instance, Stern and Susman describe a femoral head attributed to Afarensis (AL 333-3) as *"remarkably modern in most aspects of its morphology."*[71] Meanwhile, a smaller femoral head (AL 288-1ap) *"resembles that of nonhuman primates"*—an ordinary ape.

The extensive overlap of *Australopithecus* and *Homo* at Hadar and Laetoli is consistent with the Olduvai Gorge evidence, and supports the idea that humans have always lived side by side with a diversity of ape species, including the now extinct australopiths. They were our contemporaries, not our ancestors.

Latest Findings Confirm Coexistence of Australopith and Man at Ethiopia

In 2010 bones displaying slice marks (which would require tools) were found in the Hadar region. This is further evidence for the presence of humans during the time of Lucy and her kind. In Dikika, Ethiopia V-shaped cut marks were found on bones recovered just a few hundred miles away from where Afarensis bones ("Lucy's baby") were excavated. The butchered bones date to the time when Lucy is said to have lived, approximately 3.4 million years ago. The new finding of stone tools used to butcher animals comes from researchers reporting in *Nature* (2010). McPherron *et al.* note, *"these bones show unambiguous stone-tool cut marks for flesh removal and percussion marks for marrow access."*[72] In light of this recent finding, Johanson hints that there may be many more bones dating to that time period showing evidence of being butchered. Until recently, such findings would be dismissed or ignored (toolmaking has consistently been attributed to man). Johanson explains the new finding will *"prompt a reexamination of the tens of thousands of animal bones already collected from this time period at Hadar, Lucy's home, and other sites in Kenya and Tanzania."* Interestingly, even the famous knee joint attributed to Lucy's kind (specimen AL 129-1) appears to have been butchered.

In a *Science* article published in 2015, paleoanthropologists Brian Villmoare and colleagues report the discovery of a partial lower jawbone with teeth (LD 350-1) from the Ledi-Geraru research area of Afar, Ethiopia.[73] The LD 350-1 mandible is dated to 2.8 million years old. In their assessment the specimen is not an australopith nor did it align with Habilis (or the contested taxon *H. rudolfensis*). The possibility that the human-looking jaw might be Erectus or *H. sapiens* was not even considered because they assumed modern humans should not have existed that long ago—and so it was tentatively labeled an *"indeterminate species"* of *Homo*.

---

70. The Afarensis (AL 333-3) femur looks strikingly similar to the Koobi Fora femur (KNM-ER 1481) attributed to Erectus. The latter femur is described as indistinguishable from those of modern *H. sapiens*. See image opposite of p. 161 in: Johanson D. and Shreeve J., Lucy's Child, *The Discovery of a Human Ancestor*, 1989.

71. Stern J.J.T. and Susman R.L., The locomotor anatomy of *Australopithecus afarensis.*, Am J Phys Anthropol 60:279-317, 1983.

72. McPherron S.P. *et al.*, Evidence for stone-tool-assisted consumption of animal tissues before 3.39 million years ago at Dikika, Ethiopia, *Nature* 446:857-860, 2010.

73. Villmoare B., Kimbel W.H., *et al.*, Early *Homo* at 2.8 Ma from Ledi-Geraru, Afar, Ethiopia, *Science* 347:1352-1355, 2015.

The researchers suggested that the new find calls into question the *"timing and place of Homo origins"*—pushing the evolution of early man back by nearly half a million years,[74] making these bones a million years older than the earliest *Homo* bones at Olduvai Gorge, Tanzania and northern Kenya (see below).

3) Kenya—Extensive Coexistence of Australopith and Man at Koobi Fora

In addition to the many bones and human artifacts discovered by Louis and Mary Leakey at Olduvai Gorge, their son, Richard Leakey, discovered a comparable collection of bones and artifacts at the Koobi Fora formation in northern Kenya.[75,76,77,78,79,80] Although many of the bones and artifacts appear to be human, the radioisotopic ages were deemed "too old" (2.6–2.9 million years old) to belong to humans, and so the dates were revised to a much younger date to conform to the "group think"[81,82] (see next chapter). Even accepting the younger dates, there was clearly extensive coexistence of Erectus/*H. sapiens* and *Australopithecus* in northern Kenya, which confounds an ape-to-man progression.

The hominin species that coexisted in the Koobi Fora formation include: *Au. anamensis, Au. boisei, H. habilis, H. rudolfensis,* and African *H. erectus* (which some call *H. ergaster*). These fossils date from 1–4 million years ago. Paleo-experts remain divided over how to split these reputed hominin species. As "lumpers" we simply group them all into two separate genera—*Australopithecus* (gracile and robust forms) and *Homo*. In addition to hominin bones, a rich assemblage of stone tools and butchered bones was found. In many ways, the findings in Kenya's Turkana basin are comparable to the "living sites" in Tanzania's Olduvai Gorge. Both regions reveal the coexistence (for at least half a million years) of *Australopithecus* and *Homo*, and both have yielded a wealth of artifacts confirming the presence of cognitively modern human activity. Here again, it appears that the australopithecine apes were part of the diet of the Erectus/*H. sapiens* hunter-gatherer groups, (as opposed to being evolutionary precursors).

The Turkana basin of northern Kenya is home to one of the most famous regions

74. https://www.sciencedaily.com/releases/2015/03/150304141454.htm

75. Leakey R.E.F., New Hominid Remains and Early Artifacts from Northern Kenya, *Nature* 226:223-224, 1970.

76. Leakey R., Further Evidence of Lower Pleistocene Hominids from East Rudolf, North Kenya, *Nature* 231:241-245, 1971.

77. Leakey R., Further Evidence of Lower Pleistocene Hominids from East Rudolf, North Kenya, *Nature* 237:237-269, 1972.

78. Leakey R., Further Evidence of Lower Pleistocene Hominids from East Rudolf, North Kenya, *Nature* 242:170-173, 1973.

79. Leakey R., Further Evidence of Lower Pleistocene Hominids from East Rudolf, North Kenya, *Nature* 248:653-655, 1974.

80. Leakey R., Evidence for an Advanced Plio-Pleistocene Hominid from East Rudolf, Kenya, *Nature* 242:447-450, 1973.

81. Fitch F.J. and Miller J.A., Radioisotopic Age Determinations of Lake Rudolf Artifact Site, *Nature* 226:226-228, 1970.

82. Drake R.E., Curtis G.H. *et al.*, KBS Tuff dating and geochronology of tuffaceous sediments in the Koobi Fora and Shungura Formations, East Africa, *Nature* 283:368-372, 1980.

of hominin exploration. It is described as *"the continental keystone for interpreting the tempo and mode of early human evolution. … The fossils and artifacts recovered from the Lake Turkana basin have contributed much to our current understanding of early human origins."*[83] There are numerous paleontological and archaeological excavations on all sides of the 160-mile long Lake Turkana (formerly Lake Rudolf). Over the past 35 years of exploration a total of 16,000 fossils have been collected from the Turkana basin, 10,000 of which were from the Koobi Fora region, where hundreds of hominin specimens have been recovered.[84] A wide range of African fossils have also been collected, among them pig, antelope, hippo, rhino, elephant, monkeys, extinct apes, and hominin remains.[85] Pig bones in particular played a pivotal role in dating a volcanic ash layer named the Kay Behrensmeyer's Site (aka the "KBS Tuff"). The KBS Tuff served as a marker for establishing the age of important fossils and the timing of the origin of "early man." The original radioisotopic dating of the KBS Tuff sparked intense debate among the paleo-community, which raged for a full decade. The outcome of that debate gave rise to the modern theory as currently taught (see next chapter).

The Koobi Fora formation is on the east side of Lake Turkana. It includes some of the most well known hominin sites in the region. The deposit contains sedimentary sequences that are interbedded by volcanic ash layers (called tuffs). Volcanic ash layers (such as the KBS Tuff), can be potassium-argon dated, and can thus serve as markers or reference points for determining the age of bones and artifacts.

The Koobi Fora formation is where Richard Leakey, son of paleoanthropologists Louis and Mary Leakey, established himself in the field. For two decades he was the director of the National Museums of Kenya. In the 1970s, he headed up a number of expeditions under the auspices of the Koobi Fora Research Project. Richard Leakey was the first to find hominin bones on the east side of Lake Turkana (and "Turkana Boy" years later near the western shore). What Louis and Mary Leakey accomplished in over three decades of painstaking work at Olduvai Gorge, Richard Leakey ("Richard" here after) did in a single field season in East Turkana.[86] During the second field season of his first full-scale expedition in 1969, Richard found two australopithecine skulls in Ileret (part of the Koobi Fora formation), one of which (KNM-ER 406) looked remarkably similar to "Zinj" which was discovered by his father years earlier at Olduvai Gorge.[87] KNM-ER 406 was appropriately assigned to the same species as Louis's "Zinj" (*Australopithecus boisei*). The second skull (KNM-ER 407) was fragmentary and more difficult to classify, but it too was eventually identified as the same species (*Au. boisei*). It was during that same

83. Harris J.M., Leakey M.G., *et al.*, A Brief History of Research at Koobi Fora, Northern Kenya, *Ethnohistory* 53:35-69, 2006. DOI: 10.1215/00141801-53-1-35.

84. http://www.kfrp.com

85. Harris J.M., Leakey M.G., *et al.*, A Brief History of Research at Koobi Fora, Northern Kenya, *Ethnohistory* 53:35-69, 2006. DOI: 10.1215/00141801-53-1-35.

86. Lewin R., *Bones of Contention*, University of Chicago Press, Chicago, 2nd edition, 1997.

87. Leakey R.E.F., New Hominid Remains and Early Artefacts from Northern Kenya, *Nature* 226:223-224, 1970.

field season that the geologist on site, Kay Behrensmeyer, discovered stone tools. Mary Leakey herself described them as closely resembling those found in Bed I at Olduvai Gorge.[88]

Kay Behrensmeyer recovered the stones tools from the KBS Tuff itself (which was named after her soon after). Several other archaeological sites from the Koobi Fora formation revealed what are described as *"occupation sites"* or *"living sites."*[89,90] Hundreds of butchered bones and stone tools were found dating to nearly 2 million years old (originally 2.6 million years old).[91] The bones show evidence of hammer stone fractures and slice marks described as *"indistinguishable from experimentally induced cut marks."*[92] The slice marks were in *"prime locations"* for dismembering carcasses to detach meat for consumption.

The locations containing a wealth of stone tools and butchered bones are best thought of as communal centers, typical of semi-nomadic hunter-gatherer groups. Henry Bunn, paleo-expert specializing in taphonomy, reported in *Nature* (1981), *"The documentation of meat-eating and the concentration of bones at particular places by early hominids lends strong support to the food-sharing model..."*[93] Bunn writes in his *Nature* paper that some of the butchered bones were found near the shoreline, 6-10 miles away from the closest source rock from which the stone tools were presumably made from. Just like the findings at Olduvai, this level of foresight and planning clearly shows the toolmakers at Koobi Fora were Erectus/*H. sapiens*. The lifestyle and abilities reflected at Koobi Fora are undoubtedly human. One could reasonably infer that the toolmakers at those same sites must also be undoubtedly human. But common sense does not always prevail in fields of science that are strongly ideologically driven.

Richard Leakey learned from his father's error over a decade earlier, when the latter mistakenly attributed the stone tools at Olduvai to the robust australopiths ("Zinj" or *Au. boisei*). Richard knew better than to associate the stone tools with the Zinj-like skulls he found at Ileret.[94] He recounts, *"These [Olduvai-looking] implements, to my mind, show a degree of sophistication which implies that our*

88. Leakey M.D., Early Artefacts from the Koobi Fora Area, *Nature* 226:228-230, 1970.
89. Day M.H., *Guide to Fossil Man*, University of Chicago Press, Chicago, p. 197, 1986.
90. Leakey R. and Lewin R., *Origins Reconsidered: In search of what makes us human*, Anchor Books (Double-day), New York, 375 pp., 1992.
91. Bunn H.T., Archaeological evidence for meat-eating by Pliocene hominids from Koobi Fora and Olduvai Gorge, *Nature* 291:574-577, 1981.
92. Bunn H.T., Archaeological evidence for meat-eating by Pliocene hominids from Koobi Fora and Olduvai Gorge, *Nature* 291:574-577, 1981.
93. Bunn H.T., Archaeological evidence for meat-eating by Pliocene hominids from Koobi Fora and Olduvai Gorge, *Nature* 291:574-577, 1981.
94. Leakey R.E.F., New Hominid Remains and Early Artifacts from Northern Kenya, *Nature* 226:223-224, 1970. *"In view of the generally accepted opinion that A. boisei was not a toolmaker, the discovery of artefacts in the Koobi Fora deposits adds support to the evidence from the fossil material that there were two different representatives of hominids in the area we investigated."*

ancestors began making tools well before [1.8 million years ago]."[95] Richard was sure the toolmakers at Koobi Fora were mentally superior to any australopith, and so he insisted that members of our own genus *Homo* must have made the sophisticated stone tools. In light of several Erectus specimens found in the region that date close to 2 million years old, it seems obvious that the real toolmakers at Koobi Fora were Erectus/*H. sapiens*. Yet this is not what Richard concluded. Perhaps this is because there was not yet any identifiable Erectus material found in the deeper strata or because *Homo* bones were not found below the KBS Tuff until a few field seasons later in 1972.[96] Or perhaps Richard's reluctance to attribute the stone tools to Erectus was because of his conviction, shared with his father and mother: "*I feel confident that one day we will be able to follow man's fossil trail at East Rudolf* [Turkana] *back as far as four million years. There, perhaps we will find evidence of a common ancestor for Australopithecus—near-man—and the genus Homo, true man.*"[97] He believed the toolmaker was a pre-Erectus species of *Homo* that had not yet been found or fully described—a species whose bones would later be identified as the hotly contested taxon *Homo rudolfensis*.[98]

The paleo-community's strategic decision to assign a younger date to the KBS Tuff hindered Richard from advancing the model of man coexisting with Lucy and her kind. The stone tools and australopithecine specimens he and his team found were dated to at least the age of the KBS Tuff, which at that time was dated as 2.6 million years old (older than any Erectus bones found).[99] The stone tools were considered the oldest artifacts ever found—an uncomfortable finding for many experts in the field. Not long after the stone tools were found, one of Richard's field members found a human-looking skull. Richard concluded that the *Homo* genus was more than 2 million years old. That skull was infamously known as "1470."[100]

The enigmatic skull, KNM-ER 1470 had an estimated cranial capacity of about 800 cm^3. This is significantly larger than any known australopith.[101,102] Leakey

95. Leakey R.E., In Search of Man's Past, *National Geographic*, May 1970, pp. 724. (see Roger Lewin, *Bones of Contention*, The University of Chicago Press, Chicago, p. 156, 2nd edition, 1997.).

96. Day M., *Guide to Fossil Man*, University of Chicago Press, Chicago, 1986. See p. 213 for list of Koobi Fora specimens and their date of discovery. A jawbone attributed to *Homo* (KNM-ER 820) was discovered in 1971 from Ileret, Kenya.

97. Leakey R.E., Skull 1470, *National Geographic*, pp. 819-829, p. 829, June 1973. See also: Leakey L.S.B., *Homo habilis, Homo erectus*, and the australopithecines, *Nature* 209:1279–1281, 1966. DOI: 10.1038/2091279a0

98. Wood B. and Collard M., The Human Genus, *Science* 284(5411):65-71, 1999. "*H. rudolfensis was not used until the 1990s, when it was suggested that part of the H. habilis sensu lato hypodigm should be recognized as a separate species.*"

99. Fitch F.J. and Miller J.A., Radioisotopic Age Determinations of Lake Rudolf Artefact Site, *Nature* 226:226-228, 1970.

100. Leakey R., Evidence for an Advanced Plio-Pleistocene Hominid from East Rudolf, Kenya, *Nature* 242:447-450, 1973.

101. Leakey R., Evidence for an Advanced Plio-Pleistocene Hominid from East Rudolf, Kenya, *Nature* 242:447-450, 1973.

102. Leakey R.E., M.G. Leakey, A.K. Behrensmeyer, The Fossil Hominids and an Introduction to Their Context, 1968-1974, In: Leakey M.G. and Leakey R.E., Eds, *Koobi Fora Research Project, Vol. 1: The Fossil Hominids and an Introduction to their Context 1968-1974*, Clarendon Press, Oxford, 86-182, 1978.

further noted that the specimen lacked a nuchal crest and other powerful muscle attachments typical of australopiths.[103] The shape of the skull was globular, and resembled members of our own genus *Homo*. Endocast scans of the interior surface of the skull further revealed Broca's speech area—a region of the brain only found in humans.[104,105] The skull was found well below the KBS Tuff, dating close to 3 million years old. To many in the field, it was far too old to be human, and sparked the "KBS Tuff controversy." Paleo-experts were determined to prove that the stone tools and *Homo*-looking skull could not possibly be as old as the potassium-argon dates of the tuff. At a symposium held in 1973 at Nairobi, paleo-experts compared all the hominin fossils from the Turkana basin region. Meave Leakey *et al.* later described how leading paleo-experts at the symposium felt about Richard's findings:

> ... the 2.6 Ma date attributed to the KBS Tuff was controversial. If the date was accurate, stone artifacts from the KBS Tuff were the oldest known to science and the hominid fossils from below that tuff included the oldest representatives of the genus *Homo*.[106]

These findings blatantly conflicted with the "group think" of the paleo-community, and so the KBS Tuff was re-dated many, many times until (with the help of pig's teeth) a more "comfortable" age of 1.8 million years was finally accepted[107] (see chapter 12).

Specimen 1470 is not the only finding from below the KBS Tuff that was described as being human. A set of anatomically modern leg bones (KNM-ER 1472, 1475, and 1481) were also found during the 1972 field season by paleo-expert John Harris, who was working alongside Richard and the Lake Turkana team. The most complete set of bones is 1481, which preserves a nearly intact left femur and an incomplete left tibia. Specimen 1472 consists of a right femur and was described as sharing some features with the better-preserved 1481 femur. Specimen 1475 is another fragmentary femur which displays features *"which are not seen in the femurs of Australopithecus."*[108] In Richard's assessment of the anatomy of the leg bones, they align best with Erectus/*Homo sapiens*. He reports, *"The postcranial elements cannot readily be distinguished from H. sapiens if one considers the range of variation known for this species."*[109] Bernard Wood agrees, and observes that the

103. Leakey R., Evidence for an Advanced Plio-Pleistocene Hominid from East Rudolf, Kenya, *Nature* 242:447-450, 1973.

104. Dean Falk, Cerebral cortices of East African early hominids, *Science* 221, 1072-74, 1983.

105. Tobias P.V., The brain organization of *Homo habilis*: A new level of organization in cerebral evolution, *J Hum Evol* 16(7-8):741-761, 1987.

106. Harris J.M., Leakey M.G., *et al.*, A Brief History of Research at Koobi Fora, Northern Kenya, *Ethnohistory* 53:35-69, 2006. DOI: 10.1215/00141801-53-1-35

107. Drake R.E., Curtis G.H. *et al.*, KBS Tuff dating and geochronology of tuffaceous sediments in the Koobi Fora and Shungura Formations, East Africa, *Nature* 283:368-372, 1980.

108. Leakey R., Evidence for an Advanced Plio-Pleistocene Hominid from East Rudolf, Kenya, *Nature* 242:447-450, April 1973.

109. Leakey R., Evidence for an Advanced Plio-Pleistocene Hominid from East Rudolf, Kenya, *Nature* 242:447-450, April 1973.

leg bones (1472 and 1481) indicate *"modern human walking."*[110] Richard reported these findings in *Nature* stating, *"The suggestion that a large brained, fully bipedal hominid was living in East Rudolf 3 million years ago was put forward after the 1972 discoveries"*[111]—referring to skull 1470 and associated leg bones and other *Homo* material recovered from below the KBS Tuff.

Erectus bones were also been found in younger strata, including a human jawbone (KNM-ER 992), discovered by Richard in 1971. It later became the defining specimen of the African form of Erectus (*H. ergaster*). Other Erectus skulls, (such as KNM-ER 3733, with a cranial capacity of 800–900 cm³) were found in the region. Richard reported in *Nature* (1976) that the Koobi Fora findings confirm the "unequivocal occurrence" of *Homo* (i.e., Erectus) together with *Australopithecus* in East Turkana (Figure 4), stating:

> The radioisotopic dating of these tuffs, in spite of a continuing controversy over them, is not an issue here. The contemporaneity of *Homo erectus* and a robust *Australopithecus* is now clearly established over the period during which the Upper Member of the Koobi Fora Formation was deposited [between the KBS and the Koobi Fora/BBS tuff complexes]... 1.3 to earlier than 1.6 Myr ago.[112]

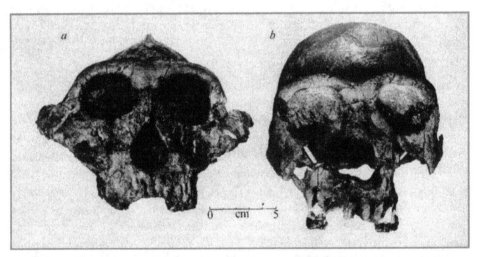

Figure 4. KNM-ER 3733 pictured right is attributed to Erectus. It was found *in situ* in the same bed (Upper Member) of the Koobi Fora Formation as the robust australopithecine skull KNM-ER 406 (left). Note: the interior of 3733 is illuminated (not shadowed). Image from Leakey and Walker, *Nature*, 261:572-574, 1976.

Let's summarize the significance of the findings from the Koobi Fora Research Project. In the 1970s Richard Leakey and his famous "Hominid Gang" found hundreds of hominin bones and artifacts in the Koobi Fora formation of northern

110. Coppens Y., Howell F.C., Isaacs G.I., and Leakey R.E. (eds.), *Remains Attributed to Homo in East Rudolf Succession, Earliest Man and Environments in the Lake Rudolf Basin*, University of Chicago Press, Chicago, p. 502, 1976.
111. Leakey R., Further Evidence of Lower Pleistocene Hominids from East Rudolf, North Kenya, *Nature* 248:653-656, 1973.
112. Leakey R., *Australopithecus, Homo erectus*, and the single species hypothesis, *Nature* 261:572-574, 1976.

Kenya. These findings consisted of a diversity of stone tools, butchered bones, human-like skulls, human jawbones, and human leg bones. These were buried above, below, and within the KBS Tuff, alongside *Australopithecus*. There can be no doubt that the artifacts were made by humans, whose remains were found in the same formation within so-called "living sites." Thus the Turkana basin—the "continental keystone" of paleo-research—clearly reveals the extensive coexistence of two separate genera (*Australopithecus* and Erectus/*H. sapiens*). As with Olduvai Gorge, Tanzania—no australopith-to-man progression can be seen at the famous Koobi Fora formation of northern Kenya. Richard Leakey himself acknowledged this when describing his team's findings in *Nature*:

> There seems no evidence, however, that the genus *Homo* at Rudolf had any direct relationship to the australopithecine population of the same time and with which it shared its habitat. The concept of the gracile australopithecine being ancestral to *Homo* in the Lower Pleistocene requires careful reexamination... The Rudolf [Lake Turkana] material seems to confirm the view developed as a result of work at Olduvai... that *Homo* and *Australopithecus* are two quite separate and distinct early Pleistocene hominids.[113]

Today it is undisputed in the paleo-community that Erectus existed nearly 2 million years ago in East Turkana. Several Erectus bones, including some more recent discoveries, have been found in the Koobi Fora deposits. Most notably, in 1984 the nearly complete "Turkana Boy" skeleton was found on the western shore of Lake Turkana. The authors of this book propose that the real toolmakers at Koobi Fora were Erectus/*H. sapiens*—just as at Olduvai Gorge, Tanzania.

The dates of these bones are contested, but regardless of dates these findings indicate that Erectus/*H. sapiens* coexisted extensively with those australopithecines that would otherwise be presumed to be our ancestors.

Latest Findings Confirm Coexistence of Australopith and Man in Kenya

New discoveries continue to confirm extensive coexistence far deeper into the geologic record. For instance, in a *Nature* publication in 2015, researchers reported the discovery of 3.3 million-year-old stone tools from the Lomekwi site in Kenya. Prior to this discovery the oldest stone tools had been dated to 2.6 million years ago, coinciding with the earliest accepted fossil evidence for man.[114] Evolutionary paleo-experts have consistently associated stone tool-making abilities with the origin of the genus *Homo*. The level of sophistication required to manufacture stone tools of the Oldowan type (flaking with a hammerstone) has always been understood to exceed the cognitive abilities of the australopithecine brains. As *Nature* science writer Ewen Callaway explains, *"Chimpanzees and other non-human*

---

113. Leakey R., Further Evidence of Lower Pleistocene Hominids from East Rudolf, North Kenya, *Nature* 231:241-245, 1971.
114. Semaw S. *et al.*, 2.6-Million-year-old stone tools and associated bones from OGS-6 and OGS-7, Gona, Afar, Ethiopia, *J Hum Evol* 45(2):169–177, 2003.

primates use stones to crack nuts, for instance, but their tools lack the craftsmanship of the Oldowan toolmakers, who would strike one rock against another, breaking off flakes to leave a sharp-edged stone core."[115] Paleoanthropologists Ian Tattersall and Jeffrey Schwartz agree that the level of intelligence required to produce stone tools greatly exceeds that of apes:

> Apes have trouble making stone tools, as experiments with a young bonobo called Kanzi have shown. … archaeologists Nick Toth and Kathy Schick conscripted him as a student of stone toolmaking, and frankly didn't get very far even after intensive coaching. To obtain a sharp flake you first have to choose a cobble of the right type, and then you have to hit this core with your hammerstone hard, and at precisely the right angle. It takes a fair bit of cognitive sophistication to figure all this out, and even after repeated demonstrations over many months, Kanzi never really got the idea. … early stone toolmaking was not simply an opportunist process, carried out as necessity demanded. The Oldowan toolmakers not only knew how to identify the kinds of stone that would produce sharp flakes when struck, but they also anticipated needing those flakes, and carried cobbles of the appropriate kind quite long distances before making them into tools as required. Such planning and foresight goes well beyond anything yet observed or inferred among living apes, even those that use rudimentary tools (stones for cracking nuts, twigs for "fishing" termites, etc).[116]

Since australopiths could not have made the stone tools (nor the slice marks on bones from Dikika, Ethiopia) that are dated to the time of Lucy, there is obviously a problem.[117] Paleo-experts are faced with a dilemma. They know they can't accept the coexistence of early Afarensis and man because that would falsify ape-to-man evolution. Yet the alternative is just as incredible—ape-like creatures making sophisticated stone tools.

A remarkable new discovery in the town of Ileret, Kenya, within the Koobi Fora formation, has revealed 97 fossilized footprints produced by at least 20 different individuals. The trackways were found between 2007 and 2014. The footprints were from five different sites within a mile of each other. They were preserved in different stratigraphical levels. They were not all on the same continuous surface like the footprints at Laetoli, Tanzania. The researchers state in their *Nature* (2016) paper that a number of the measured Ileret footprints are *"statistically indistinguishable from those of modern humans"* and *"provide the first direct fossil evidence of a human-like pattern of external foot motion in H. erectus, and a bipedal gait that mirrored what is seen in humans today."*[118] In their study they compared the preserved footprints to those of local indigenous people. These authors found that *"The Ileret footprints are generally comparable in size (length and breadth) to those of footprints produced in the same substrate by habitually barefoot Daasanach people*

115. Callaway E., Oldest stone tools raise questions about their creators, *Nature* 520:421, 2015.
116. Tattersall I. and Schwartz J., *Extinct Humans*, Westview Press, New York, p. 120, 2000.
117. http://www.livescience.com/50908-oldest-stone-tools-predate-humans.html
118. Hatala K.G. *et al.*, Footprints reveal direct evidence of group behavior and locomotion of *Homo erectus*, *Nature: Scientific Reports* 28766:1-9, 2016.

living near Ileret today." They further state that the parallel hominin trackways suggest the group traveled together, reflecting *"human-like social behaviors"* and cooperation. Everything about the footprints suggests anatomically modern humans formed them, just as we saw with the Laetoli footprints (see chapter 7).

The researchers made some additional noteworthy observations in their paper. The footprints were said to *"preserve fine detail, indicating that they were rapidly hardened and covered with sediment."* They explain further:

> Multiple lines of geological, sedimentary, and taphonomic evidence suggest that the hominin tracks on any of the Ileret footprint surfaces were formed and buried within the same day, perhaps within a few hours. First, many of the Ileret fossil tracks and trackways show similarly fine-detailed preservation states, and track surfaces lack evidence of soil development or root traces. The depositional context and the lack of mud cracks on any of the footprint layers suggest that these sites were rapidly buried by fine or silty sand before any drying occurred.[119]

All of the footprints were found within a single geologic formation, what is known as the "Ileret tuff complex." This is the same site where Richard Leakey discovered the Zinj-like skull from his early expedition to East Turkana in 1969. It is also where Erectus bones have been found such as the recently discovered partial upper jawbone (KNM-ER 42703) and skull (KNM-ER 42700) cited earlier.[120] Now paleo-experts are finding footprints in the same area dating to roughly the same age (1.5 million years ago) of Erectus. The Ileret formation is another example showing the coexistence of *Australopithecus* and Erectus/*H. sapiens* in the same habitat.

Here again we are not seeing an australopith-to-man progression—rather we are seeing extensive coexistence of two distinct forms (*Homo* and *Australopithecus*), which is in keeping with our alternative model (see chapter 14).

Conclusions—Implications of Extensive Coexistence

The 1970s are described by paleo-experts as the "Golden Age" of paleo-research. Prior to the excavations at key sites in Tanzania, Kenya, and Ethiopia, there really wasn't much of a hominin fossil record. However, the "science" of paleoanthropology was established with the explosion of fossil discoveries that took place during the 60s and especially the 70s. It was in east Africa that the australopith-to-man story was formulated based on archeological and paleontological records. It is from that era in history and upon that framework that the modern theory was built. With that in mind those key East African sites described in this chapter can be seen as "Holy Ground"—and it is at those sites where excavations are continuing to shape and revise the modern theory. Yet it is ironic that at those key sites, no ape-to-man progression can be seen. Instead, we have a rich record of human

---

119. Hatala K.G. *et al.*, Footprints reveal direct evidence of group behavior and locomotion of *Homo erectus*, *Nature: Scientific Reports* 28766:1-9, 2016.
120. Spoor F., Leakey M.G. *et al.*, Implication of new early *Homo* fossils from Ileret, east of Lake Turkana, Kenya, *Nature* 448:688-691, 2007.

bones, human artifacts, and butchered bones of all kinds of different species. This is unequivocal evidence of behavior and lifestyles that can only be described as human. Moreover, within these so-called "living sites" or "occupation sites" are the bones of *Australopithecus*. The extensive coexistence of *Australopithecus* and Erectus/*H. sapiens* at the most famous sites of paleoanthropological research—Tanzania, Ethiopia, and Kenya—casts strong doubt on the australopith-to-man story, as some paleo-experts freely confess.

Almost all of the famous hominin sites indicate the extensive coexistence of hominin species claimed to have ancestor/descendant relationships (Figure 5). How can the ape-to-man story account for modern-looking human bones, human footprints, and human artifacts coexisting with Lucy? After 150 years of collecting and studying hominin fossils, what we actually see is that humans have always coexisted with diverse forms of ape types, including the extinct australopiths. Unfortunately, when human bones are found too early in the fossil record, such bones are either reclassified (i.e., Mary Leakey's *Homo* bones and footprints); or re-dated (Richard Leakey's 1470 skull and stone tools); or are ignored ("Oldoway Man" from Olduvai Gorge).

**Latest Developments

In late 2017 new findings of anatomically modern human-looking footprints from Trachilos in western Crete were reported in *Proceedings of the Geologists' Association*.[121] We had concluded just prior to this discovery that the earliest known occurrence of human fossils are the 3.7 million-year-old Laetoli footprints (see chapter 7 and 11). However, the new findings from Crete suggest *Homo sapiens*/Erectus lived at least 5.7 million years ago—significantly predating the earliest australopiths. This would require the paleo-community to abandon hominins such as Lucy and Ardi as our ancestor, because humans were apparently already around long before their time (cladogenesis cannot be invoked). To preserve the theory paleo-experts would essentially have to start from scratch, and find the bones of a much older common ancestor to *Homo* and *Australopithecus*, just as Richard Leakey had insisted decades ago: *"...I would expect that the genus Homo will eventually be traced into the Pliocene at an age of between 4 and 6 million years, together with Australopithecus."*[122] Charles Oxnard, an expert on australopithecine fossils, has recently made a compatible observation that seems to be a fulfillment of Richard Leakey's prediction: *"There are now many more fossils more similar to humans and older than australopithecines than are any of the australopithecines themselves. Hence A* [australopithecines, including Lucy's kind are] *not on a direct line to humans."*[123] The Trachilos footprints appear to be the latest confirmation of the extensive coexistence of australopith and man. These findings, as well as many

121. Gierlinski G.D. *et al.*, Possible hominin footprints from the late Miocene (c. 5.7 Ma) of Crete? *Proceedings of the Geologists' Association*, 621:1-14, 2017. DOI: 10.1016/j.pgeola.2017.07.006
122. Leakey R.E., Hominids in Africa, *American Scientist*, 64(2):174-178, 1976.
123. Personal communication, 2016.

other findings cited in Figure 5 (next page), appear to falsify the ape-to-man story that has been advocated from the 70s to the present.

The Problem of Extensive Coexistence of Ancestor/Descendant Species

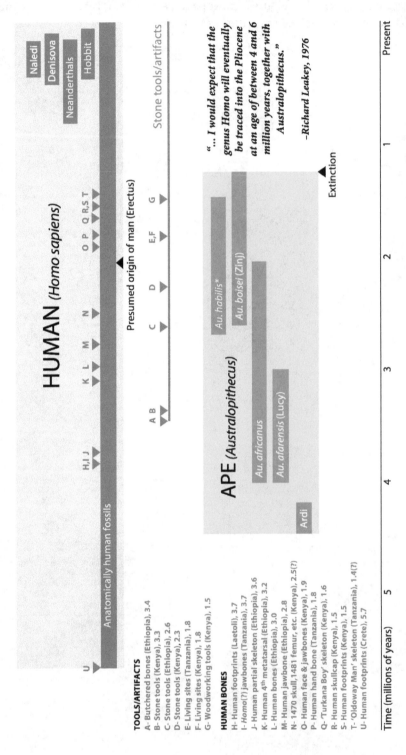

HUMAN *(Homo sapiens)*

Naledi
Denisova
Neanderthals
Hobbit

Stone tools/artifacts

Presumed origin of man (Erectus)

Anatomically human fossils

U

H,I,J   K L M   N   O P   Q R,S T

A B   C   D   E,F   G

APE *(Australopithecus)*

Au. habilis*
Au. boisei (Zinj)

Au. africanus

Au. afarensis (Lucy)

Ardi

Extinction

" ... I would expect that the genus Homo will eventually be traced into the Pliocene at an age of between 4 and 6 million years, together with Australopithecus."

–Richard Leakey, 1976

TOOLS/ARTIFACTS

A- Butchered bones (Ethiopia), 3.4
B- Stone tools (Kenya), 3.3
C- Stone tools (Ethiopia), 2.6
D- Stone tools (Kenya), 2.3
E- Living sites (Tanzania), 1.8
F- Living sites (Kenya), 1.8
G- Woodworking tools (Kenya), 1.5

HUMAN BONES

H- Human footprints (Laetoli), 3.7
I- *Homo*(?) jawbones (Tanzania), 3.7
J- Human partial skeleton (Ethiopia), 3.6
K- Human 4th metatarsal (Ethiopia), 3.2
L- Human bones (Ethiopia), 3.0
M- Human jawbone (Ethiopia), 2.8
N- 1470 skull, 1481 femur, etc. (Kenya), 2.5(?)
O- Human face & jawbones (Kenya), 1.9
P- Human hand bone (Tanzania), 1.8
Q- 'Turkana Boy' skeleton (Kenya), 1.6
R- Human skullcap (Kenya), 1.5
S- Human footprints (Kenya), 1.5
T- 'Oldoway Man' skeleton (Tanzania), 1.4(?)
U- Human footprints (Crete), 5.7

| Time (millions of years) | 5 | 4 | 3 | 2 | 1 | Present |

Figure 5. The diagram (previous page) reveals the extensive coexistence of *Australopithecus* and *Homo*, assuming conventionally assigned dates. The enduring coexistence of these two genera confounds their presumed ancestor/descendant relationship. Anatomically modern bones indistinguishable from *H. sapiens*, modern human-looking footprints, sophisticated stone tools, and butchered bones have all been found dating to the time of Lucy's kind, Afarensis (3–4 million years ago). Here cladogenesis cannot be invoked. Such findings falsify the ape-to-man story. The extensive coexistence of these two genera strongly supports our alternative model—humans have always lived alongside the australopiths (they were apparently part of their hunter-gatherer diet) until the time of their extinction. *An *Australopithecus* designation of Habilis is consistent with an earlier assessment by Wood (2003), among others who have noted its australopith-like body plan.

References

Stone Tools/Artifacts
A. McPherron S. *et al.*, *Nature*, 2010.
B. Harmand S. *et al.*, *Nature*, 2015.
C. Semaw S. *et al.*, *J Hum Evol*, 2003.
D. Roche H. *et al.*, *Nature*, 1999.
E. Leakey M., *Olduvai Gorge*, 1979.
F. Leakey M., *Nature*, 1970.
G. Dominguez-Rodrigo M. *et al.*, *J Hum Evo*, 2001.

Human Bones
H. Leakey M. *et al.*, *Nature*, 1979.
I. Leakey M. *et al.*, *Nature*, 1976.
J. Haile-Selassie Y. *et al.*, *Proc Natl Acad Sci*, 2010.
K. Ward C., *et al.*, *Science*, 2011.
L. Johanson D. *et al.*, *Nature*, 1976.
M. Villmoare B. *et al.*, *Science*, 2015.
N. Leakey R., *Nature*, 1973.
O. Leakey Meave *et al.*, *Nature*, 2012.
P. Domínguez-Rodrigo M. *et al.*, *Nature*, 2015.
Q. Leakey L. *et al.*, *Nature*, 1933.
R. Brown F. *et al.*, *Nature*, 1985.
S. Spoor F., Leakey M.G., *Nature*, 2007.
T. Hatala K. *et al.*, *Scientific Reports*, 2015.
U. Gierlinski G. *et al.*, *Proc Geol Assoc*, 2017.

CHAPTER 12

Dating Methods
Do We Really Know How Old Bones Are?

Sounds like faith, not science, doesn't it?[1]

Late Paleoanthropologist Clark Howell of the University of California Berkeley

How Are Hominin Bones Dated?

Paleoanthropologists have at their disposal multiple dating methods that are commonly used to date hominins. Some dating methods are used to determine the age of the bones themselves. To do this, they would use carbon-14, luminescence techniques, and DNA analysis. However, most methods do not actually date the hominin bones themselves, but attempt to date things associated with the bones (such as artifacts, rocks, ash layers, flowstones, etc.). These things may be dated using potassium-argon/argon-argon isotopes, uranium-series isotopes, paleomagnetic analysis, and biostratigraphy. Each technique has its own problems, as summarized below.

The potassium-argon radioisotope dating method was the primary method used to establish the current hominin timeframe. In the 1960s groundbreaking paleoanthropological research was conducted at Olduvai Gorge, Tanzania. Lava flows that were inter-bedding the outcrop at Olduvai Gorge were potassium-argon dated. A decade later, additional fossils were discovered in the Hadar region of Ethiopia and in Laetoli, Tanzania. At both locations there were neighboring layers of volcanic ash (ash "tuffs"), which were dated using potassium-argon, and later the related argon-argon method. Many other key hominin sites, and the majority of major hominin species, in Africa, Europe, and Asia have been dated using the potassium-argon or argon-argon method. Since the potassium-argon method has played such a foundational role in establishing the currently accepted hominin timeline, it will be the main focus of this chapter. Other dating methods have been calibrated to conform to the potassium-argon-based hominin timeline. Contrary to common thought, the hominin dating methods are not truly independent

---

1. Lewin R., *Bones of Contention*, University of Chicago Press, Chicago, p. 226, 1987. Howell made this comment during the Geological Society of London in 1975, in the midst of the famous KBS Tuff controversy.

dating methods—there is a great deal of cross-calibration and data adjustments aimed at harmonizing conflicting dates.

Paleo-experts often use more than one method to date the same hominin site. In theory, the different methods should consistently agree, especially since they are often cross-calibrated. However, as we will show, these methods routinely yield conflicting ages. Those dates that do not agree with the expected or desired age of a particular hominin species are very often discarded. This may sometimes be justified due to contamination, poor samples, resetting events, etc. However, when a date is assigned to a hominin based on a given method, and later it is decided that that date is problematic for the ape-to-man narrative, the very same bones will be re-dated using various alternative methods. After many trials, a bone will be assigned a date that fits the paradigm. Selectively using dates that seem most compatible with the hominin timescale, while rejecting dates that do not agree, can lock a field into incorrect understanding. Selective use of data, whether it is deliberate or passive, is bad science. Selective use of data is a common snare and temptation for all scientists.

The Difference Between Precision and Accuracy

Throughout this book we have referenced the standard evolutionary timescale (e.g., —"Lucy lived 3.2 million years ago."). Outside the field of paleoanthropology it is generally assumed that the various dating methods used to date hominin fossils are extremely reliable. Few people realize that there are many problems with these dating methods, as is acknowledged in the technical scientific literature. The truth is, the popular dating methods routinely produce conflicting dates. Behind the very sophisticated technologies that are used to date samples, are many layers of questionable assumptions. Such underlying assumptions are rarely discussed when a date is published. The resulting dates are typically accepted as valid without reservation. Dates that are assigned to specific fossils are often reported with a very small margin of error. This gives the impression that since precise physical measurements are possible—therefore those measurements translate into equally precise dates. In reality, those small margins of errors are misleading. The sophisticated dating instruments are capable of providing extremely *precise* measurements. They tell us precisely about the exact nature of the specimen (i.e., isotopic composition)—but not its age. Precision is not the same as *accuracy*. It is possible to be precise but not accurate. Consider a rifle that is not properly sighted in. The resulting hits on a target can be tightly clustered (consistent, controlled, precise) yet still they may all completely miss the bullseye (inaccurate). The same is true of dating methods. Physically precise measurements taken in the present do not automatically translate into correct dating of past events.

The Difference Between "Relative Age" and "Absolute Age"

There is an important distinction to make between a "relative age" and an "absolute age." The hominin timescale was established based on the relative age of stratigraphical sequences, which can be correlated based on similar sedimentary characteristics or similar types of fossils and artifacts found within them. This is based on the law of superposition (youngest sequences at the top and oldest at the bottom). Making certain questionable assumptions, it is possible to use index fossils or similar artifacts to determine whether separate sequences are roughly equivalent to each other in age. One can then reasonably infer the relative age of surrounding strata beside, above, or below it. Yet to determine an absolute age— meaning the actual age of those sequences—a rock sample must be collected that can be directly dated (using potassium-argon, argon-argon, fission track, etc.). So the absolute age (for example, 1.8 million years old plus or minus 0.25 million years) is determined separately by radioisotope dating methods. Thus it is entirely feasible to accurately correlate stratigraphical sequences using relative dating methods (such as faunal correlations or paleomagnetic reversals) yet still obtain an absolute age (a radioisotope age) that is absolutely wrong. On a case-by-case basis, we can trust the stratigraphical methods used to obtain relative ages, even while we question the underlying assumptions of absolute radioisotope dating.

How Does Radioisotope Dating Work?

There are at least three variables that must be known in order to date ash, rocks, or bones using radioactive dating methods like carbon-14, or potassium-argon/argon-argon. These are: 1) initial quantity of radioactive atoms; 2) the quantity of daughter atoms derived from the decay of their radioactive parent atoms; and 3) the decay rate. The decay rate is measured by the half-life, which is the time it takes for half of any given amount of radioactive atoms to decay into daughter atoms.

An hourglass is a simple way to illustrate the radioactive decay process. Imagine the sand in the top chamber represents initial radioactive atoms. These may be called "parent atoms." The sand in the bottom chamber represents stable atoms called "daughter atoms." The rate that sand trickles down represents the decay rate. In an hourglass, the time it takes for half of the "parent atoms" (sand particles) to "decay" into the daughter atoms is half an hour. Radioisotope dating methods such as potassium-argon works similarly to an hourglass. The quantity of both the radioactive parent atoms (potassium-40) and the quantity of stable daughter atoms (argon-40) in a given sample is measured using an accelerator mass spectrometer (AMS) instrument. The half-life of radioactive potassium-40 is already known. The time it takes for half of the potassium-40 to decay into argon-40 is 1.251×10^9 years, based on today's measured rate. Together these three variables can be used to calculate the age of a sample—given certain critical assumptions.

All Dating Methods Critically Depend on Assumptions

All dating methods are only as reliable as the assumptions upon which they are built. To the extent that the underlying assumptions are routinely correct, the dating method can be trusted. However, if any of those assumptions are routinely violated, the dating method cannot be trusted. To be clear, we do not doubt the precision of the instruments used to measure the isotopic composition of samples being dated. The instruments that are used to quantify atoms (for example, an AMS) are extremely precise. That is undisputed. What can be disputed is the interpretation of the resulting measurements—what do those measurements mean in terms of the timing of past events? The interpretations of those measurements critically depend on a series of assumptions. If any of the underlying assumptions are not correct, the dating techniques cannot give a reliable age.

The radioisotope dating methods commonly used to date hominins (i.e., carbon-14, uranium-series, potassium-argon, and argon-argon) all rely on the following three critical assumptions:

1) **Initial Conditions:** No daughter atoms or decay products were initially present in the system.

2) **Closed System:** Parent and daughter atoms cannot enter or leave the system. All daughter atoms measured must be derived from the *in situ* radioactive decay of the parent atoms.

3) **Constant Decay Rate:** The rate at which parent atoms decay into daughter atoms (the half-life) must have been constant in the past, and the same as today's measured rate.

The hourglass analogy may be useful for understanding the nature of these three assumptions. For assumption 1, the initial amount of sand in the upper and lower portions of the hourglass must be known in order to determine how much time has elapsed. But imagine if no one was present when the hourglass was turned over (just like no one was there long ago when the rocks surrounding hominin sites formed). What if some sand was already in the lower chamber? In that situation, it would appear as though more time had passed than actually did.

For assumption 2, it is assumed that the hourglass is completely shielded from external influences. But suppose in your absence someone came in and added and/or removed sand grains from the top and/or bottom of the hourglass. The hourglass could no longer be considered an accurate indicator of elapsed time.

For assumption 3, suppose someone came into the room at an unknown point in time and sped up the rate at which the sand fell into the bottom chamber by widening the neck of the hourglass. If one assumed the rate of flow (decay rate) had remained constant in the past, they would have wrongly concluded that a full hour had passed when the actual elapsed time was much shorter.

Some may be surprised to learn that there is a large body of evidence from the peer-reviewed scientific literature that calls all three of these assumptions into question. In this chapter we will be focusing on the first two assumptions, which are especially relevant to the potassium-argon and uranium-series dating methods, the ones most commonly used to date hominin sites.

Potassium-Argon/Argon-Argon Dating

The volcanic rocks and ash layers used to date hominin bones are said to have formed millions of years ago. However, there were no eyewitnesses or other records to verify what the initial conditions of the system were. No scientists were there to measure the quantity of parent and daughter atoms when the rocks/ash formed. Consequently, it can only be assumed that no daughter atoms were present when the rock last crystallized (assumption 1). It is further assumed that all daughter atoms measured today derived from the *in situ* radioactive decay of parent atoms (assumption 2). Yet there are certain physical processes that can incorporate external daughter atoms into the system to yield exaggerated ages. In other cases, excess daughter atoms may not be effectively eliminated from the lava prior to crystallization, again resulting in samples that date significantly older than their true age. The potassium-argon dating method is especially prone to these types of error.

The potassium-argon dating method is commonly used to estimate the age of igneous material (granite, basalt, and ash) that forms from molten lava. The "clock" starts ticking when the igneous material cools and crystallizes. The radioactive parent isotope (potassium-40) becomes trapped inside mineral crystals, and begins to decay into daughter atoms (argon-40). Prior to crystallization, it is assumed that all of the gaseous daughter isotope escapes from the lava. Geochronologists understand this is essential in order to accurately date rocks or ash using the potassium-argon method:

> The K-Ar method is the only decay scheme that can be used with little or no concern for the initial presence of the daughter isotope. This is because ^{40}Ar is an inert gas that does not combine chemically with any other element and so escapes easily from rocks when they are heated. Thus, while a rock is molten, the ^{40}Ar formed by the decay of ^{40}K escapes from the liquid.[2]

In theory the complete degassing of argon should leave only the parent atoms within the newly formed rock. On this basis, it is assumed that all of the daughter atoms measured in rock samples are the "direct descendants" of those initial parent isotopes. However, if there is even a trace of excess argon trapped in the crystals, a sample can yield a date that is much older than its true age. This raises a critical question: how do we know that all the excess argon is effectively removed from the system (outgassing) before the lava solidifies? Since we do not have direct access to the past (no one was present to measure the initial isotopic concentrations), there is only one sure way to test the validity of this critical assumption—by dating rocks

2. Dalrymple G.B., *The Age of the Earth*, Stanford University Press, Stanford, CA, p. 91, 1991.

of known age which formed in recorded history. Numerous studies published in the peer-reviewed scientific literature have done that and the results are surprising.

A noteworthy example is Mount Ngauruhoe in New Zealand (Mount Doom in *Lord of the Rings* movies). A series of known lava flows occurred in the 1950s and again in the 1970s with no further eruptions since 1975. In January 1996, 11 whole rock samples from 5 lava flows were collected. Care was taken to ensure each lava flow was correctly identified.[3] The samples were prepared and sent to the respected Geochron Laboratories in Cambridge, Massachusetts for whole-rock potassium-argon dating. The lab did not know the origin or expected age. However, the laboratory technicians were cautioned that the sample may have contained "low argon" (potentially yielding a young age), to encourage careful analytical work. Given that we know when the rocks formed (because we know when the eruptions occurred) the potassium-argon dating should have yielded the true age of the Mount Ngauruhoe samples (approximately 20–50 years old). However, the dated age of the samples ranged from a minimum of a quarter million years to a maximum of 3.5 million years, dramatically older than their actual age. The study confirmed that the source of error was excess argon trapped in the lava during crystallization. In other words, the argon measured in the samples did not originate from the *in situ* radioactive decay of parent potassium-40 isotopes. So assumption 1 was incorrect—yielding a false date. While a rock is molten, much of the gaseous argon is *not* effectively removed from the system, resulting in greatly inflated ages.

The second example is the lava dome that formed in the crater of Mount St. Helens in Washington state. The dome formed in 1984, and crystallized by 1986 (the actual age of the rock), providing geologists with an opportunity to test the reliability of the potassium-argon method. A decade later, five samples (1 whole-rock sample and 4 component minerals) were sent to Geochron Laboratories.[4] As before, no information was provided about where the sample was collected or the actual age of the rock, though the laboratory technicians were again advised to expect "low argon." The results of the potassium-argon analysis indicated that the solidified lava dome was anywhere between 340,000 and 2.8 million years old. Furthermore, different crystals within the same rock sample yielded different ages, all of which were dramatically older than the true age of the recently formed lava dome. The most reasonable explanation for this discrepancy is that excess argon (i.e., not from *in situ* radioactive decay of parent isotopes), possibly inherited from the mantle, was incorporated into the lava prior to crystallization. Interestingly, the mineral with the tightest crystalline structure (pyroxene) dated as being the

---

3. Snelling A., Andesite flows at Mt Ngauruhoe, New Zealand, and the implications for Potassium-Argon "Dating," 1998. https://www.researchgate.net/publication/237527549_The_Cause_of_Anomalous_Potassium-Argon_Ages_for_Recent_Andesite_Flows_at_Mt_Ngauruhoe_New_Zealand_and_the_Implications_for_Potassium-Argon_Dating
4. Austin S.A., Excess Argon within mineral concentrates from the New Dacite Lava Dome at Mount St. Helens Volcano, *Creation Ex Nihilo Technical Journal* Vol. 10 (Part 3), 1996.

oldest. This may be because its tighter crystalline structure, allowed for greater argon retention, and as a consequence "dated" much older than the other minerals.[5] Put more simply, argon is not being excluded from the molten lava as typically assumed. Other researchers have come to similar conclusions. For instance, Broadhurst and colleagues report in the *Geochimica et Cosmochimica Acta* journal that *"the solubility of Ar in theminerals is surprisingly high."*[6] In other words, argon does not appear to readily escape from the lava prior to crystallization as is commonly assumed (refuting assumption 1). These researchers concluded that non-radiogenic argon was retained in the lattice vacancies of the minerals, giving the superficial appearance of great age.

Table 1. Young rocks from recent eruptions (<1000 years old) yield greatly exaggerated apparent ages. The data used in this table was retrieved from mainstream scientific journals.[7,8,9,10,11,12]

Location	When Lava Extrude	Measured Age
Hualalai basalt	1800-1801 A.D.	1.6 million years
Mount Etna basalt	122 B.C.	0.25 million years
Mount Etna basalt	1792 A.D.	0.35 million years
Mount Lassen basalt	1915 A.D.	0.11 million years
Sunset Crater basalt	1064-1065 A.D.	0.27 million year
Kilauea basalt	<200 years ago	21 million years
Kilauea basalt	<1,000 years ago	42.9 million years
Kilauea basalt	<1,000 years ago	30.3 million years
Kilauea Iki basalt	1959 A.D.	8.5 million years
Mount Stromboli	1963 A.D.	2.4 million years
Hualalai basalt	1800-1801 A.D.	22.8 million years
Rangitoto basalt	<800 years ago	0.15 million years
Mount Erebus	1984 A.D.	0.64 million years
Mount Etna basalt	1964 A.D.	0.7 million years
Medicine Lake obsidian	<500 years ago	12.6 million years

*Literature review and compilation of listed data credited to Dr. Andrew Snelling[13]

5. Austin S.A., Excess Argon within mineral concentrates from the New Dacite Lava Dome at Mount St. Helens Volcano, *Creation Ex Nihilo Technical Journal* Vol. 10 (Part 3), 1996.
6. Broadhurst C.L. *et al.*, Solubility and partitioning of Ar in anorthic, diopside, Forsterite, spinel and synthetic basaltic liquids, *Geochimica et Cosmochimica* 54:299-309, 1990.
7. Dalrymple G.B., $^{40}Ar/^{36}Ar$ Analyses of Historic lava flows, *Earth and Planetary Science Letters* 6:47-55, 1969.
8. Noble C.S. and Naughton J.J., Deep-ocean basalts: inert gas content and uncertainties in age dating, *Science* 162:265-267, 1968.
9. Dalrymple G.B. and Moore J.G., Argon 40: Excess in submarine pillow basalts form Kilaueau Volcano, Hawaii, *Science* 161:1132-1135, 1968.
10. Krummenacher D., Isotopic composition of Argon in modern surface volcanic rocks, *Earth and Planetary Science Letters* 8:109-117, 1970.
11. McDougall I. *et al.*, Excess radiogenic argon in young subaerial basalts from the Auckland volcanic field, New Zealand, *Geochimica et Cosmochimica Acta* 33:1485-1520, 1969.
12. Esser R.P. *et al.*, Excess Argon in melt inclusions in zero-age Anorthoclase feldspar from Mt Erebus, Anartica, as revealed by a $^{40}Ar/^{39}Ar$ method, *Geochimica et Cosmochimica Acta* 61:3789-3801, 1997.
13. http://static.icr.org/i/pdf/technical/The-Cause-of-Anomalous-Potassium-Argon-Ages.pdf

Many other examples of exaggerated ages have been reported in the scientific literature (Table 1). Dalrymple reported in *Earth and Planetary Science Letters* the age of five historic lava flows.[14] Each yielded dates that greatly exceeded their true ages. For example, a rock that formed just 85 years ago from a lava flow at Mt Lassen, California dated to over a quarter million years old. Hualalai basalt that formed between 1800-1801, just 200 years ago, potassium-argon dated to 1.6 million years old. A year later, Dr. Krummenacher potassium-argon dated the same lava flow in Hawaii.[15] The new date indicated it was over 16 million years old. Mt. Stromboli in Italy erupted in 1963—samples collected from the site dated to 2 million years old. Many additional studies published in *Nature*, *Science*, and other peer-reviewed geological science journals have reported highly discrepant ages when testing the accuracy of the potassium-argon method on rocks of known age.[16,17,18,19,20,2122,23,24,25,26]

These anomalous dates are not due to systematic errors in the analytical procedure or the equipment. The excess argon is real and measurable. All of these studies, and many others, have confirmed that excess argon is routinely trapped in lava when it cools.[27,28] The argon does not appear to be effectively degassing from the system. Studies have indicated excess argon is readily retained in the minerals during crystallization.[29] This undermines the most fundamental assumption of potassium-argon dating—the daughter atoms (argon-40) measured today do not consistently derive from the *in situ* radioactive decay of parent atoms (potassium-40). This

14. Dalrymple G.B., $^{40}Ar/^{36}Ar$ analyses of historical lava flows, *Earth and Planetary Science Letters* 6:47-55, 1969.

15. Krummenacher D., Isotopic composition of Argon in modern surface volcanic rocks, *Earth and Planetary Science Letters* 8:109-117, 1970.

16. Laughlin A.W. *et al.*, Dating of Quaternary Basalts Using the Cosmogenic 3He and 14C Methods with Implications for Excess 40Ar, *Geology* 22:135-138, 1994.

17. Patterson D.B. *et al.*, Noble Gases in Mafic Phenocrysts and Xenoliths from New Zealand, *Geochimica et Cosmochimica Acta*, 58:4411-4427, 1994.

18. Armstrong R.L., K-Ar Dating: Late Cenozoic McMurdo Volcanic Group and Dry Valley Glacial History, Victoria Land, Antarctica, *New Zealand J Geol and Geophys* 21(6):685-698, 1978.

19. Fisher D.E., Heavy Rare Gases in a Pacific Seamount, *Earth and Planetary Science Letters* 9:331-335, 1970.

20. Fisher D.E., U/He Ages as Indicators of Excess Argon in Deep Sea Basalts, *Earth and Planetary Science Letters* 14:255-258, 1972.

21. Fisher D.E., Excess rare gases in a subaerial basalt from Nigeria, *Nature*, 232:60–61, 1971.

22. Funkhouser J.G. and Naughton J.J., Radiogenic Helium and Argon in Ultramafic Inclusions from Hawaii, *J Geophys Res* 73:4601-4607, 1968.

23. Funkhouser J.G. *et al.*, Problems in the Dating of Volcanic Rocks by the Potassium-Argon Method, *Bulletin of Volcanology* 29:709-717, 1966.

24. Funkhouser J.G. *et al.*, Excess Argon in Deep-Sea Rocks, *Earth and Planetary Science Letters* 5:95-100, 1968.

25. Honda M. *et al.*, Noble Gases in Submarine Pillow Basalt Glasses from Loihi and Kilauea, Hawaii: a Solar Component in the Earth, *Geochimica et Cosmochimica Acta* 57:859-874, 1993.

26. McDougall I., The Geochronology and Evolution of the Young Volcanic Island of Reunion, Indian Ocean, *Geochimica et Cosmochimica Acta* 35:261-288, 1971.

27. Damon P.E. *et al.*, Problem of excess argon-40 in volcanic rocks, In *Radioactive Dating and Methods of Low-level Counting*, pp. 463-431. Int. Atomic Energy Agency, Vienna, 1967.

28. Poths J. *et al.*, Ubiquitous Excess Argon in Very Young Basalts, *Geological Society of America Abstracts With Programs* 25: p. A-462, 1993.

29. Broadhurst C.L. *et al.*, Solubility and partitioning of Ar in anorthite, diopside, forsterite, spinel, and synthetic basaltic liquids, *Geochimica et Cosmochimica Acta* 54:299-309, 1990.

gives the superficial appearance of great age. The official United States Geological Survey website (USGS.gov) acknowledges excess argon as a cause for concern:

> The conventional K-Ar dating method depends on the assumption that the rocks contained no argon at the time of formation and that all the subsequent radiogenic argon (i.e., ^{40}Ar) was quantitatively retained. ... Under some circumstances the requirements for successful K-Ar dating may be violated. ... if excess ^{40}Ar is present in the rock, the calculated age-dates are too old.

The New Mexico Geochronology Research Laboratory at the Institute of Mining and Technology cautions similarly stating, *"Argon loss and excess argon are two common problems that may cause erroneous ages to be determined. ... excess argon can cause the calculated K/Ar age to be older than the "true" age of the dated material."*[30] In *Geological Society of America Bulletin*, Cumbest and colleagues affirm,

> A significant problem in K/Ar isotopic dating is the sitting of "excess" ^{40}Ar acquired by minerals from their environment (that is, ^{40}Ar not produced by radiogenic decay within the mineral).[31]

Morozova and colleagues make the same observation, *"K-Ar dating is based on the decay of potassium to ^{40}Ar. A major constraint is the possibility that a mineral may contain excess radiogenic argon, which results in anomalously high ages."*[32] Poths *et al.* acknowledge further that the presence of excess argon is *"ubiquitous"* in basaltic rock that formed from recent eruptions.[33] It is for this reason that geochronologists have largely abandoned the potassium-argon method in favor of improved techniques such as argon-argon dating, which can allegedly detect excess argon.[34]

Yet it was the highly questionable potassium-argon method that laid the foundation for the currently accepted hominin timescale (and indeed the geologic timescale as a whole). Later refinements were made using the argon-argon method, but the general age framework was already firmly established prior to its invention and widespread use. The major breakthrough fossil discoveries were made in the 60s at Olduvai Gorge and other sites in east Africa during the 70s, the era Donald Johanson refers to as "The Golden Decade" when the conventional potassium-argon dating dominated the field. The argon-argon method was not commonly

30. New Mexico Geochronology Research Laboratory, Argon Lab: K/Ar and $^{40}Ar/^{39}Ar$ Methods, New Mexico's Institute of Mining and Technology.
31. Cumbest R.J. *et al.*, Argon composition of metamorphic fluids: Implications for $^{40}Ar/^{39}Ar$ geochronology, *Geological Society of America Bulletin* 106:942-951, 1991.
32. Morozova, I.M. *et al.*, Inheritance of radiogenic argon by newly formed minerals during glauconite transformation, *Transactions (Doklady) of the Russian Academy of Sciences: Earth Science Sections* 344(7):52-57, 1996.
33. Poths J. *et al.*, Ubiquitous Excess Argon in Very Young Basalts, *Geological Society of America Abstracts With Programs* 25: p. A-462, 1993.
34. https://ageofrocks.org/2015/04/13/argon-argon-dating-how-does-it-work-is-it-reliable/ Most labs now use argon-argon dating in place of the conventional potassium-argon method.

used until around the late 1980s.[35] While the argon-argon method apparently has improvements, it is a much more complicated process that incorporates many new potential sources of experimental error, requires many additional correction factors, and requires many new assumptions. Moreover, the argon-argon method fails in the same way that the potassium-argon method fails—recent lava flows still yield dates of millions of years. Even with argon-argon, the first assumption is still routinely violated. The "improved" argon-argon method does not detect excess argon as successfully as we are told.[36] Contrary to popular claims, assumptions 1 and 2 still apply to this method. For instance, Inger *et al.* acknowledge that excess argon is not always detected:

> Excess argon, which would lead to spuriously old ages, can sometimes be identified from $^{39}Ar/^{40}Ar$ versus $^{36}Ar/^{40}Ar$ correlation plots. These can demonstrate a contribution of ^{40}Ar which is not accounted for by the air correction, and so does not result from radiogenic decay since the mineral was last closed to Ar loss.[37]

It is also worth mentioning that the "improved" argon-argon method is not an independent dating method—it is still based on the decay of potassium into argon. In argon-argon dating, the concentration of potassium in a sample is still measured (as in the traditional potassium-argon method) it is just not measured directly. Instead, a rock sample is bombarded (irradiated) with neutrons to transform some of its potassium-39 content (a sister isotope of potassium-40) into argon-39. The amount of irradiated argon-39 is then used as a proxy to indirectly measure the relative abundance of potassium-40 in a sample (the logic here is based on the added assumption that potassium-39 is proportional to the amount of potassium-40 in any natural setting).[38] However, the only way scientists can know how much neutron flux to bombard a sample with (i.e., how much ^{39}Ar to produce) is if they calibrate the system by using a sample of "known age," called a monitor or standard. Interestingly, the standard of supposedly "known age" must be dated separately, most commonly with the potassium-argon method. Thus the age of a sample in question is usually dated using the argon-argon method that is first calibrated by the very unreliable potassium-argon method. Consequently, the argon-argon method is not at all an independent dating method, and therefore cannot possibly be anymore accurate than the potassium-argon system upon which it is founded. Obradovich acknowledges this stating:

> The $^{40}Ar/^{39}Ar$ technique is a relative method that depends on the age of the

---

35. Lo Bello P. *et al.*, $^{40}Ar/^{39}Ar$ stop-heating and laser fusion dating of a Quaternary pumice from Neschers, Massif Central, France: The defeat of xenocrystic contamination, *Chemical Geology* (Isotope Geoscience) 66: 61-67, 1987.

36. McDougall I. and Harrison T.M., *Geochronology and Thermochronology by the $^{40}Ar/^{39}Ar$ Method*, Oxford University Press, New York, p.110, 1988. Age spectra can be difficult to interpret and often yield misleading release patterns. For instance, samples that date too old, and so are known to contain excess argon can still exhibit flat release patterns (so-called "false plateaus") suggesting a "reliable" age.

37. Inger S. *et al.*, Metamorphic evolution of the Sesia-Lanzo zone, western Alps, *Contributions to Mineralogy and Petrology* 126:152-168, p. 158, 1996.

38. Swisher C. *et al.*, *Java Man*, Scribner, New York, p. 23, 2000.

monitor mineral being accurately known. It is, therefore, still dependent upon the conventional K-Ar technique being able to measure accurately the quantities of K and ^{40}Ar in the monitor mineral.[39]

In light of these findings, it is very likely that the hominin sites dated using either the potassium-argon or argon-argon method, including many australopith sites, Lucy, Ardi, Habilis, Erectus, etc., are all much younger than their reported ages. If eruptions occurring in recorded history, (such as Mt. Ngauruhoe and numerous other sites), consistently date to be millions of years old, how can we be sure the same error is not occurring when dating material from past eruptions in Laetoli, Hadar, Olduvai, and other famous hominin sites? The rocks that are known to be young are giving dates very similar to the deposits at all of these hominin sites (i.e., Pleistocene and Pliocene ages). There is no way to know whether or not all of the measured daughter atoms were from the *in situ* radioactive decay of parent atoms—it is an unjustified assumption.[40] As geologist Snelling notes:

> Because [radiogenic] ^{40}Ar* is indistinguishable from non-radiogenic ^{40}Ar, there is no way of knowing whether the ^{40}Ar measured in all samples has been produced by *in situ* radioactive decay of ^{40}K, whether it is primordial ^{40}Ar inherited from the mantle, or whether it is mobile ^{40}Ar acquired from other crustal rocks via fluid transport.[41]

The best way to test the validity of any dating method is to date rocks of known age. Whenever scientists do this they routinely obtain dates that are much older than their true age. If we cannot trust these dating methods on rocks or ash of known age, how can we trust these same methods on rocks of unknown age?

Uranium-Thorium (U-Th) Dating

All radioisotope dating methods discussed here require the dated material to have remained a closed system throughout its existence. When dating volcanic rock, ash deposits, flowstones, etc. it is assumed that all daughter atoms are derived exclusively from the *in situ* radioactive decay of parent atoms (assumption 2). However, the "closed system" assumption is routinely violated. A number of studies show that these parent-daughter systems are not effectively shielded from external processes (such as ground water transportation) that can add or remove isotopes. This can lead to erroneous ages. The uranium-thorium dating method is especially prone to this type of error—a phenomenon we will call "open system behavior," which undermines the second critical assumption of radioisotope dating.

39. Obradovich J.D., A Cretaceous time scale, In: Caldwell G.E. and Kauffman E.G. (eds.), *Evolution of the Western Interior Basin*, Geological Association of Canada Special Paper 39, 680 pp., p. 382, 1993.
40. As Richards and McDougall write in the *Geochimica et Cosmochimica Acta* journal, "*Excess ^{40}Ar contamination cannot be conclusively proven by conventional K-Ar dating techniques...*" Geochronology of the Porgera gold deposit, Papua New Guinea: Resolving the effects of excess argon on K-Ar and ^{40}Ar/^{39}Ar age estimates for magmatism and mineralization, *Geochimica et Cosmochimica Acta* 54:1397-1415, 1990.
41. Snelling A., *Radioisotopes and the Age of the Earth*, Volume II, Chapter 6, Isochron discordances and the role of inheritance and mixing of radioisotopes in the mantle iand crust, p. 396, 2005.

Many famous hominin fossils have been found in caves that have been dated using the uranium-series techniques (either U-Th or U-Pb). For example, the recently discovered species Sediba and Naledi were found in limestone pits or caves. Anyone who has visited such a cave or hot spring will immediately recognize the flowstone (such as stalactites and stalagmites) that rapidly form. Flowstone forms when water drips into caves through cracks and fissures in limestone rock, leaving behind calcium carbonate deposits. Calcium carbonate can form layered deposits on the walls and along the floors of caves. Cave deposits can be dated using the uranium-thorium method, also known as the uranium-series dating. Artifacts found in caves that have been covered by flowstone or are sandwiched between flowstone layers are assumed to have the same date as the flowstone. This includes cave wall paintings, stone tools, bones, and teeth.

Uranium-234 is a radioactive isotope (half-life of 245,000 years) that decays into thorium-230, which itself is radioactive and continues along a decay chain into the stable daughter product lead-206. Since thorium-230 is unstable, an age cannot be calculated by simply measuring the amount produced from its parent (U-234) like other conventional dating methods (i.e., K-Ar dating). Instead, an age must be calculated based on the degree to which "secular equilibrium"[42] has been restored between uranium-234 and thorium-230. Without getting any more technical, uranium-thorium dating is useful for dating flowstone samples believed to be less than 500,000 years old (to date material older than this, uranium-lead dating is used, discussed next).[43] Like all dating methods, the uranium-thorium method depends on certain critical assumptions that may be false.

Uranium-thorium dating is possible because of the difference in solubility between uranium and thorium. Uranium is soluble in water (dissolves readily) and so it can be easily transported through ground water into caves. Thorium, on the other hand, is largely insoluble (does not dissolve in water), and tends to absorb onto the surface of clay minerals and other particles, which reduces its mobility through soil or rock. These observations led to the primary assumption of uranium-thorium dating. It is assumed that all thorium is effectively filtered out of drip water at the soil/limestone boundary, and only uranium is assumed to be deposited, together with calcium carbonate, to form flowstone/dripstone. The second assumption is that the flowstone/dripstone, once it forms, is a closed system, and there is no thorium-230 or uranium-234 exchange with the outside environment.[44] Under these two assumptions, any thorium-230 that is measured in a flowstone sample is assumed to be from the *in situ* radioactive decay of uranium-234.

However, both assumptions are unrealistic when considering any natural cave

---

42. Secular equilibrium is the point at which the production rate of thorium-230 from its radioactive parent (uranium-234) is equal to the loss rate of thorium-230 by decay.
43. Uranium-238/Lead-206 or U-Pb dating is used to date hominin-bearing cave deposits from South Africa.
44. Liritzis I., Uranium-Thorium Dating in Cave Art, 1989. https://www.researchgate.net/publica-tion/272677356_uranium_-thorium_dating_in_cave_art

setting.[45,46] Just like potassium-argon dating, if there is any excess daughter product (in this case thorium-230) present in the system when the flowstone formed this violates the first assumption. If any excess thorium was later incorporated into the system, or if any uranium was washed out, this violates the second assumption. In either case, the samples will date significantly older than their true age. A handbook from the Department of Geological Sciences at the University of Florida points out these two critical assumptions (and a third, the decay rate, which we will not discuss here):

> Ultimately, the accuracy of these ages is dependent upon: (1) how well the decay constants for these three nuclides are known; (2) the condition that no ^{230}Th was initially present in the sample at the time of growth; and (3) the condition that the U-series decay chain has remained closed to isotopic exchange with the surrounding environment since formation.[47]

Let's consider some of the conditions that might violate these critical assumptions. When water drains through surface soils overlying caves and carries new minerals into the cave, this is known as leaching. While it is true that thorium by itself is insoluble, and not directly leachable from soils, thorium can bind to other minerals or molecules that are soluble and hence be transported into a cave. The principal constituent of limestone is calcium carbonate ($CaCO_3$), and calcium carbonate plus water gives rise to the carbonate ion (CO_3^{-2}). It is acknowledged that *"The presence of ions or ligands (CO_3^{-2}, humic matter) that can form soluble complexes with thorium should increase its mobility in soil."*[48] This means thorium can in fact be carried (leached) from surface soils and surrounding rock into caves. This invalidates the primary assumption of uranium-thorium dating. The following statement made by Georges Sauvet *et al.* in the journal *Quaternary International* (2015) reflects the common assumption, which they challenge in their paper: *"Calcite incorporates some uranium when it crystallizes (because uranium compounds are soluble in water), but no thorium compounds which are insoluble. At this moment, the meter is set to zero."*[49] The researchers go on to explain that *"several sources of error may seriously undermine this method... calcite may behave as an open system. In that case, uranium removal or thorium input could lead to overestimation of the age."* Indeed, thorium isotopes can be brought into solution and leached into caves:

> The contamination of groundwater through the transport of thorium from soil to ground water will not occur in most soils, except soils that have low sorption

45. http://www.atsdr.cdc.gov/toxprofiles/tp147-c5.pdf Thorium is known to be ubiquitous in our environment and occurs naturally in the earth's crust—it is found in most rocks and soil.
46. *"Thorium is found in small amounts in most rocks and soils; it is three times more abundant than tin in the Earth's crust and is about as common as lead. Soil commonly contains an average of around 6 parts per million (ppm) of thorium."* https://en.wikipedia.org/wiki/Occurrence_of_thorium
47. Dutton A., Chapter 26- Uranium-thorium dating, In: Shennan I. *et al.* (eds), *Handbook of Sea-Level Research*, Wiley, Hoboken, N.J., p.386, 2015.
48. http://www.atsdr.cdc.gov/toxprofiles/tp147-c5.pdf
49. Sauvet G. *et al.*, Uranium-thorium dating method and Palaeolithic rock art, *Quaternary International Journal* 432:86-92, 2015. DOI: 10.1016/j.quaint.2015.03.053

characteristics and have the capability to form soluble complexes. Chelating agents [organic compounds] produced by certain microorganisms (*Pseudomonas aeruginosa*) present in soils may enhance dissolution of thorium in soils (Premuzic *et al.* 1985).[50]

Liritzis also shows that thorium can be transported into caves by water:

Many elements that are picked up in solution as a result of acid leaching in soil zone e.g. Si, Al, Na, K, will remain in solution when $CaCO_3$ is precipitated. A detrital calcite will contain soil particles and this imposes serious problems into the dating, as the conditions of closed system is no longer valid and Th isotopes will participate in the initial calcitic deposit.[51]

Detrital calcite is a form of calcium carbonate associated with biodegradation of organic matter by microorganisms. Detritus (humus) is a major component of soil and upland streams. Sauvet *et al.* report on the surprisingly high solubility of thorium when bound to certain salts:

A spectacular confirmation of ^{230}Th solubility was given by Whitehead *et al.* (1999). A 'contemporary' straw stalactite (i.e. less than a century old that could be assimilated to "zero age") was sampled in a cave of New Zealand and gave a U/Th age of 3520 ± 170 ka. As ^{232}Th was virtually absent, thorium could not come from detrital particles, but was incorporated as soluble salts, probably organic ones. This study demonstrates that soluble ^{232}Th may be coprecipitated with calcite at the very moment of its formation giving it a false age of a few thousands of years. We cannot reject the hypothesis that ^{232}Th, present in the limestone of the cave, continues to percolate through the porosity and to accumulate during the growth of the speleothem leading to increasingly erroneous ages.[52]

It is clear that there are multiple ways that thorium can be incorporated into drip water. These include water percolating through soils and sedimentary rocks with low absorption, or binding with soluble organic complexes, ionic compounds, soluble salts of organic origin, or binding with chelating agents produced by microorganisms, or tiny clay particles. None of these conditions are unusual and all will tend to give old dates for young rock.

As we have just shown, the uranium-thorium method is certainly not immune to open-system behavior. Flowstone/dripstone samples appear to readily exchange thorium-230 and uranium-234 with the environment. Any attempt to detect excess thorium (thorium-230 that did not derive from the *in situ* radioactive decay of uranium-234) requires additional complicating assumptions. For example, the detection of initial or detrital thorium-230 is based on the simultaneous measurement of the longer-lived thorium-232 isotope, which serves as a vicarious measurement of thorium-230 content that is presumed to have been initially

50. http://www.atsdr.cdc.gov/toxprofiles/tp147-c5.pdf
51. Liritzis I., Uranium-Thorium Dating in Cave Art, 1989. https://www.researchgate.net/publication/272677356_uranium_-thorium_dating_in_cave_art
52. Sauvet G. *et al.*, Uranium-thorium dating method and Palaeolithic rock art, *Quaternary International Journal* 432:86-92, 2015. DOI: 10.1016/j.quaint.2015.03.053

present in the system.[53] This, of course, is only possible given the shaky assumption that thorium-230 exists in constant proportion with thorium-232 in any natural setting over time:

> One of the possible reasons leading to age overestimation is the presence of thorium trapped in calcite during crystallization. As thorium is presumed to be insoluble, it would have to be imbedded in solid particles of detrital material such as silt or clay. In such particles, both isotopes of thorium, ^{230}Th and ^{232}Th, are assumed to be present in their natural proportions.[54]

Pentecost acknowledges the difficulties with detecting excess detrital thorium: *"Since most travertines contain a few percent detrital material, the selection of samples is crucial. Fortunately, detrital thorium can be detected as it occurs with ^{232}Th, but corrections are sometimes difficult and may not be very reliable."*[55]

Sauvet *et al.* in *Quaternary International* (2015) journal provide an eye-opening explanation of an alternative source of excess thorium-230 that is much harder to detect than detrital sources:

> Correction for detrital thorium-containing particles is standard practice for specialists. However, there is another source of error, much more confusing because it is captious and difficult to detect. This derived from the opening of the system after the deposition of calcite. This cause of error is well known in the case of corals, but much more difficult to detect in the case of speleothems (Scholz and Hoffmann, 2008). The possibility of such error is seldom mentioned in spite of well-documented examples. ...An input of ^{230}Th seems more probable as, contrarily to what is usually claimed, ^{230}Th is not rigorously insoluble, particularly when occurring as salts of organic acids such as fulvic and humic acids. The introduction of a very small quantity of ^{230}Th, not correlated with the incorporation of detrital thorium, may be responsible for ^{230}Th/^{234}U activity ratios that are greater than 1. The same phenomenon probably also takes place when this ratio is lower than one, causing an overestimation of the ages.[56]

These researchers cite convincing evidence indicative of open-system behavior. They found that excess thorium-230 is introduced into the system after initial flowstone deposition, resulting in an overestimation of a sample's age. Uranium loss through leaching is another problem for uranium-thorium dating that can result in exaggerated ages. For example, one source says: *"Clark et al. (1991) found evidence of uranium loss by natural travertine dissolution."*[57] Sauvet and colleagues acknowledge this problem as well:

---

53. Dutton A., Chapter 26- Uranium-thorium dating, In: Shennan I. *et al.* (eds), *Handbook of Sea-Level Research*, Wiley, Hoboken, NJ, p.386, 2015.

54. Sauvet G. *et al.*, Uranium-thorium dating method and Palaeolithic rock art, *Quaternary International Journal* 432:86-92, 2015. DOI: 10.1016/j.quaint.2015.03.053

55. Pentecost A., *Travertine*, Springer, Netherlands, p. 249, 2005.

56. Sauvet G. *et al.*, Uranium-thorium dating method and Palaeolithic rock art, *Quaternary International Journal* 432:86-92, 2015. DOI: 10.1016/j.quaint.2015.03.053

57. Pentecost A., *Travertine*, Springer, Netherlands, p. 249, 2005.

Moreover, a much more serious but rarely considered source of error contradicts the assumption of a closed system. In thin layers of carbonate deposits and in damp media, the uranium incorporated into the calcite during its crystallization may be partially eliminated because of its solubility in water. Uranium leaching causes an artificial increase of the age that may reach considerable proportions (e.g. a negative hand in a cave in Borneo was dated to 27,000 years by U/Th whereas its ^{14}C age was only 8–10,000 cal BP; Plagnes *et al.*, 2003).[58]

Uranium-Lead (U-Pb) Dating

Uranium-thorium dating is useful for dating cave deposits less than 500,000 years old. To date hominin-bearing cave deposits older than this uranium-lead dating is the method of choice. Yet uranium-lead dating suffers from the same problem as seen with uranium-thorium dating—open system behavior (i.e., mobility of U, Th, and Pb) leading to exaggerated ages. As a doctoral thesis on this topic acknowledges, *"Published studies in the area* [South African hominin sites] *have revealed major ^{234}U excess in ground water and speleothem. Where conventional age calculations are used this effect could result in an age much greater than the true age."*[59] Surprisingly, fundamental processes involved in uranium-lead dating (such as the movement of lead in the environment and how it incorporates into flowstone) are not well understood. Woodhead *et al.* acknowledge this in *Quaternary Geochronology:*

> Controls on the movement of Pb in the environment and its incorporation into calcite are relatively poorly known. Most Pb salts with common anions are only slightly soluble and the average concentration in river waters is <100 ppt (Gaillardet *et al.*, 2003) and just a few ppt in ocean water (Chester, 2000). Pb is incorporated into the calcite structure (Rimstidt *et al.*, 1998; Reeder *et al.*, 1999) but given Pb(II)'s relative insolubility, most natural calcites should have relatively low levels of Pb (Rasbury and Cole, 2009). Adsorption and complexation with Fe and Mn oxides and organic matter, however, may promote Pb mobilisation (Borsato *et al.*, 2007; Dawson *et al.*, 2010) and subsequent availability. Alternatively, Pb may be incorporated into speleothems associated with fine detrital particles or as sub-micron sized colloids (Fairchild and Treble, 2009).[60]

Aware of the problem of open system behavior, geochronologists devise complex models to account for uranium-thorium-lead loss and uptake. These hotly contested models are continually revised or replaced by promising "new" models. Models are needed because dated carbonate samples from caves contain a mixture of radiogenic lead and non-radiogenic (common) lead. Non-radiogenic lead from the environment can also be added to a sample during sample preparation in the laboratory. Since radiogenic lead (Pb-206) and non-radiogenic lead (Pb-206) are analytically indistinguishable, researchers have to indirectly determine which

58. Sauvet G. *et al.*, Uranium-thorium dating method and Palaeolithic rock art, *Quaternary International Journal* 432:86-92, 2015. DOI: 10.1016/j.quaint.2015.03.053
59. Walker J., Uranium-lead dating of hominid fossil sites in South Africa, Univ. of Leeds, 2005.
60. Woodhead J. *et al.*, U and Pb variability in older speleothems and strategies for their chronology, *Quaternary Geochronology* 14:105-113, 2012.

lead isotopes derived from the *in situ* decay of uranium and which did not. This distinction is made by using other isotopes (i.e., thorium) as a proxy for estimating the initial amount of lead in a sample at the time of flowstone formation. This requires additional assumptions about past conditions that are continually debated by experts. For instance, Woodhead *et al.* write:

> We have argued previously (Woodhead *et al.*, 2006) that compilations of speleothem U and Pb concentration data derived from the literature and as measured by conventional ICPMS (or other instrumental methods) may seriously over-estimate the Pb abundance in many samples. This possibility arises from the ubiquitous contamination of anthropogenic Pb in the environment and the fact that micrograms of this Pb can be easily added to a sample by simple crushing and handling. In many cases the Pb blank added during such procedures is orders of magnitude above the natural Pb content of typical samples. In an attempt to circumvent this problem, Woodhead *et al.* (2006) employed Th as a proxy for Pb content using an assumed crustal Th/Pb ratio, and suggested that a typical Pb content for many speleothems may be less than 100 ppb with $^{238}U/^{204}Pb$ ratios in the 10^2–10^6 range, many of which would be suitable for U–Pb geochronology. This hypothesis was not an ideal construct, however, since it relied upon Th as a proxy for Pb content.[61]

In an attempt to avoid these problems, geochronologists have developed complex pre-screening processes to ensure that they are choosing only the best samples. The problem is, there are very few "ideal" flowstone samples when it comes to dating hominins (most all samples are expected to contain initial amounts of non-radiogenic lead, detrital thorium, and excess uranium). To date, over 600 hominin fossils have been discovered in South Africa in various caves, *"the richest collection outside the East African Rift system."*[62] All of these cave settings are open systems, such that even a tiny bit of excess common lead, if mistaken for radiogenic lead, will result in greatly exaggerated ages.

The bottom line is, no one was present long ago to measure the initial conditions (i.e., initial isotopic concentrations) of a given cave system. Therefore, there is no way to directly verify how much uranium, thorium, or lead was initially present, or whether the system has always remained closed throughout its history. Consequently, any hominin bones or artifacts that have been found in caves that have been dated using the uranium-thorium or uranium-lead method are inherently uncertain. The actual age of all such hominin bones that have been dated using these methods (Neanderthals, Erectus, Hobbit, Sediba, Naledi, etc.) are very likely significantly younger than their reported ages.

---

61. Woodhead J. *et al.*, U and Pb variability in older speleothems and strategies for their chronology, *Quaternary Geochronology*, 14:105-113, 2012.
62. Pickering R. *et al.*, U-Pb dating of calcite-aragonite layers in speleothems from hominin sites in South Africa by MC-ICP-MS, *Quaternary Geochronology* 5:544-558, 2010.

Carbon-14—A Serious Challenge to the Hominin Timescale

Most people are confused about carbon-14 dating. It is often thought that carbon-14 shows how very old things are. Actually carbon-14 usually shows us how young things are. Carbon-14 mostly arises in the upper atmosphere, where cosmic rays turn nitrogen into carbon-14. The resulting carbon-14 immediately begins to revert back to nitrogen. Some of this carbon-14 enters into living plants and animals. Because carbon-14 no longer enters living things after they die, the carbon-14 "clock" starts ticking at death. The carbon-14 in a biological sample disappears at a very steady rate, with its half-life being just 5,730 years. This means that no detectable carbon-14 should remain in any biological remains after about 100,000 years.

It is remarkable, but essentially everything in the fossil record contains measurable levels of carbon-14.[63] This seems contrary to popular wisdom, but is widely recognized within the carbon-14 community. Taken at face value, this suggests that the entire fossil record is less than 100,000 years old. Many will be offended by this idea—but like it or not, this is what the carbon-14 dating appears to be showing. When bones of the *Homo* genus have been carbon-14 dated, they have consistently yielded young dates—ranging from thousands to tens of thousands of years.[64] It appears that Naledi has been carbon-dated, but the resulting dates (33,000–35,000 years old) were rejected, because the dates conflicted with expectation, and conflicted with other dating methods. So those dates were discarded, being assumed to be caused by contamination.[65] We suggest that many more hominin bones should be carbon-14 dated, including bones of the genus *Australopithecus*.

Some will argue that any carbon-14 detected in fossils must be modern carbon-14 that has somehow infiltrated the sample.[66] Three lines of evidence suggest that this is not the case. First, the carbon-14 levels in biological samples of the same type buried at the same time are remarkably consistent. Secondly, many samples such as coal deposits are too massive and too deeply buried to be significantly contaminated by modern carbon. Thirdly, carbon samples not subject to contamination (such as diamond) still reveal measurable levels of carbon-14.

Some have argued that new C-14 may have been created by heavy radiation of biological samples by nearby uranium deposits.[67] However, uranium deposits are rare and diffuse, and such radiation could never be intense enough to create carbon-14 faster than it decays. Geophysicist John Baumgardner directly responds

63. For a list of 90 peer-reviewed journal articles reporting measurable amounts of carbon-14 in samples from every part of the Phanerozoic record, see Table compiled by P. Giem and D.R. Humphrey *et al.* in the following report: http://www.icr.org/i/pdf/research/RATE_ICC_Baumgardner.pdf

64. Day M.H., *Guide to Fossil Man*, University of Chicago Press, Chicago, 432 pp., 1986.

65. Dirks P. *et al.*, The age of *Homo naledi* and associated sediments in the Rising Star Cave, South Africa, *eLife* 2017;6e24231. DOI: 10.7554/eLife.24231.

66. Nadeau M.J. *et al.*, Carbonate ¹⁴C background: does it have multiple personalities? *Radiocarbon* 43(2A):169-176, 2001.

67. Zito R. *et al.*, Possible subsurface production of carbon-14, *Geophysical Research Letters* 7(4):235-238, 1980.

to this objection as well, both in his technical report on this topic and through personal communication with the authors of this book: *"The currently measured rates of U and Th decay are too small to generate any significant amount of C-14 in these contexts, so any attempt to explain the measured C-14 levels such as we and others have reported for coal by this mechanism is hopeless."*[68]

One way that geochronologists have tried to bring carbon-14 dates into alignment with the hominin timeline has been to add a control, such as natural gas, to each experiment, and then reduce the carbon-14 level of a sample by the amount of carbon-14 in the natural gas. The assumption is that natural gas is too old to retain carbon-14, so any carbon-14 in it must be contamination. The problem with this approach is that natural gas is not a fair control—it contains highly reproducible levels of carbon-14, which suggests that it also is less than 100,000 years old. Ubiquitous carbon-14 throughout the fossil record is a very real, and brings into question dating methodology and standard timelines.

The Remarkable Story of the Dating and Re-dating of the Pivotal KBS Tuff

Paleo-experts expect the different dating methods to agree with one another when dating the same hominin bones. The radioisotope age, paleomagnetic age, bio-stratigraphic age, luminescence age, fission track age, etc. should generally agree. However, this is often not the case. The apparent consistency and presumed reliability of the dating methods is in part because the dates that do not agree are routinely omitted. Selective use of data is bad science yet it is surprisingly common practice when it comes to dating methods. The scientific literature is replete with such examples. The dated material is deemed "contaminated," and new samples are often dated and re-dated multiple times until the desired age is achieved. In some cases, the various dating methods only align after some reworking of the data. Massaging the data can often lead to apparent resolution of conflicting dates.

But what happens when multiple dating methods agree on an apparent age that conflicts with the ape-to-man story? In such cases, the paradigm will consistently take precedence over the data. The dating of an important stratigraphic marker, called the KBS Tuff, is a classic example of this. The KBS Tuff controversy is well documented, and provides a rare inside look at how the dating of hominin bones actually plays out.

In the 1970s Richard Leakey headed the Koobi Fora Research Project in the Lake Turkana basin of Northern Kenya. During those expeditions Richard and his "hominin gang" found human artifacts,[69] two occupation sites (including a hippo

---

68. Personal correspondence, 12-11-2013.
69. Leakey R.E.F., New Hominid Remains and Early Artefacts from Northern Kenya, *Nature* 226:223-224, 1970.

butchery site),[70,71] a human skull,[72] human jawbones, human teeth, and human leg bones.[73] These specimens were found in and below an ash deposit known as the KBS Tuff, which predated the earliest known human ancestors. These findings threw the paleo-community into a frenzy, and the debate that ensued lasted for over a decade. In the early 70s, all the various dating methods available at that time (all of which are still used today) agreed on the same age for the KBS Tuff. This included faunal dating,[74,75] paleomagnetic dating,[76] fission-track dating,[77] potassium-argon, and argon-argon dating.[78] All of those separate analyses were reported in *Nature*. The researchers insisted that great care was taken to avoid contamination and that standard laboratory procedures were rigorously followed. Nevertheless, the dates obtained conflicted with the established ape-to-man story that reigned at that time.

At that time, Johanson and other like-minded experts were convinced the genus *Homo* had emerged only around 1.8 million years ago. This did not fit with the new dates from Koobi Fora, Kenya. How could human artifacts and human bones, and an essentially modern human-looking skull, be dated at nearly 3 million years old (long before the first humans were said to have evolved)? Even more problematic, how could man have coexisted with the earliest australopithecine ancestors? The data did not support the standard paradigm.

After passionate debate, the KBS Tuff was repeatedly re-dated until a more "comfortable" age was obtained—an age that conveniently agreed with the "group think" of the paleo-community. The modified dates were necessary to preserve the paradigm. The controversy was a clear demonstration of "scientific politics." As prize-winning British science writer Roger Lewin notes, *"It is also a story that demonstrates how very unscientific the process of scientific inquiry sometimes can be."*[79]

1970: Multiple Dating Methods Initially Agreed on Age of KBS Tuff

During the second field season of the Koobi Fora Research Project in 1969, the

70. Hay R.I., The KBS Tuff controversy may be ended, *Nature* 284:401, 1980.

71. Isaac, G. L., Leakey, R. E. F., and Behrensmeyer, A. K., Archeological Traces of Early Hominid Activities, East of Lake Rudolf, Kenya, *Science* 173:1129–1134, 1971.

72. Leakey R.E.F., Evidence for an Advanced Plio-Pleistocene Hominid from East Rudolf, Kenya, *Nature* 242:447-450, 1973.

73. Leakey R.E.F., Further Evidence of Lower Pleistocene Hominids from East Rudolf, North Kenya, 1972, *Nature* 242:170-173, 1973. See Table 2 for material attributed to *Homo*.

74. Maglio V.I., Vertebrate Faunas and Chronology of Hominid-bearing Sediments East of Lake Rudolf, Kenya, *Nature* 239:379-385, 1972.

75. Leakey R.E.F., Evidence for an Advanced Plio-Pleistocene Hominid from East Rudolf, Kenya, *Nature* 242:447-450, 1973.

76. Brock A. and Isaac G.L.I., Paleomagnetic stratigraphy and chronology of hominind-bearing sediments east of Lake Rudolf, Kenya, *Nature* 247:344-348, 1974.

77. Hurford A.J., Fission track dating of a vitric tuff from East Rudolf, North Kenya, *Nature* 249:236-237, 1974.

78. Fitch F.J. and Miller J.A., Radioisotopic Age Determinations of Lake Rudolf Artefact Site, *Nature* 226:226-228, 1970.

79. Lewin R., *Bones of Contention* 2nd Edition, The University of Chicago Press, Chicago, p.190, 1987.

geologist on site, Kay Behrensmeyer, found sophisticated stone tools similar to the type found at Olduvai Gorge. These human artifacts were found embedded in a volcanic ash deposit that was subsequently named after her (the Kay Behrensmeyer Site, or "KBS Tuff").[80] Embedded pumice samples were sent to respected geochronologists Jack Miller of Cambridge University and Frank Fitch of Birkbeck College, London. Potassium-argon dating gave the first samples an average age of 221 million years![81] Obviously a dinosaur-era age for the stone tools was unacceptable. They concluded that the volcanic material must have been contaminated by the inclusion of older "basement" rock. They write, *"Exploratory conventional K-Ar dating in 1969 revealed the presence of detrital impurities in the vitric tuff sample that made its apparent ages discrepantly high (>200 Myr)."*[82] What evidence indicated that the sample was contaminated?[83] Only the extremely old dates. They "knew" it was contamination from older rock, because it was an impossible age for the ape-to-man story. Richard Leakey then sent Miller and Fitch "better" samples from the KBS Tuff. The new samples yielded an age of 2.6 million years.[84] The younger age was believed to be closer to the true age of the KBS Tuff, and was therefore assumed to be uncontaminated.

By the 70s the argon-argon dating method was in use, as described earlier.[85] The argon-argon technique was a refinement of the conventional potassium-argon method. It was heralded as a superior dating technique in terms of both precision and accuracy. With the "superior" argon-argon method at their disposal, Fitch and Miller re-dated the KBS Tuff to yield an *"incontrovertible"* age with *"greater accuracy than any other site in Africa or elsewhere."*[86] They used the argon-argon method in concert with the conventional potassium-argon method. Separate studies of faunal correlations (elephant fossils),[87,88] paleomagnetism,[89] and fission

---

80. Behrensmeyer A.K., New Hominid Remains and Early Artefacts from Northern Kenya: Preliminary Geological Interpretation of a New Hominid Site in the Lake Rudolf Basin, *Nature* 226:225-226, 1970.

81. Fitch F.J. and Miller J.A., Radioisotopic Age Determinations of Lake Rudolf Artifact Site, *Nature* 226:226-228, 1970.

82. Fitch F.J. *et al.*, 40Ar/39Ar dating of the KBS Tuff in Koobi Fora Formation, East Rudolf, Kenya, *Nature* 263:740-744, 1976.

83. Fitch F.J. and Miller J.A., Radioisotopic Age Determinations of Lake Rudolf Artifact Site, *Nature* 226:226-228, 1970. They attribute the contamination to *"the possible presence of extraneous argon derived from inclusions of pre-existing rocks."*

84. This age was later revised by Fitch *et al.* to 2.42 Ma and then to 2.48 and then to 2.5 Ma. Fitch F.J. *et al.*, Dating of the KBS Tuff and *Homo rudolfensis, J Hum Evol* 30:277-286, 1996.

85. Argon-argon dating was first described in 1962, but not commonly used until years later.

86. Letter, Fitch to R. Leakey, 7 August 1969. Quotation recorded on p. 192, In: Lewin R., *Bones of Contention,* University of Chicago Press, Chicago, 1987.

87. Maglio V.I., Vertebrate Faunas and Chronology of Hominid-bearing Sediments East of Lake Rudolf, Kenya, *Nature* 239:379-385, 1972.

88. Curtis G.H. *et al.* in *Nature* 258:396, 1975. The authors write, *"Although Maglio found that the morphology of elephant fossils fit with a 2.5 Myr date* [here they cite Maglio, *Nature*, 239, 1972], *Cooke and Maglio, in 1972, pointed out that fossil pigs from below the KBS Tuff horizon at East Rudolf seemed to correlate best with those from beds dating close to 2 Myr in the Omo River area to the north in Ethiopia."*

89. Brock A. and Isaac G.L.I., Paleomagnetic stratigraphy and chronology of hominid-bearing sediments east of Lake Rudolf, Kenya, *Nature* 247:344-348, 1974.

track dating[90] confirmed Fitch and Miller's potassium-argon and argon-argon age. All of those dating methods agreed that the specimens were 2.6 million years old. Fitch, Findlater, and Watkins commented on their seemingly remarkable concordance, saying, *"The compatibility of independent evidence is a very strong argument for accepting the chronology now proposed for East Rudolf* [Turkana]."[91] The age of the KBS Tuff was reported in *Nature* to be *"securely dated at 2.6 m.y."*[92] Richard Leakey affirmed their confidence in the reported age and its agreement with multiple dating methods stating:

> ... there is no evidence to suggest that the 2.61 +- 0.26 m.y. BP date from the KBS Tuff is unreliable (personal communication from J.A. Miller). The continued paleomagnetic studies by Dr. A Brock (University of Nairobi) together with faunal correlations further strengthen confidence in this date.[93]

The argon date (2.6 mya) was published and accepted without issue in 1970.[94] This was the calm before the storm. A few years later the human-looking skull KNM-ER 1470 was discovered.[95] Its stratigraphic position beneath the KBS Tuff indicated it was 2.9 million years old. Then more anatomically modern human bones were found beneath the KBS Tuff. These new findings made many paleo-experts extremely uncomfortable. The age of the KBS Tuff, associated artifacts, and human bones were *"much questioned in private anthropological and paleontological circles."*[96] Researchers sought to re-date the KBS Tuff in hopes of obtaining the required earlier age (1.8 million years old) compatible with the age of the *Homo* bones seen at Olduvai Gorge. Eventually they succeeded—the desired age was "determined" (pre-determined), but only thanks to selective use of data.

1975: New Dates Conflict—Previous Dates Dismissed as "Contamination"

Curtis, Drake, and Hampel were the first to contest the potassium-argon and argon-argon age of 2.6 million years. New samples were collected and re-dated using the potassium-argon method. In the journal *Nature* (1975) they reported a revised age for the KBS Tuff.[97] The new dates ranged from 1.5 million years old to 6.9 million years old. Ages in the range of 2.0–6.9 million years old were seen as discrepant and *"thought to be caused by detrital contamination."*[98] Those unwelcome

90. Hurford A.J., Fission track dating of a vitric tuff from East Rudolf, North Kenya, *Nature* 249:236-237, 1974.

91. Fitch F.J. *et al.*, Dating of the rock succession containing fossil hominids at East Rudolf, Kenya, *Nature* 251:214, 1974.

92. Leakey R., Evidence for an Advanced Plio-Pleistocene Hominid from East Rudolf, Kenya, *Nature* 242:447-450, April 1973.

93. Leakey R., Further Evidence of Lower Pleistocene Hominids from East Rudolf, North Kenya, 1972, *Nature* 242:170-173, March 1973.

94. Fitch F.J. and Miller J.A., Radioisotopic Age Determinations of Lake Rudolf Artefact Site, *Nature* 226:226-228, 1970.

95. Leakey R.E., Evidence for an Advanced Plio-Pleistocene Hominid from East Rudolf, Kenya, *Nature* 242:447, 1973.

96. Hurford A.J. *et al.*, Fission-track dating of pumice from KBS Tuff, East Rudolf, Kenya, *Nature* 263:738-740, 1976.

97. Curtis G.H. *et al.*, Age of KBS Tuff in Koobi Fora Formation, East Rudolf, Kenya, *Nature* 258:395-398, 1975

98. McDougall I. *et al.*, K-Ar age estimate for the KBS Tuff, East Turkana, Kenya, *Nature* 284:230-234, 1980.

dates were omitted. The researchers noted another puzzling observation: samples taken from different areas of the KBS Tuff yielded different ages. They reported two ages for what was previously thought to be the same volcanic event, 1.6 million years old and 1.82 million years old. Which was the correct age for the KBS Tuff? Curtis and colleagues suggested that the conflicting ages were caused by *"different eruptive centers"*—whereby two different pumices had been sampled.[99] The samples were thought to come from two eruptions, separated in time by 200,000 years.[100] In a later publication, Curtis *et al.* suggested another idea. The younger age of 1.6 million years was supposedly caused by an error in potassium analyses, not different eruptive centers.[101,102] Eliminating this younger age was necessary to accept the more agreeable age of 1.82 million years that was more attractive for the origin of *Homo*. Regardless, neither of those dates (1.6 mya and 1.82 mya) agreed with the argon ages (2.6 mya) previously reported by Fitch and Miller. To explain this discrepancy, Curtis *et al.* assumed that the older age resulted from the presence of older pumice blocks in the KBS Tuff.[103] Curtis wrote: *"in spite of great care to prevent contamination, contamination nevertheless occurred in the samples used by Fitch and Miller. Significantly, the Ar/Ar method did not indicate this contamination."*[104] How could this be? Miller and Fitch insisted their samples were pure and free of contamination:

> … competence was shown at every stage in the process of extraction, selection, preparation and cleaning of the various feldspar sub-subsamples dated in 1969 and 1981, sufficient to eliminate any possible contamination risk. For example, both the 1969 K-Ar and $^{40}Ar/^{39}Ar$ step heating sub-samples were prepared from individual hand picked selections of the very best of the clean-looking, sharply reflective euhedra, mostly between 5 mm and 10 mm in diameter, in the Behrensmeyer concentrate.[105]

Nevertheless, Curtis and colleagues assumed contamination, even though both teams agreed there was no direct evidence of contamination. Perhaps the problem was not contamination. Perhaps the real problem was that the dates did not agree with the accepted ape-to-man timeline that the paleo-community had adopted. Curtis *et al.* rejected the 2.6 million year age of the KBS Tuff proposed by Fitch and Miller, and further rejected their own potassium-argon ages (2.0–6.9 mya and 1.6 mya). All of the "disagreeable" dates were dismissed. This conveniently allowed them to settle on 1.82 million years for the age of the KBS Tuff, exactly where they wanted it to be. The dates were forced to submit to the established narrative.

99. Curtis G.H. *et al.*, Age of KBS Tuff in Koobi Fora Formation, East Rudolf, Kenya, *Nature* 258:395-398, 1975.

100. Hillhouse J.W. *et al.*, Additional results on paleomagnetic stratigraphy of the Koobi Fora Formation, east of Lake Turkana (Lake Rudolf), Kenya, *Nature* 265, 1977, p.412.

101. Drake R.E. *et al.*, KBS Tuff dating and geochronology of tuffaceous sediments in the Koobi For a and Shungura Formations, East Africa, *Nature* 283:368-371, 1980.

102. Hay R.L., The KBS Tuff controversy may be ended, *Nature* 284:401, 1980.

103. Curtis G.H. *et al.*, Age of KBS Tuff in Koobi Fora Formation, East Rudolf, Kenya, *Nature* 258:395-398, 1975.

104. Curtis G.H., Improvements in potassium-argon dating: 1962-1975, *World Archaeology* 7:2, 198-209, 1975.

105. Fitch F.J. *et al.*, Dating of the KBS Tuff and *Homo rudolfensis*, *J Hum Evol* 30:277-286, 1996.

1976: Recomputation of Previous Analyses—Bad Dates Due to "Argon Loss"?

A year after Curtis *et al.'s* publication, Fitch, Hooker, and Miller reported in *Nature* (1976) a recomputation of their original argon data from the samples collected in 1969.[106] This time they used a more accurate "constant of proportionality" value (J) in their calculations. They also adjusted their previous age of 2.6 million years down to 2.42 million years using an isochron analysis. The same samples collected in 1969 from the KBS Tuff were also re-dated using potassium-argon and argon-argon techniques. Additional samples retrieved from 1971–1973 were further subjected to argon-argon analyses. These new argon dates further confirmed their revised age of ~2.4 million years. But complications arose. The apparent ages were broadly scattered between 0.5–2.4 million years old. Was the KBS Tuff much younger than they had thought? A younger age was unacceptable to them. So they assumed thermal activity had resulted in "argon loss." This allegedly produced the misleading appearance of a much younger age. Fitch *et al.* explain:

> Because great care was taken in their preparation… the results are very unlikely to be marred by contamination. The scatter of apparent ages obtained must be explained, therefore, by the loss of varying amounts of Ar from the feldspars. If it is accepted that contamination is not significant in these samples, then a minimum age of 2.4 Myr for the KBS Tuff is indicated…. [107]

An age of 2.4 million years still conflicted with the younger dates obtained by other researchers. To deal with this Fitch and colleagues took issue with the potassium-argon age (1.82 mya) published a year earlier by Curtis *et al.* These younger age estimates were assumed to be *"the date of total argon loss."*[108] In other words, the younger apparent ages reported by Curtis *et al.* were dismissed, and assumed to be caused by a thermal heating event that reset the argon "clock" (just like Fitch *et al.* assumed with their own anomalously young dates). They also rejected Curtis *et al.'s* claim that their previously published argon ages of 2.6 million years old was due to contamination from older pumice material mixed into the KBS Tuff. Their new isochron age supposedly confirmed that the true age of the KBS Tuff was 2.4 million years, and was not influenced by the contamination of older pumice blocks.

Here we see when a sample is "too old" for a research team's liking, contamination from an older eruption can be assumed without any clear evidence. And when a sample is "too young" for a competing research team's liking, it can be blamed on "argon loss" without any clear evidence. As Brent Dalrymple, geophysicist of the U.S. Geological Survey, Menlo Park, California criticized, *"These two mechanisms*

106. Fitch F.J. *et al.*, ^{40}Ar/^{39}Ar dating of the KBS Tuff in Koobi Fora Formation, East Rudolf, Kenya, *Nature* 263:740-744, 1976.

107. Fitch F.J. *et al.*, ^{40}Ar/^{39}Ar dating of the KBS Tuff in Koobi Fora Formation, East Rudolf, Kenya, *Nature* 263:740-744, 1976.

108. Fitch F.J. *et al.*, ^{40}Ar/^{39}Ar dating of the KBS Tuff in Koobi Fora Formation, East Rudolf, Kenya, *Nature* 263:740-744, 1976.

[invoking contamination and argon loss] *could be used to explain anything, as their effects on potassium-technique are exactly opposite.*"[109]

The KBS Tuff controversy reveals that what determines the age of hominin bones is not actual dating methods, but rather the researcher's *a priori* commitment to a particular model of hominin evolution. Fitch and Miller agreed with Leakey's view that *Homo* had evolved more than 2 million years ago. Not surprisingly their dates ranged from 2.4–2.6 million years. Curtis and colleagues, on the other hand, agreed with Johanson and the popular "group think" of most of the paleo-community, that the origin of the genus *Homo* was established roughly 1.8 million years ago, consistent with the findings at Olduvai Gorge. Not surprisingly, their dates were around 1.8 million years. The dates obtained by each of these research teams reflected their respective personal biases. This well-documented exchange between two competing research teams exposes the role of "scientific politics" when dating rocks and ash tuffs associated with bones and artifacts. The hominin timeline was not established simply on the basis of objective scientific inquiry. Instead, dates have often been force-fitted to align with whatever ape-to-man story is preferred by a certain group of paleo-researchers. A broad scatter of apparent ages and selective use of desirable dates makes this possible.

1976: Fission Track Dates Support a KBS Tuff Age of 2.4–2.6 Million Years?

Anthony Hurford from Birkbeck College, University London and colleagues dated pumice samples from the KBS Tuff using fission track methods. The goal of the new fission track analyses was to bring resolution to the conflict between the potassium-argon ages determined by Curtis *et al.* (1.82 mya) and the potassium-argon and argon-argon ages determined by Fitch *et al.* (2.4–2.6 mya). Their results were published in the same issue of *Nature* as Fitch *et al.*'s recalculation, in 1976.[110]

Hurford *et al.* dated two pumice samples from the KBS Tuff. One of these was the same one that was potassium-argon dated by Curtis *et al.* Interestingly, neither of those samples yielded an age consistent with what Curtis *et al.* reported (1.82 mya). Instead they obtained an average age of 2.44 million years. Their findings led them to reject the claims made by Curtis *et al.* that the original argon analyses by Fitch *et al.* were due to contamination from older pumice blocks mixed into the KBS Tuff. Their new fission track age seemed to confirm Fitch and Miller's estimation of 2.4–2.6 million years old. They also noted its agreement with the paleomagnetic stratigraphy reported earlier by Brock and Isaac.[111] But how did they explain the younger potassium-argon ages proposed by Curtis *et al.*? Hurford assumed that there must have been a reheating event (argon loss) that resulted

---

109. Lewin R., *Bones of Contention*, 2nd Edition, Univ. Chicago Press, Chicago, p. 204, 1987.

110. Hurford A.J. *et al.*, Fission-track dating of pumice from KBS Tuff, East Rudolf, Kenya, *Nature* 263:738-740, 1976.

111. A. Brock A. and Isaac G.L.I., Paleomagnetic stratigraphy and chronology of hominind-bearing sediments east of Lake Rudolf, Kenya, *Nature* 247:344-348, 1974.

in an anomalously young apparent age. This seems to be a popular explanation whenever a date is "too young" for a particular theory.

It is interesting that Hurford *et al.* noted in their paper that different grains within the same pumice sample gave different fission track ages. Some yielded an average age of 2.44 million years, whereas others ranged from 290 million years old to 380 million years old! How could pumice samples taken from the same eruption event (the KBS Tuff) result in such widely discrepant ages? The answer offered by these researchers was that the older dates were of course, caused by contamination. They write, *"These results confirm that the pumice blocks had been contaminated by older zircons, possibly during eruption, or by the penetration of detrital grains into the pumice vesicle, during transportation or on deposition."*[112] These older zircon grains (and all other grains of a similar type that would have yielded much older ages) were excluded from the fission track analysis. Yet there was no way to prove zircon contamination.

There is a pattern here. Whenever dates are "too old" to agree with the popular narrative, they are assumed to have been inherited from an older source rock. Whenever the dates are "too young," a reheating event is assumed to have occurred some time in the past. In the end, only the dates that agree with the paradigm are seen as acceptable. Fission track dating is especially susceptible to the "cherry picking" of dates that agree with the paradigm. This is because fission track dating (just like single crystal argon-argon analysis) involves separating out individual zircon grains. Different zircon grains commonly yield very different ages. This allows researchers to "shop around" for specific grains that give them an age they are looking for. Zircon grains that do not give the "correct" age are excluded for any number of unverifiable reasons (penetration of detrital contamination, argon loss, etc.). All too often, the desired dates are selectively chosen simply because they support a particular hominin theory.

1977–1981: All Previous Dates Rejected to Agree with "Group Think"

By the late 1970s and early 80s all of the previously published dates for the KBS Tuff in the range of 2.4–2.6 million years old had been rejected. The potassium-argon dates, argon-argon dates, paleomagnetic dates, fission track dates, and faunal correlations were all abandoned. New dates were offered to replace these older dates. Remarkably, all of those same dating methods were made to agree with the pre-decided age of 1.8 million years—which satisfied the paleo-community. But this was only possible by the selective use of data and preferentially omitting dates that were not compatible with the ape-to-man story. Below is a brief summary of the subsequent studies that have sought to re-date the KBS Tuff.

---

112. Hurford A.J. *et al.*, Fission-track dating of pumice from KBS Tuff, East Rudolf, Kenya, *Nature* 263:738-740, 1976.

A faunal study by White and Harris (*Science*, 1977)[113] based on pig teeth (instead of the elephant fossils cited earlier) suggested that *"deposits below the KBS tuff were equivalent to fossiliferous beds in the Omo basin and Olduvai Gorge that had been dated about 1.8 Myr."*[114] Hillhouse *et al.* published a new paleomagnetic age (*Nature*, 1977) that agreed with Curtis *et al.*'s potassium-argon age of 1.8 million years.[115] Curtis *et al.* published new potassium-argon ages to confirm their earlier age estimates (*Nature*, 1980).[116] In their paper they omitted the 1.6-million-year-old potassium-argon age that they had previously reported. These younger dates were allegedly caused by *"systematic error in potassium analyses in all KBS analyses which had given a 1.6 Myr date."* This conveniently brought all of the discrepant ages of 1.6 million years old up to 1.8 million years old, as their narrative required.

Gleadow from the University of Melbourne obtained new fission track ages (*Nature*, 1980),[117] yet the dates were widely scattered. As in Hurford's fission analysis, different mineral grains yielded different ages. An age that was "too young" (1.54 mya) was considered anomalous and was excluded from their age estimates. Other mineral grains sampled from the KBS Tuff seemed to be from 24-million-years-old to 550-million-years-old. These were assumed to be *"inherited zircons"* from much older volcanic eruptions *"probably to the east or north-east."* Consequently, only the zircon grains that yielded the desired age were chosen. Gleadow explained that the fission track technique they utilized allowed them to pick and choose specific mineral grains that agreed with the sought-after age. Gleadow explained:

> Some detrital contamination was present in all zircon concentrations dated, presumably from the small amounts of tuffaceous matrix which worked deep into vesicles and fractures in the pumice. One of the major advantages of the external detector method of fission track dating, however, is that it permits the determination of ages on individual mineral grains, even at very small grain size (<100 μm). Thus it is possible to discriminate between the young primary igneous zircons and the old detrital zircons.[118]

How did Gleadow explain the older fission track and argon ages published by other researchers? Gleadow dismissed the fission track dates reported previously by Hurford, and offered his own fission track age for the KBS Tuff of 1.87 million years old (but only after excluding all zircon grains that did not agree with this age). He then rejected the potassium-argon and argon-argon ages determined by

113. White T.D. and Harris J.M., Suid Evolution and Correlations of African Hominid Localities, *Science* 198(4312):13-21, 1977.
114. Hay R.L., The KBS Tuff controversy may be ended, *Nature* 284:401, 1980.
115. Hillhouse J.W. *et al.*, Additional results on paleomagnetic stratigraphy of the Koobi Fora Formation, east of Lake Turkana (Lake Rudolf), Kenya, *Nature* 265:412, 1977.
116. Drake R.E. *et al.*, KBS Tuff dating and geochronology of tuffaceous sediments in the Koobi Fora and Shungura Formations, East Africa, *Nature* 283:368-371, 1980.
117. Gleadow A.J.W., Fission track age of the KBS Tuff and associated hominid remains in northern Kenya, *Nature* 284:225-230, 1980.
118. Gleadow A.J.W., Fission track age of the KBS Tuff and associated hominid remains in northern Kenya, *Nature* 284:225-230, 1980.

Fitch and Miller. Gleadow reasoned, *"The preservation of these detrital mineral ages fully justifies contamination as a plausible explanation for the older K-Ar ages and is strong evidence against the existence of previously postulated overprinting* [thermal reheating] *events."*[119] Individual mineral grains in the same sample often yield very different ages. It seems that ages that disagree with what the researchers are hoping to confirm (in this case an age of around 1.8 million years) can be discarded at will.

Another study published by McDougall, Gleadow, and colleagues (*Nature*, 1980)[120] reported new potassium-argon age estimates for the KBS Tuff. Not surprisingly, these new dates were in *"excellent agreement"* with Gleadow's fission track ages described above (and reported in the same issue of *Nature*). The new potassium-argon ages averaged 1.89 million years old. But once again, "anomalously old" dates (7.46 mya and 4.11 mya) were discarded. McDougall *et al.* explained that these older ages were allegedly caused by *"small amounts of old detrital K-feldspar in the aliquants used in the argon extractions."*[121] This was assumed to be true even though they admit that such *"old detrital K-feldspar"* could not be identified upon careful examination of the mineral concentrate.

Finally, Ian McDougall of Australian National University performed an argon-argon analysis on pumice samples taken from the KBS Tuff (*Nature*, 1981).[122] The new argon-argon measurements yielded a "concordant" age of 1.88 million years.

Table 2. How dates can be revised to agree with the "group think" of the paleo-community and the ape-to-man narrative as a whole. Compare the dates before and after finding *Homo* bones below the KBS Tuff (i.e., after the 1975 Bishop Conference in London pre-decided its age).

Dating Method	Age (mya) Before Finding *Homo* below KBS Tuff	Age (mya) After Finding *Homo* below KBS Tuff
Potassium-Argon	2.61 (Fitch & Miller, 1970) 2.42 (Fitch & Miller, 1976)*	1.82 (Curtis *et al.*, 1975) 1.89 (Gleadow *et al.*, 1980) 1.8 (Drake & Curtis *et al.*, 1980)
Argon-Argon	2.6 (Fitch & Miller, 1970)	1.88 (McDougall, 1981)
Fission Track	2.6 (Hurford, 1974)	1.87 (Gleadow, 1980)
Paleomagnetic	2.61 (Brock & Isaac, 1974)	1.8 (Hillhouse, 1977)
Faunal Correlation	2.5 (Maglio, 1972)	1.8 (White & Harris, 1977)

*Reported after the Bishop Conference in 1975, yet Fitch *et al.* defended their earlier estimates.

In summary, all of the dating methods that had aligned to confirm an age of 2.4–2.6 million years for the KBS Tuff were tossed out, and all of those same dating methods were then forced to align with a new age that was acceptable to the paleo-community (roughly 1.8 million years) (Table 2). In 1980, a paper was published

---

119. Gleadow A.J.W., Fission track age of the KBS Tuff and associated hominid remains in northern Kenya, *Nature* 284:225-230, 1980.
120. McDougall I. *et al.*, K-Ar age estimate for the KBS Tuff, East Turkana, Kenya, *Nature* 284:230-234, 1980.
121. McDougall I. *et al.*, K-Ar age estimate for the KBS Tuff, East Turkana, Kenya, *Nature* 284:230-234, 1980.
122. McDougall I., ^{40}Ar/^{39}Ar age spectra from the KBS Tuff, Koobi Fora Formation, *Nature* 294:120-124, 1981.

in *Nature* that headlined *"The KBS Tuff controversy may be ended."*[123] However, subsequent publications continued to call into question the age of the KBS Tuff. For instance, Miller and Fitch published a paper in the *Journal of Human Evolution* in 1996.[124] They remained convinced that the true age of the KBS Tuff is definitely older than 1.9 million years, and possibly as old as 2.5 million years, in accord with their earlier analyses.

Concluding Remarks on Dating of KBS Tuff and Impact on Modern Theory

The dating of the KBS Tuff was a pivotal point in the history of paleoanthropology. Its presumed age gave rise to the modern theory that is now universally taught. The dating of the KBS Tuff represented the collision of two competing views regarding the origin of early man: the Lake Turkana group headed by Richard Leakey and the Berkeley group headed by Clark Howell.

Richard Leakey had adopted the view of his father and mother, Louis and Mary Leakey, that the genus *Homo* was much older than 2 million years. Their view was that *Australopithecus* and *Homo* coexisted and were two parallel lineages, rather than a single evolving lineage wherein an *Australopithecus* ancestor gave rise to *Homo*. Richard Leakey's Lake Turkana research team (Fitch, Miller, Isaac, Brock, Harris, and others) embraced the Leakey model of the "great antiquity" of man. The discoveries at Koobi Fora, Kenya in the late 60s and early 70s, including occupation sites, stone tools, human-looking bones, and the human-looking skull (KNM-ER 1470) found below the KBS Tuff (then dated at 2.9 mya), were seen as strong support for their model.

Many other leading members of the paleo-community accepted an opposing model of human origins. Researchers from Berkeley, such as Clark Howell, Donald Johanson, Garniss Curtis, and those who had sided with them (Cooke, White, McDougall, and others) believed the origin of the genus *Homo* was closer to 1.8 million years ago. The Berkeley group maintained that *Australopithecus* gave rise to *Homo,* and these scientists wished to claim that the KBS Tuff controversy was *"settled."* If the KBS Tuff had not been re-dated closer to 1.8 million years old, Lucy's kind (*Australopithecus afarensis*), could not have been promoted as the direct ancestor to the genus *Homo*. Lucy would have been seen as just another "side-branch," an extinct australopithecine ape of little importance. John Reader speaks of these two competing views:

> Richard Leakey shared his father's belief's that human evolution had been a very lengthy affair, and *Australopithecus* had played no part in it since the two lines split from the common ancestor about six or seven million years ago. Some of his contemporaries championed the opposite view, that *Australopithecus* was indeed the human ancestor, and that the *Homo* and *Australopithecus* lineages split from a

123. Hay R.L., The KBS Tuff controversy may be ended, *Nature* 284:401, 1980.
124. Fitch F.J. *et al.*, Dating of the KBS Tuff and *Homo rudolfensis*, *J Hum Evol* 30:277-286, 1996.

common ancestor little more than two million years ago.[125]

Thus the lines were drawn in the sand, even before the age of the KBS Tuff had been re-dated. The truth about the KBS Tuff controversy is that half of the paleo-community had already pre-decided its "revised age" from the moment the human skull KNM-ER 1470 was found in underlying strata. An age of 2.9 million years was simply not going to work with their preferred timeline regarding the origin of man (2.9 was too old for their model). Richard Leakey saw what was at stake: *"Either we toss out this skull, or we toss out our theories of man... It simply fits no previous models of human beings"* and *"leaves in ruins the notion that all early fossils can be arranged in an orderly sequence of evolutionary change."*[126] And so the Berkeley team "knew" the KBS Tuff could not possibly be as old as the dating methods indicated. From that point on, they were determined to keep re-dating the KBS Tuff until they obtained the age that fit their model.

It was in 1975 at the Bishop Conference on anthropology and geology in London that the age of the KBS Tuff was pre-decided (before the re-dating). It was there that the Lake Turkana team went toe to toe with the Berkeley team. The central focus of the meeting was to determine the "true" age of the KBS Tuff. Geologist Basil Cooke from Dalhousie University, Halifax was called upon to share the results of his studies on pig fossils from various sites in East Africa. Cooke strongly advocated that pig teeth from below the KBS Tuff in East Turkana, Kenya, correlated with those found in beds nearby in Omo and in Bed I at Olduvai Gorge, Tanzania, which at that time was believed to represent the origin of *Homo*.[127] Both sites were dated to 1.8 million years using the potassium-argon method. These dates were assumed to be reliable. This meant that the KBS Tuff needed to be revised to the same age (assuming his faunal study of pig teeth was accurate). Leading members of the paleo-community favored the revised age of 1.8 million years. Johanson spoke of the impact Cooke's presentation made on the paleo-community writing, *"Nearly everyone but the Lake Turkana team went away convinced that the KBS tuff and the skull-1470 dates would have to be corrected."*[128] John Reader wrote similarly that paleo-experts *"were prepared to accept the word of one geologist, Basil Cooke, before that of an entire multi-disciplinary [East Turkana] research team."*[129] It is no coincidence that not long after the conference in London, a flurry of papers were published that all confirmed the "new" age of 1.8 million years (from authors who had attended the meeting).

Fossil pig teeth were pivotal in establishing the current paradigm. If the dates of

125. Reader J., *Missing Links: In Search of Human Origins*, Oxford University Press, New York, p. 340, 2011.

126. Leakey R., Skull 1470, *National Geographic* 143:819-829, 1973.

127. Cooke, H.B.S., Suidae from Plio-Pleistocene strata of the Rudolf Basin, In: Coppens, Y., *et al.* (eds.) *Remains Attributed to Homo in East Rudolf Succession, Earliest Man and Environments in the Lake Rudolf Basin*, University of Chicago Press, Chicago, pp. 251-263, 1976.

128. Johanson D.C. and Edey M.A., *Lucy: The Beginnings of Humankind*, Simon & Schuster, New York, p. 240, 1981.

129. Reader J., *Missing Links: In Search of Human Origins*, Oxford University Press, New York, p. 353, 2011.

Leakey's stone tools, human bones, and human skull had not been revised, the Leakey model would be the basis of the modern theory of human evolution. Because the pig teeth correlations suggested by Cooke won out, the model of *Australopithecus* as the ancestor to *Homo* became the currently reigning paradigm, which centers on Lucy and Johanson. The pig teeth won. As Marvin Lubenow, life-long researcher of human evolution writes:

> In the 10-year controversy over the dating of one of the most important human fossils ever discovered, the pigs won. The pigs won over the elephants. The pigs won over potassium-argon dating. The pigs won over argon[40]/argon[39] dating. The pigs won over fission-track dating. They won over paleomagnetism. The pigs took it all. But in reality, it wasn't the pigs that won. It was evolution [the ape-to-man story] that won. In the dating game, evolution always wins.[130]

Examples like the KBS Tuff show that when it comes to dating hominin bones and artifacts the paradigm overrides the data. The paradigm wins over data, even when all of the dating methods point to a specific age (such as 2.4–2.6 million years). All of those dates can be dismissed and then all of the same dating methods can then be used to yield an entirely different age (such as ~1.8 million years). The power of the paradigm and the "group think" of the paleo-community is a major factor in determining the "age" of specific hominins and the hominin timeline in general.

Earlier in this chapter we discussed the problems with the various absolute dating methods that have been used to date the KBS Tuff and other hominin sites. In particular, we discussed the well-documented problem of samples from volcanic eruptions occurring in recorded history (within the last thousand years) that yield potassium-argon ages that are millions of years old. In fact, many times the dates from recent eruptions often produce apparent ages that are compatible with the ape-to-man timeline (1–6 million years). Yet we know those dated samples cannot possibly be that old because eyewitness records verify the young age of those eruptions. This raises a very serious concern. The primary dating methods used by paleo-experts to provide an "independent check" for radioisotope ages are themselves calibrated and/or correlated by radioisotope dating—primarily the conventional potassium-argon method. This includes argon-argon dating, faunal dating, and paleomagnetic dating. Even the so-called "paleontological clock" based on pig teeth evolution is calibrated by using the potassium-argon dated beds in which the pig teeth are found.

Thus, the hominin timeline is still fundamentally based upon the assumed reliability of the potassium-argon method. As Curtis explains:

> The very important paleo-magnetic time-scale is based almost entirely on radiometric dates obtained by the conventional K/Ar method (Cox 1969), and almost all of the dates calibrating the evolution of man in south-east Asia and

---

130. Lubenow M., The Pigs Took it All, *Creation* 17(3):36-38, June 1995.

Africa have been made by this method.[131]

Therefore we conclude that it is highly probable that the true ages of the KBS Tuff and many other east African hominin sites are much younger than their potassium-argon, argon-argon, and paleomagnetic ages. The various dating methods do not provide independently-derived age estimates. This calls into question the widely accepted hominin timescale and the ape-to-man story upon which it is built.

Selective Use of Dates that Agree with the Paradigm is Common Practice

Some might think we should give the dating of the KBS Tuff a pass since the incident took place back in the 1970s. Some have even championed the controversy as a perfect example of the "progress of science."[132] It may be assumed that the selective use of data is something of the past, especially with the aid of superior analytical equipment and improved methodologies. While it is true that new techniques have been added to scientist's repertoire, all the same basic dating methods from the past are still widely used today (with some refinements and improvements). Most importantly, the potassium-argon and argon-argon dated stratigraphical record still serves as the framework for the hominin timescale.[133] All other dating methods are built on this framework, which was established in the 60s and 70s. Consequently, the most recently dated hominin bones are still plagued by the same basic problems. The KBS Tuff is not an isolated example of dating uncertainties.

Dating Naledi—The Latest Example of Selective Use of Data

In 2013 paleo-expert Lee Berger discovered over a thousand bones deep in a South African cave. The bones were said to belong to a new "almost human" species named *Homo naledi* (see chapter 10). When the discovery was announced to the world in 2015, Berger had expressed his desire for Naledi to be assigned an age ranging somewhere between 2–3 million years. This would fit nicely with his proposed status of Naledi as a transitional "bridge" species linking the australopiths to the genus *Homo*, falling directly on the path leading to modern humans (just as he had hoped with Sediba). This expectation had not been met, however, because the various dating methods he employed conflicted. At that time, Berger explained that the age of Naledi would not be reported until the discrepancies could be "resolved" and until various dating methods agreed. That was very unusual. The age of hominin bones are customarily reported concurrently with the publication of the discovery paper. But because of the complications summarized in chapter

131. Curtis G.H., Improvements in potassium-argon dating: 1962-1975, *World Archaeology* 7:2, 198-209, 1975.
132. Hay R.I., The KBS Tuff controversy may be ended, *Nature* 284:401, 1980; Hay writes that the KBS Tuff controversy *"illustrates the process of trial and error by which science progresses."*
133. Walter R.C., Age of Lucy and the First Family: Single-crystal ^{40}Ar/^{39}Ar dating of the Denen Dora and lower Kada Hadar members of the Hadar Formation, Ethiopia, *Geology* 22, 1994. *"The tempo of hominid evolution at Hadar is now precisely established, and the grain-discrete ^{40}Ar/^{39}Ar dating method was essential for this resolution."* The potassium-argon method formed the framework for the modern hominin time. Argon-argon dating refined these ages with more precise dates.

10, it took two years of testing various methodologies before the age of Naledi was reported.

In 2017, an age for Naledi was finally published by Paul Dirks *et al.* in the journal *eLife*.[134] We are now told that Naledi lived sometime between 236,000–335,000 years ago—an age far too young to serve as a critical "bridge" species as Berger had hoped. This further confirms that Naledi was fully human (see chapter 10).

Three strategies were used to constrain the age of the Naledi fossils found within the Dinaledi cave chamber: 1) reconstruct the stratigraphy of the sedimentary units at the time of fossil deposition, 2) date the surrounding sedimentary and flowstone deposits to bracket the age of the Naledi remains, and 3) directly date Naledi bones and associated fossils. Dirks *et al.* ran into serious complications with all three objectives.

It is important to realize that the reported age critically depended on correctly interpreting the depositional history of the cave sediments (its stratigraphy). Without a proper understanding of the stratigraphy the dates have no meaning. Dirks *et al.* acknowledge, "*...all efforts* [to date Naledi] *are strongly dependent on the stratigraphic interpretation of the fossils or units that are being dated.*"[135] The sedimentary units in most caves are described by paleo-experts as "*complex, discontinuous and frequently reworked*"—the Dinaledi Chamber was no exception. Most of the sedimentary units did not form clearly separated, stratified layers nor did they occur in direct contact with one another. Each unit and the fossils they contained (units 3a and 3b) were thoroughly mixed from periodic flooding events and sediment removal via drains in the bottom of the cave, which "*resulted in contrasting stratigraphic relationships across the cave.*" Dirks *et al.* note, "*...the fossils are contained in mostly unconsolidated muddy sediment with clear evidence of a mixed taphonomy* [fossil] *signature indicative of repeated cycles of reworking and more than one episode of primary deposition.*" Thus it was extremely difficult (if not impossible) for the researchers to discern the original sequence of the sedimentary units. This is a serious problem because none of the "ages" obtained using the various dating methods have any meaning if the stratigraphy cannot be reconstructed.

Dirks *et al.* emphasize the importance of understanding the depositional history of the cave sediments and associated fossils. The Dinaledi chamber is not the only hominin site that has been plagued by this problem:

> The importance of a deep understanding of the stratigraphic position of the fossils and the geological processes that led to their deposition cannot be overstated considering the extremely complex fill in many cave systems involving repeated

134. Dirks P. *et al.*, The age of *Homo naledi* and associated sediments in the Rising Star Cave, South Africa, *eLife*, 2017. DOI: 10.7554/eLife.24231
135. Dirks P. *et al.*, The age of *Homo naledi* and associated sediments in the Rising Star Cave, South Africa, *eLife*, 2017. DOI: 10.7554/eLife.24231

cycles of deposition, erosion and reworking, leading to complex and sometimes contradictory age results. This problem is well illustrated with the ongoing debate on the age of Stw 573 ('little foot') in the nearby Sterkfontein Cave, where after 20 years of dating efforts no definitive age is yet established. Another good example illustrating the difficulties of linking cave stratigraphy to a definitive age for the hominin fossils they contain is presented by the *H. floresiensis* ['Hobbit'] remains in the Liang Bau cave, Indonesia.[136]

The authors of the *eLife* paper cautioned that the stratigraphic interpretation of caves should rarely be considered conclusive. Not surprisingly, the researcher's initial interpretation of the stratigraphy did not consistently agree with the dating methods that were later applied to those units. The researchers puzzled over these conflicts: *"This apparent paradox may indicate that OSL ages are unreliable, but could mean that sub-unit 1b was deposited in reverse stratigraphic order in relation to the flowstone."*[137] At the end of their analysis they had to reinterpret the stratigraphy to agree with ages obtained from the dating methods. This introduces a dilemma: does the stratigraphy give meaning to the age estimates (as they stated in the paper) or do the age estimates give meaning to the stratigraphy (as their reevaluation assumed)? Expect the stratigraphy of the cave and the age of Naledi to be revised in upcoming papers—just as we saw with Hobbit (see chapter 5).

Several dating methods were used to date bones, teeth, and flowstones in the cave chamber.[138] Dirks explained in a *Science Daily* article upon publication of the Naledi age estimates that, *"The dating of naledi was extremely challenging. Eventually, six independent dating methods allowed us to constrain the age of this population of Homo naledi to a period known as the late Middle Pleistocene"*.[139] The claim that numerous dating methods were able to "constrain" the age of Naledi sounds impressive. However, careful examination of the technical science paper by Dirks *et al.* shows that most of those dating methods did not agree. A number of unverifiable just-so scenarios were invoked to explain away conflicting dates. The various dating methods yielded a wide range of apparent ages from which the "true" age of Naledi was selected.

All of the dating methods required several questionable assumptions that the authors were forthright in acknowledging, to their credit. The unfiltered dates obtained by each of the dating methods conflicted. To make sense out of the wide range of dates, minimum and maximum apparent ages were used to bracket the age of the Naledi fossils. The dates were further filtered to obtain more precise age constraints. Several conflicting age estimates (and even entire dating methods)

136. Dirks P. *et al.*, The age of *Homo naledi* and associated sediments in the Rising Star Cave, South Africa, *eLife*, 2017. DOI: 10.7554/eLife.24231

137. Dirks P. *et al.*, The age of *Homo naledi* and associated sediments in the Rising Star Cave, South Africa, *eLife*, 2017. DOI: 10.7554/eLife.24231

138. Dirks *et al.*, report, *"In this paper we present results of uranium-thorium (U-Th) disequilibrium, electron spin resonance (ESR), radiocarbon, and optically stimulated luminescence (OSL) dating in combination with paleomagnetic analyses, to provide ages for the fossils and surrounding deposits in the Dinaledi Chamber..."*

139. https://www.sciencedaily.com/releases/2017/05/170509083554.htm

were excluded from the analysis for variety of speculative reasons, many of which could not be validated. The selective use of dates ultimately led to "concordant ages." It is likely that none of the dates obtained represent the true age of the Naledi fossils. Below is a summary of the various methods used to date Naledi.

Carbon-14 dating was used to date the fossil material, yet those results gave an age for Naledi that was too young (33,000 and 35,500 years old for two of the dated bones), and so these dates were rejected on the basis of presumed contamination.[140]

Uranium-lead (U-Pb) was used to date the flowstone deposits surrounding the fossils, but the researchers found that the flowstones were rich in clay, which is known to contribute to open system behavior (producing erroneous ages). Dirks *et al.* note, *"flowstones in the Dinaledi Chamber contained excessive common Pb caused by the inclusion of detrital material (mainly clays) making them unsuitable for U-Pb dating."*[141] Uranium-thorium (U-Th) dating is also susceptible to open system behavior due to clay contamination. The researchers acknowledged this in their paper, yet they decided to use U-Th as a primary dating method anyway.

Optically stimulated luminescence (OSL) was used but the results conflicted with other dating methods and so the method was deemed unreliable and not useful. Dirks *et al.* write, *"OSL dating of cave sediments is complex and difficult to interpret (e.g., Roberts et al., 2009), and probably imprecise."*[142]

Paleomagnetic dating was used, but it merely gave a minimum age estimate for the cave itself, but did not help to precisely date the fossils themselves. The only dating methods that actually addressed the age of the bones, and were acceptable to the researchers, was uranium-thorium dating (U-Th) and electron spin resonance (ESR). Yet even those two methods yielded conflicting dates. For instance, the baboon tooth found just centimeters below the Naledi remains gave an ESR age of 721,000 years, yet its U-Th age was 115,000 years. Obviously both ages cannot be correct. The U-Th age was omitted in favor of the ESR age and it was assumed that the significantly older baboon tooth was reworked into the younger Naledi deposit.

Different parts of the same tooth gave different ages (i.e., dentin versus enamel). All of the three Naledi teeth that were U-Th dated were rejected, apparently because the age estimates were too young (43,000–146,000 years).[143] Different parts of the same flowstone sample, separated by just a few centimeters, gave

140. The source of contamination was said to have been caused by *"extensive secondary $CaCO_3$ replacement..."* Dirks P. *et al.*, *eLife*, 2017, p. 26.

141. Dirks P. *et al.*, The age of *Homo naledi* and associated sediments in the Rising Star Cave, South Africa, *eLife*, 2017. DOI: 10.7554/eLife.24231

142. Dirks P. *et al.*, The age of *Homo naledi* and associated sediments in the Rising Star Cave, South Africa, *eLife*, 2017. DOI: 10.7554/eLife.24231

143. Dirks *et al.* insist that the U-Th dates for the teeth are *"minimum age estimates"* and not the depositional age of the fossils. It was assumed that the young ages represented uranium uptake events during wet periods in the chamber.

widely differing ages (88,000 and 242,000 years). The different ages for the same samples was difficult to interpret.[144] Both of the dating methods used to date Naledi (U-Th and ESR) relied upon several unknown variables and assumptions about past conditions that are not testable (all measurements taken were based on present-day conditions). Some of those unknowns include the intensity of radiation in the cave since the bones were deposited (relevant to ESR dating) and the initial flowstone concentration of uranium and thorium, among many other uncertainties. Indeed, the U-Th method yielded a very wide scatter of ages (9,000 to 500,000 years)—a clear indicator that this widely-used dating method is subject to open system behavior, and is therefore unreliable.

The many dating methods employed by Berger et al. gave an incredible spectrum of ages (an 840,000 year gap between the youngest and oldest dates). Yet the authors apparently had no problem selectively ignoring almost all of the data (based upon untestable speculations), and chose the dates they were most comfortable with. It seems quite clear that the true age of Naledi is still unknown. But it is evident that Naledi did not live millions of years ago, was not a sub-human precursor, and co-existed with modern man. Separate evidence suggests that the Naledi bones are significantly younger than their reported ages (see chapter 10).

Ongoing Problems with Dating Erectus

Erectus has also been plagued with dating problems. In 1996, published dates (using ESR and U-series) for Erectus in Java suggested they lived as recent as 35,000–50,000 thousand years ago. This means Erectus would have overlapped with modern humans in the region. This extensive coexistence in time and space led the researchers to conclude that Erectus is unlikely to be the direct ancestor to modern humans. Many paleo-experts ("splitters") did not like this possibility, and the dates were rejected or ignored by many in the field. Since then, the same Java sites have been re-dated using some of the same techniques. The new dates show that Erectus did not live in the region quite as recently as earlier estimates. Yet the new dating methods did not agree with one another, leaving scientists with an enigma. Researchers in the journal *PLOS ONE* report:

> Here, we report $^{40}Ar/^{39}Ar$ incremental heating analyses and new ESR/U-series age estimates from the "20 m terrace" at Ngandong and Jigar. Both data sets are internally consistent and provide no evidence for reworking, yet they are inconsistent with one another. The $^{40}Ar/^{39}Ar$ analyses give an average age of 546±12 ka (sd ± 5 se) for both sites, the first reliable radiometric indications of a middle Pleistocene component for the terrace. Given the technical accuracy and consistency of the analyses, the argon ages represent either the actual age or the maximum age for the terrace and are significantly older than previous estimates. Most of the ESR/U-series results are older as well, but the oldest that meets all modeling criteria is 143 ka+20/-17. Most samples indicated leaching of uranium

---

144. Dirks *et al.* write, "The U uptake history appears complex and heterogeous, and probably involved several episodes." p. 21

and likely represent either the actual or the minimum age of the terrace. Given known sources of error, the U-series results could be consistent with a middle Pleistocene age. However, the ESR and ^{40}Ar/^{39}Ar ages preclude one another."[145]

To summarize, in 1996, researchers concluded using different dating methods that Erectus from Java lived recently, about 35,000–40,000 years ago. More recently the same sites were re-dated to be significantly older, yet this time the two different techniques gave two different answers. The argon-argon age is 550,000 years whereas the ESR/U-series age is 140,000 years. The researchers note that both methods provide internally consistent results yet they clearly disagree with one another.

Conclusion—No Hominin Bones are "Securely" Dated

Almost every hominin and hominin-bearing site that has ever been discovered (i.e., Erectus sites in Indonesia and Australia, several Neanderthal sites, Hobbit, Naledi, Lucy and her kind Afarensis, Habilis, the KBS Tuff, and various australopith sites in South Africa, etc.) have been dated and re-dated multiple times as techniques change and as theories are continually revised with new fossil discoveries. On a regular basis, dates that were once accepted as "secure" are abandoned, and new dates that are considered "more reasonable" are established.

**Latest Developments

Most recently, new findings of fossilized modern human-looking footprints from Crete were reported in *Proceedings of the Geologists' Association* (2017).[146] The footprints present a serious evolutionary dilemma for the paleo-community because of their presumed age: 5.7 million years (2 million years older than the Laetoli footprints). This leaves them with only two possible resolutions—both of which are problematic for those who hope to hold on to the ape-to-man story. The first solution is to push back the origin of the genus *Homo* much earlier than previously thought. But this would mean Lucy and Ardi (and any other Pliocene-age candidates) can no longer be seen as credible ancestors to man. This would also require a total rewrite of the modern theory and would essentially erase the last 50 years of paleo-research—all previous claims about the origin of man would be invalid. An alternate solution would be to call into question the reliability of the dating methods, and re-date the Crete footprints to obtain an age that agrees with the current ape-to-man narrative (just as they did with the KBS Tuff). In *Contested Bones* we suggest a third possibility—that the dating methods are fundamentally flawed and that the ape-to-man story is untenable.

---

145. Indriati E. *et al.*, The Age of the 20 Meter Solo River Terrace, Java, Indonesia and the Survival of *Homo erectus* in Asia, *PLOS ONE* 6(6):e21562l, 2011. DOI: 10.1371/journal.pone.0021562.
146. Gierlinski G.D. *et al.*, Possible hominin footprints from the late Miocene (c. 5.7 Ma) of Crete? *Proceedings of the Geologists' Association* 621:1-14, 2017. DOI: 10.1016/j.pgeola.2017.07.006

CHAPTER 13

Genetic Evidence
Validation of the Ape-to-Man Story?

If ENCODE is right, then evolution is wrong.[1]

Evolutionary geneticist Dan Graur of the University of Houston

Does Genetic Evidence Prove What the Fossil Record Has Failed to Show?

This book is primarily about the bones that are claimed to prove the evolutionary transition from ape to man. We have outlined a series of major problems that apply broadly to the hominin fossil record. We have shown evidence that human artifacts and *Homo* bones are routinely found in the same bone beds (and hence are in the same timeframe) as the earliest presumed precursors. We have further shown that virtually all the important hominin fossils are still fiercely contested within the paleo-community. The fossil evidence, while sometimes suggestive, does not bring any type of certainty to the proposition that apes evolved into humans.

However, most paleoanthropologists, even the ones who openly acknowledge all the problems in their field, remain 100% certain that apes evolved into man. Why is this? We suggest that this is due partly to the power of the broader evolutionary paradigm, and partly to the power of consensus (group) thinking. But there are more specific reasons why so many are so certain.

It is true that most scientists are committed to the evolutionary framework, yet it is surprising that this strong commitment is not usually based upon the scientist's own personal experience or expertise. Most scientists need to look to experts in other fields (or even the popular media), to find support for their certainty about human evolution. This can become circular—scientists are consistently looking to other scientists to justify their personal certainty about human evolution. But there is one field that most boldly claims that it has the real proof of human evolution. That field is not paleoanthropology, but is genetics. For this reason it is important for us to briefly look at the genetic evidence that bears on the ape-to-man question.

---

1. Grauer D., Presentation given at 2013 meeting of the Society for Molecular Biology, http://www.slideshare.net/dangrauer1953/update-version-of-the-smbesesbe-lecture-on-encode-junk-dna-graur-december-2013.

One of us has studied genetics for nearly 40 years (focusing on the topic of human evolution for the last 10–15 years), and the other author has been studying genetic questions associated with the origin of man for more than six years. Contrary to popular opinion, the genetic evidence does not support ape-to-man evolution. In fact, it strongly refutes it.

Four Profound Genetic Problems with Ape-to-Man Evolution

Problem 1—Creating Networks of New Biological Information: Every form of life is genetically programmed to be what it is, and to do what it does. This is not a figure of speech—life is literally programmed. Each form of life has, within its genome, the programing that makes that living thing "alive." The genetic operating system that enables life to be alive is vast, and specifies what each living thing is and how it operates. Chimpanzees are genetically programmed to be chimps, and human beings are genetically programmed to be humans. The program that specifies "human being" must be incredibly advanced and incredibly specific, in order to explain mankind's unique capabilities. The networks of executable programs that make us human cannot be derived by random genetic mutations (isolated letter changes) within an ape genome, combined with some reproductive filtering (natural selection). What is required for creating new biological programs is much more profound than isolated letter changes and random rearrangements of pre-existing genetic code. Random tinkering within an ape genome cannot establish the amazing attributes that make us human.

Paleoanthropologists do not generally pay much attention to the question of how new genetic information might arise. They often seem to think that a limited number of beneficial letter changes in an ape genome can result in a few superficial morphological modifications—resulting in human beings. Looking just at the bones, a paleo-expert might say that the ape-to-human transformation is very simple—just find "the ape that stood up." Genetically, this is extremely naïve. To transform an ape into a human would require a vast number of biological changes, and each biological change would require large numbers of co-dependent sets of mutations resulting in new genetic programming. To have the ape-to-man story work, a large amount of new biological information (extremely specific new instructions) must somehow arise in a very short evolutionary timeframe.

Let's just consider the simplest step—the restructuring of the ape foot into a human foot. This would be an extremely complex genetic undertaking. Many bones, ligaments, muscles, and neurons would have to be reprogrammed, requiring the creation or reworking of many genes. But as we will soon see, in the ape-to-man scenario there is not enough time to significantly rework even a small portion of a single gene. Furthermore, putting human feet onto an ape would by itself accomplish very little. Enabling an ape to walk like a human would simultaneously require the reworking of the feet, legs, knees, hips, backbone, neck, and brain.

Reworking any one of these traits would require the "fixation" of many very specific and mutually dependent mutational events. We can show that this is impossible in any length of time, and is certainly impossible in just a few million years (see Problem 3, below).

"Reprogramming" an ape so it could walk like a man would certainly not result in a human being. To change an ape to a man requires so much more: hands capable of making sophisticated tools, vocal chords suitable for high-level verbal communication, and special brain structures as required for language. Yet all this is like nothing compared to the programming required for vastly increasing brain capacity, enabling conscious thought, and the full emergence of modern man. We cannot even guess how much new information would be required to accomplish all this—we can only say that today's best computer scientists cannot accomplish anything comparable. If a host of brilliant scientists and engineers cannot design and implement such high-level programming, how can anyone believe this could arise by the trial-and-error process of mutation/selection?

In the cell, biological programming starts with the prescriptive information that is stored within the genome's DNA. Such information is like the dormant programs stored on a computer's hard drive. Each gene in the genome can be seen as a separate executable program, which when activated becomes an actively running program. The genes within the genome produce a multitude of RNAs and proteins that can be seen as the RAM of the cell. Each cell has millions of actively operating RNA and protein molecules, all of which can be considered active information. Among those millions of information molecules, there is a vast amount of interactive "cross-talking." There are uncounted information networks within the cell, akin to an intracellular Internet. For example, these intricate communication networks would include the many signal transduction pathways of the cell.

We are only beginning to learn how all these biological information systems are implemented through systems of chemical interactions that involve information reading, writing, erasing and signaling. In addition to the better-known genetic systems, there are the epigenetic systems, the epitranscriptomic systems, the glycomic systems, the protein interactomic systems, the phosphoproteomic systems, and the lipidomic systems. There are countless chemical systems that process the many information systems of the cell.[2,3,4] In addition to all this, there are doubtless other layers of information waiting to be discovered within the cell. Far above and beyond all this, there are the information networks operating at the whole-organism level (for example, the brain and nervous system). We each contain

2. Satterlee J., Enabling Exploration of the Eukarytic Epistranscriptome, DPCPSI Council of Councils, National Institutes of Health, January 2015. Document available at: https://dpcpsi.nih.gov/sites/default/files/council%20jan%2030%202015%20Pres%20E4.pdf
3. Method of the year 2016: Epitranscriptome Analysis, *Nature Methods* 14:1, 2017. DOI:10.1038/nmeth.4142; Published online 29 December 2016.
4. Gabius HJ. and Roth J., An introduction to the sugar code, *Histochem Cell Biol* 147:111–117, 2017. DOI: 10.1007/s00418-016-1521-9; Published online: 14 December 2016 © Springer-Verlag Berlin Heidelberg 2016.

information and information systems, which greatly exceed our comprehension. Where does all this specified complexity come from?

Many scientists now widely acknowledge that the cell's biological information systems are vastly superior to any existing human information system.[5] According to Bill Gates, cofounder and CEO of Microsoft Corporation,

> The understanding of life is a great subject. Biological information is the most important information we can discover, because over the next several decades it will revolutionize medicine. Human DNA is like a computer program but far, far more advanced than any software ever created.[6]

The nature of biological information has been described in depth in the symposium proceedings *Biological Information—New Perspectives.*[7] This volume critically examines how such information systems might have arisen. The 29 contributing scientists from diverse fields unanimously agreed that these biological information systems, and all of the associated prescriptive information content flowing through them, could never arise by trial-and-error. This is a profound problem with the ape-to-man story. Neither the Darwinian mutation/selection process, nor any other naturalistic trial and error process, can build information networks containing vast amounts of very specific, prescriptive information. It should be obvious that information systems and detailed biological specifications cannot arise spontaneously.

Remarkably, there are a few scientists who are still trying to deny that there is genuine information in living systems. They argue that "biological information" is merely organic chemistry (hence not real information). This is like saying that an encyclopedia has no real information—it is just paper and ink; or that a computer contains no real information—it is just electricity flowing through circuits. Information is information, regardless of the medium. Information can be encoded on a blackboard, it can be carved into rock, it can be incorporated into a circuit board, or it can be communicated using molecular structures. The language or code can be Morse code, English, ASCI, the genetic code, the epigenetic code, etc. Regardless of the medium or the specific code, information is the same basic thing. We suggest that information is best defined as "functional specificity communicated via language or code."

The bottom line is simply that the functional information that would be required to change an ape into a human could not arise spontaneously in any amount of time. This is because what is required is the establishment of a vast network of mutually-dependent, massively-integrated genetic changes. It is foolish to think that "Mother Nature" could change an ape into a human simply by favoring

5. Marks II R.J. *et al.* (eds.), *Biological Information—New Perspectives*, World Scientific Publishing Co., Singapore, 559 pp., 2013.
6. Gates B., *The Road Ahead*, Penguin, London, Revised, p. 228, 1996.
7. Marks II R.J. *et al.* (eds.), *Biological Information—New Perspectives*, World Scientific Publishing Co., Singapore, 559 pp., 2013.

independently arising random mutations scattered throughout the genome. It would be like trying to develop a new operating system via trial and error—testing random and independently arising binary bit changes. Random mutations and natural selection simply cannot establish the integrated and mutually dependent genetic modifications required to convert an ape into a man.

While much of the ape and human genomes are similarly programmed, and so are very similar genetically, the genetic differences are still profound. If the human and chimp genomes differed by just 1%, this would still represent 30 million letter differences. However, the outdated claim that the genetic differences are just 1–2% is incorrect—this misinformation arose in part because of ideological commitment, and in part because of simplifying assumptions. For example, the early analyses of the genomic differences only considered single-letter differences, and excluded the analysis of those parts of the genome that are most different. When multi-nucleotide differences ("indels") are included in the analysis, and when the whole genome is taken into consideration, it appears the genetic difference will be closer to 10% (about 300 million letter changes). Whether it's 30 million or 300 million letters, these differences must represent a huge amount of human-specifying information—as is required to program a human to be a human. In the big picture, the most important differences between the ape and human genomes may not be the nucleotide sequences themselves, but may be how the genome is expressed (how its programs are executed). We are beginning to see that there are profound ape/human differences that transcend DNA sequences. This includes many epigenetic systems such as differential nucleosome formation, 3-D DNA structure, DNA methylation, transcription, RNA splicing, RNA editing, protein translation, and protein glycosylation.

Problem 2—Extreme Rarity of Truly Beneficial Mutations: It is widely understood that within the functional part of the genome, most mutations are deleterious, while beneficial mutations are very rare. The famous Lenski LTEE experiment shows that beneficial mutations may be as rare as one in a million.[8] It is thought that beneficial mutations may be so rare that their rarity cannot be accurately measured.[9] The evidence that beneficial mutations are extremely rare is continuing to grow.[10,11] This indicates that while mutations are themselves common, mutations that are truly beneficial are exceedingly rare. This should be intuitively obvious—it is the logical consequence of making random changes in

---

8. Lenski R.E., Evolution in action: a 50,000-generation salute to Charles Darwin. *Microbe* 6(1):30-33, 2011.

9. Bataillon T., Estimation of spontaneous genome-wide mutation rate parameters: whither beneficial mutations? *Heredity* 84:497-501, 2000.

10. Montañez G.R. *et al.*, Multiple overlapping genetic codes profoundly reduce the probability of beneficial mutation, In: Marks II R.J. *et al.* (eds), *Biological Information—New Perspectives*, pp 139-167, 2013. http://www.worldscientific.com/doi/pdf/10.1142/9789814508728_0006.

11. Sanford J. *et al.*, Selection threshold severely constrains capture of beneficial mutations, In:. Marks II R.J. et al. (eds), *Biological Information—New Perspectives*, pp 264-297, 2013. http://www.worldscientific.com/doi/pdf/10.1142/9789814508728_0011.

either an instruction manual or a computer code. Random changes will consistently degrade useful information, and will almost never enhance useful information.

The exception proves the point. Some *Homo* populations appear to have undergone genetic degeneration due to inbreeding and due to being under perpetual starvation conditions for many generations. This seems to have led to reduced body size and reduced brain volume (see chapter 5). This is called "reductive evolution," which is actually evolution going backwards. Although such reductive evolution involves reduced functions and loss of information, such mutational changes can still be "beneficial" in terms of allowing adaptation to a specific environment. However, mutations that enable reductive evolution are only beneficial in an artificial and narrow sense. Such mutations routinely result in broken or lost genes, so in the long run they are deleterious. In a reductive biological situation, a population is put under very special conditions that favor the purging of functional information that is non-essential for the moment (e.g., the LTEE of Lenski *et al.*).[12] These loss-of-function mutations appear to be beneficial because organisms can temporarily grow faster. However, such reductive mutations are actually destroying information and narrowing the organism's ecological range. On closer examination, such mutations consistently represent genetic degeneration. Reductive evolution is also very commonly seen when microorganisms are grown continuously under very uniform and artificial conditions (e.g., in a test tube). Under these conditions loss of genes and functions can temporarily speed up growth. It is deceptive to refer to such reductive mutations as being beneficial because what is really happening is not evolution, but de-evolution.

Problem 3—The Waiting Time Problem in a Hominin Population: It is widely believed that an ape-like population evolved into modern man over a period of about six million years, and that the evolving population had an effective population size of about 10,000 individuals. Population geneticists have understood for a long time that in a relatively small population of this kind, one has to wait a long time if one is waiting for a specific nucleotide to be replaced by a specific alternative nucleotide, and for this change to become established ("fixed"). This "waiting time problem" appears to be the most fundamental rate-limiting factor in terms of what evolution can accomplish. The waiting time problem becomes much worse when two mutations are required to create a specific selectable benefit. When just five mutations are required to reach the "functional threshold" for a given beneficial trait (the point where natural selection becomes effective)—the waiting time becomes entirely prohibitive, exceeding the estimated age of the earth (Figure 1).

---

12. Rupe C. and Sanford J., The most famous evolution experiment of all time shows that evolution goes the wrong way, 2015. http://logosra.org/lenski

Table 1. Findings from Sanford *et al.* reveal an inordinately long waiting time for even a trivial number of pre-specified beneficial mutations to arise and become fixed in a model hominin-sized population (10,000). This is because the target nucleotide string must arise numerous times before it can "catch hold" in the population. In most instances the target string will quickly be lost from the population due to genetic drift before it can be amplified by positive selection, thereby preventing fixation. This is true even when assigning unrealistically high beneficial fitness effects to the completed (functional) target strings. For instance, string lengths ranging from 1-8 nucleotides must arise 12 times on average before they can be expected to become fixed in the population (assuming an extremely high beneficial fitness reward of 10%).

String Length	Average number of instances before fixation	Average waiting time to 1st instance (yrs)	Total average waiting time (yrs)
1	27.4	1.89×10^5	1.53×10^6
2	15.0	2.79×10^7	8.41×10^7
3	6.8	2.20×10^8	3.76×10^8
4	12.6	8.30×10^8	1.22×10^9
5	9.0	1.70×10^9	2.31×10^9
6	8.2	3.16×10^9	4.24×10^9
7	6.4	5.52×10^9	8.59×10^9
8	9.3	1.11×10^{10}	1.85×10^{10}

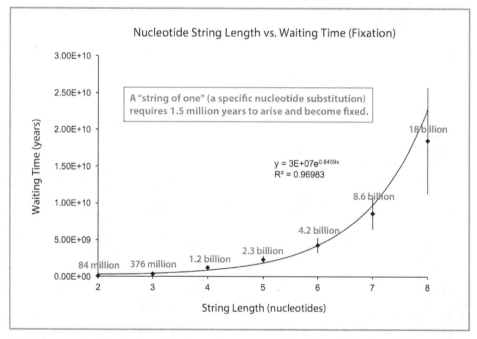

Figure 1. As nucleotide string length increases, the waiting time for those pre-specified sets of mutations to become fixed in a model hominin-sized population (10,000) increases exponentially. For instance, the fixation of just 2 co-dependent mutations would require 84 million years, greatly exceeding the 6 million year ape-to-man timeline. A nucleotide string of 8 exceeds the reputed age of the big bang universe.

Numerous authors have shown that this is a profound problem—starting with Michael Behe.[13,14,15] John Sanford, co-author of this book and his collaborators, have published research on this problem.[16] That publication has conclusively shown that given a hominin population of 10,000, and given the known human mutation rate, and even allowing for extremely large fitness benefits—the fixation of two specific co-dependent mutations requires over 80 million years. This tiny genetic modification greatly exceeds the ape-to-man time scale (six million years). Fixing eight specific mutations in such a population would require over 18 billion years—greatly exceeding the estimated time since the Big Bang (Table 1). To put this problem in perspective, eight nucleotides have an information content that is similar to a word such as "no" or "yes."

Problem 4—Genetic Entropy and the Problem of Net-loss of Information: In addition to the enormous genetic problems listed above, there is another genetic problem that we believe eclipses them all. This problem is the continuous accumulation of deleterious mutations. Contrary to popular understanding, natural selection cannot stop the accumulation of most harmful mutations. One of the authors of this book has spent most of the last 15 years focusing on the subject of genetic degeneration.[17,18,19,20,21,22,23,24,25] He is arguably one of the world's experts on this topic.

13. Behe M.J., Waiting longer for two mutations, *Genetics* 181:819-820, 2009.

14. Behe M.J. and Snoke D.W., Simulating evolution by gene duplication of protein features that require multiple amino acid residues, *Protein Sci* 13:2651-2654, 2004.

15. Behe M.J., The mathematical limits of Darwinism, In: Behe M.J. (ed.), *The Edge of Evolution*, Free Press, NY, pp. 44-63, 2007.

16. Sanford J. *et al.*, The waiting time problem in a model hominin population, *Theor Biol and Med Modeling* 12:18, 2015.

17. Sanford J.C., *Genetic Entropy*. FMS Publications, Waterloo, NY., 271 pp. 2014.

18. Sanford *et al.*, Using computer simulation to understand mutation accumulation dynamics and genetic load, In: Shi *et al.* (eds.), International Conference on Computational Science 2007, Part II, LNCS 4488 (pp. 386-392), Springer-Verlag, Berlin, Heidelberg. http://bioinformatics.cau.edu.cn/lecture/chinaproof.pdf.

19. Gibson *et al.*, Can biological information be sustained by purifying natural selection?, In: Marks II R.J. et al. (eds.), *Biological Information—New Perspectives*, pp. 232-263, 2013. http://www.worldscientific.com/doi/pdf/10.1142/9789814508728_0010

20. Nelson C.W. and Sanford J.C., The effects of low-impact mutations in digital organisms, *Theor Biol and Med Modeling* 8:9, 2011.

21. Sanford J. and Nelson C. The next step in understanding population dynamics: comprehensive numerical simulation, studies in population genetics, In: Fuste M.C. (ed.) ISBN: 978-953-51-0588-6, *InTech*, 2012.

22. Brewer W. *et al.*, Using numerical simulation to test "Mutation-Count" hypothesis, In: Marks II R.J. *et al.* (eds.), *Biological Information—New Perspectives*, pp 298-311, 2013. http://www.worldscientific.com/doi/pdf/10.1142/9789814508728_0012

23. Brewer W. *et al.*, Information loss: potential for accelerating natural genetic attenuation of RNA viruses, In: Marks II R.J. *et al.* (eds.), *Biological Information—New Perspectives*, pp 369-384, 2013. http://www.worldscientific.com/doi/pdf/10.1142/9789814508728_0015.

24. Baumgardner J. *et al.*, Can synergistic epistasis halt mutation accumulation? Results from numerical simulation, In: Marks II R.J. *et al.* (eds.), *Biological Information—New Perspectives*, pp 312-337, 2013. http://www.worldscientific.com/doi/pdf/10.1142/9789814508728_0013.

25. Nelson C. and Sanford J., Computational evolution experiments reveal a net loss of genetic information despite selection, In: Marks II R.J. *et al.* (eds.), *Biological Information—New Perspectives*, pp 338-368, 2013. http://www.worldscientific.com/doi/pdf/10.1142/9789814508728_0014

As described above, to transform an ape into a human requires the creation of a large amount of new information, which requires prohibitively large amount of time. Yet the flip side of this issue reflects an even more profound problem. While waiting for such new biological information to arise, countless deleterious mutations will be continuously accumulating within all lineages. This means that even if a significant number of beneficial mutations were continuously arising and being fixed within a population, a vastly larger number of deleterious mutations would be accumulating. This ensures that there will consistently be a net-loss of information. So species such as man or chimpanzee should not evolve, but rather should degenerate. This is consistent with the extinction of the australopithecines and the degeneration of Neanderthal, Erectus, Hobbit, and Naledi (see chapter 14). Long before a specific pair of co-dependent beneficial mutations could arise and be established, a hominin population should go extinct.[26,27,28]

Why can't natural selection filter out all the bad mutations? There are two reasons: A) there are too many bad mutations continuously pouring into the population; and B) most bad mutations are too subtle to be selectively removed. Epigenetic mutations will consistently magnify this problem.

A) There are Too Many Bad Mutations: The human mutation rate is roughly 100 new mutations per person per generation. The ape mutation rate is similar. Almost none of these mutations are beneficial. The new ENCODE findings reveal that most of the human genome is functional, hence most random changes in the genome must be deleterious.[29] Even if 90% of the genome is perfectly neutral "junk DNA" (this is no longer feasible), there would still be about 10 harmful mutations arising in every person every generation. Even the most "fit" individuals are still more mutant than their parents, so even intense selection against "the less fit" cannot stop mutation accumulation. Because most deleterious mutations cannot be selected away, they will accumulate continuously from one generation to the next. Even while a population is waiting for its first beneficial mutation, many bad mutations will have already accumulated. Waiting for just one specific beneficial mutation to be fixed in a hominin population requires over 50,000 generations, (over 1 million years). However in that same time, about 5 million mutations will have accumulated per individual (50,000 generations times 100 mutations per generation). The large majority of those accumulating mutations would be deleterious, and most of those could not be selectively removed. Even if half of all deleterious mutations could be removed, that would still leave 2.5

26. The ENCODE Project Consortium, An integrated encyclopedia of DNA elements in the human genome, *Nature* 489:57-74, 2012.

27. Gibson P. *et al.*, Can biological information be sustained by purifying natural selection? In: Marks II R.J. *et al.* (eds.), *Biological Information—New Perspectives*, pp 232-263, http:www.worldscientific.com/doi/pdf/10.11 42/9789814508728_0010.

28. Carter R.W. and Sanford J.C., A new look at an old virus: patterns of mutation accumulation in the human H1N1 influenza virus since 1918, *Theo Biol Med Modeling* 9:42, 2012.

29. Muller H.J., Our load of mutations, *Amer J Human Genetics* 2:111-176, 1950.

million deleterious mutations per person. Even if only one tenth of the genome were functional, this still means 250,000 deleterious mutations per person. Such a heavy "genetic load" would certainly be lethal, causing extinction of all hominid lineages. This would happen long before the first waited-for beneficial fixation could happen.

The Nobel laureate Hermann J. Muller, was the first to recognize the problem of bad mutations flowing into a population faster than they could be selected away.[30] He calculated that if the human mutation rate was as high as 0.5 per person per generation, this mutation rate would ensure continuous genetic degeneration and eventual extinction. Yet the actual mutation rate is roughly 200 times greater than this.

B) Most Bad Mutations are Too Subtle to be Selectively Removed: As if this was not bad enough, there is a deeper problem still. The vast majority of mutations are "nearly neutral," which means that their harmful biological effect is too subtle to allow selective elimination. This fundamental problem is well known, and led one population geneticist to publish a paper entitled, *"Why aren't we dead 100 times over?"*[31] Either of these two well-established problems (too many bad mutations, and most mutations being too subtle), virtually guarantees that most bad mutations will continuously accumulate within all ape and human lineages. Only the worst deleterious mutations can be selected away. All the rest accumulate like rust on a car. These two profound problems, when combined, are absolutely fatal to the Darwinian premise that mutation/selection can transform an ape population into a human population.

In this book, the topic of genetic degeneration has come up repeatedly. It is clear that small isolated hominin tribes must undergo long-term inbreeding—which will always accelerate genetic degeneration. This genetic outcome is certain. Evolutionary paleo-experts apply this logic to explain abnormal morphologies in isolated populations of modern man.[32] We have argued that this same mechanism can explain the deviant morphologies of all the aberrant hominin bones that fall within the genus *Homo*. This includes Erectus, Naledi, and Hobbit. This would mean that the aberrant skulls commonly referred to as *Homo erectus* are simply *Homo sapiens* that have become too inbred, and thus have become genetically compromised.

Refuting Genetic Evidences Claimed to Prove Ape-to-man Evolution

We have just reviewed four profound genetic problems that make ape-to-man evolution essentially impossible. However, some will still argue that there are powerful genetic evidences that conclusively prove ape-to-man evolution. These

30. Muller H.J., Our load of mutations, *Amer J Human Genetics* 2:111-176, 1950.
31. Kondrashov A.S., Contamination of the genome by very slightly deleterious mutations: Why have we not died 100 times over? *J Theor Biol* 175:583-594, 1995.
32. Berger L.R. *et al.*, Small-bodied humans from Palau, Micronesia, *PLOS ONE* 3(3):e1780, 2008.

are discussed below.

Human and Chimp DNA Similarity: Physical and genetic similarities can be explained in terms of either a common ancestor, or by a common designer. So physical and genetic similarities between ape and human are not, by themselves, compelling evidence for common ancestry. Furthermore, the genetic similarities between ape and man are much less than the 98% similarity that is commonly cited. For example, primate evolutionist Todd Preuss states in a study published in the *Proceedings of the National Academy of Sciences* (2012), *"It is now clear that the genetic differences between humans and chimpanzees are far more extensive than previously thought; their genomes are not 98% or 99% identical."*[33] The latest analyses indicate that the genetic similarity between chimp and man is more like 90% (in other words the genomes are 10% different). Even if the genetic difference were just 1% (which is false), this would still be 30 million genetic letter differences. Regardless of the degree of genetic similarity between man and ape, mere similarity is a very weak argument for common ancestry.

Shared Mutational Mistakes: It is commonly argued that while similarity is not proof of ape/man common ancestry, "shared mistakes" provide a powerful argument for common descent. At the heart of this argument is the idea that apes and man share the same "junk DNA," and so have similar "genetic fossils," and have similar "genetic mistakes." However, if these shared genomic regions are *not* really junk DNA, then the entire shared mistakes argument falls apart. The powerful new ENCODE evidence very seriously undermines the "shared mistakes" argument because most of what was previously thought to be "junk" in our genome is now shown to be functional and essential to life. ENCODE[34,35] is an on-going, massive, international consortium of scientists. ENCODE has shown that most of the human genome is functional (not junk), and so most "shared-mistakes" are not actually mistakes at all—but are shared functions. Shared functions support the idea of similarity by design. In the words of one prominent evolutionist, *"If ENCODE is right, then evolution is wrong."*[36] In this light, all the shared mistakes arguments appear to be collapsing.

In the past, it was claimed that junk DNA arose as the result of a long history of accumulating genetic damage and the relentless invasion and amplification of "selfish genes." Our previous work[37] has shown that the genome is indeed subject to many degenerative processes. This is problematic for evolution because it causes

33. Preuss T.M., Human brain evolution: from gene discovery to phenotype discovery, *Proc Natl Acad Sci*, USA 109 Suppl 1:10709-10716, 2012.
34. The ENCODE Project Consortium, Identification and analysis of functional elements in 1% of the human genome by the ENCODE pilot project, *Nature* 447:799-816, 2007.
35. The ENCODE Project Consortium, An integrated encyclopedia of DNA elements in the human genome, *Nature* 489:57-74, 2012.
36. Grauer D., Presentation given at 2013 meeting of the Society for Molecular Biology, http://www.slideshare. net/dangrauer1953/update-version-of-the-smbesesbe-lecture-on-encode-junk-dna-graur-december-2013.
37. Sanford J.C., *Genetic Entropy*, FMS Publications, Waterloo, NY., 271 pp., 2014.

evolution to go the wrong way. This degeneration problem also limits the time available for the evolution of new traits, because all populations must be moving toward extinction (see above). In spite of the fact that ENCODE has already largely falsified the junk DNA paradigm, some people continue to advance the argument that the "junk DNA" found in both the chimp and human genomes proves human evolution. The most commonly used shared mistakes arguments have involved two types of "junk DNA"—pseudogenes and dispersed repeats. We will briefly examine a few of the most famous arguments:

A) Beta-globin Pseudogene: The beta-globin pseudogene was used very prominently as evidence for human evolution in the famous Kitzmiller v. Dover court case in 2005. Kenneth Miller, a Brown University biology professor, presented key evidence to support the belief that humans evolved from a chimp-like ancestor. Exhibit A was the hemoglobin protein found in red blood cells that transports oxygen throughout the body's circulatory system. The hemoglobin protein is made up of alpha and beta sub-protein structures. Put most simply, there are six genes which encode the beta-globin protein structure. Until recently, it has been claimed by evolutionists that five of the six genes code for functional proteins,[38] while the sixth gene, known as HBBP1, has been thought to be a broken gene that had lost its function. It did not appear to be functional because it could not code for a protein, but could only make RNA. The HBBP1 "pseudogene" was found to have matching nucleotides in humans and apes, in the positions that were assumed to be where the gene was broken. Advocates of ape-to-man evolution used these presumed "shared mutational mistakes" as proof of common ancestry. They argued that there is no way identical random mutations could arise in the same positions independently in three separate species (chimps, humans, and gorillas). The best explanation seemed to be that all three evolved from a common ancestor.

A decade has passed since the Dover trial. Geneticists now know that the evidence presented by Miller has been overwhelmingly refuted. It is categorically false to say that HBBP1 is a broken, non-functional "pseudogene" that proves common ancestry. Multiple lines of evidence published in leading scientific journals have clearly revealed that this beta globin RNA gene is actively transcribed, is highly functional, and is essential to maintaining health. Three separate scientific publications in *Human Genetics*[39] and in *Hemoglobin*[40,41] have shown that this gene is essential, and when the HBBP1 "pseudogene" is mutated, it results in the human

---

38. Harris S. *et al.*, The primate psi beta 1 gene. An ancient beta-globin pseudogene, *J Mol Biol* 180(4):785-801, 1984.
39. Nuinoon M. *et al.*, A genome-wide association identified the common genetic variants influence disease severity in β-thalassemia/hemoglobin E, *Human Genetics* 127(3):303-314, 2010.
40. Giannopoulou E. *et al.*, A single nucleotide polymorphism in the HBBP1 gene in the human β-globin locus is associated with a mild β-thalassemia disease phenotype, *Hemoglobin* 36(5):433-445, 2012.
41. Roy P., Influence of BCL11A, HBS1L-MYB, HBBP1 single nucleotide polymorphisms and the HBG2 XmnI polymorphism on Hb F levels, *Hemoglobin* 36(6):592-599, 2012.

disease known as β-thalassemia.[42] A number of additional studies (in the journals *Genome Biology and Evolution, Cell, Genome Research, Genes and Development, Nature,* and more), have shown that HBBP1 is more active than any of the other five genes in the beta globin cluster. The HBBP1 beta globin "pseudogene" encodes multiple regulatory RNA transcripts that are crucial during development and are expressed in at least 251 different human cell and tissue types. Evolutionary geneticists discovered through comparative analysis of the HBBP1 "pseudogene" that it was far more conserved than the other functional genes in the beta protein cluster. "Conserved" is a genetics term—when a gene is conserved, it means it is the same in a very wide range of organisms (indicating a widely shared function). Such conservation confirms the gene is not useless "junk," but is vital. These researchers published their results in the *PLOS Journal of Computational Biology.* They report, *"Analyses, based on classic neutrality tests, empirical and haplotype based studies, revealed that HDB and its neighbor pseudogene HBBP1 have mainly evolved under purifying selection, suggesting that their roles are essential and nonredundant."*[43] It is ironic that the most famous example of a "shared mistake" actually involves a shared functional (essential) gene sequence. The Dover trial was a serious miscarriage of justice. The new data reveals a highly functional and very sophisticated multi-purpose gene that is shared in ape and man—providing strong evidence for shared design.

B) **Vitamin C Pseudogene:** Vitamin C (also known as ascorbic acid) is essential for our health. Many animals are able to synthesize their own vitamin C, but humans, apes, guinea pigs, bats, and many bird species are unable to synthesize vitamin C and must get it from their diet (i.e., fruits and vegetables). Some have assumed that since both man and apes lack this function, this is a shared defect inherited from a distant primate ancestor. Advocates of ape-to-man evolution have said that people and apes have exactly the same broken gene, and that this broken gene once enabled vitamin C biosynthesis. They are referring to the functional GULO gene (found in rats, mice, etc., which enables vitamin C synthesis), and a somewhat similar "pseudogene" found in humans and apes (not enabling vitamin C synthesis). The human/ape "GULO gene" is very different from the GULO gene found in rats. It has a few of the characteristics of a normal vitamin C gene but does not enable vitamin C synthesis. A key question is this: Is it correct to assume that the human/ape gene once had the same function as the very different rat GULO gene, and so is now a dead gene—hence representing a shared mistake?

In most animals that make their own vitamin C, there are four genes required. The first three genes perform additional unrelated functions, but they also synthesize

42. Tomkins J.P., The human Beta-Globin Pseudogene is non-viable and functional, *Answers Research Journal* 6:293-301, 2013.
43. Svensson Ö. *et al.*, Genome-wide survey for biologically functional pseudogenes, *PLOS Computational Biology* 2(5):e46, 2006.

the precursor of vitamin C. The fourth gene (called the GULO gene), converts that precursor into vitamin C. Humans and apes also have the first three genes, which are fully operational and essential. However, where the last gene should be, apes and humans have another gene that is only slightly similar to the GULO gene. This last gene does not make a protein, and so is assumed to be an ancient broken gene (junk DNA). Although it is very different from the GULO genes that make vitamin C, it is still called a GULO gene. In humans and apes, the GULO gene is said to show evidence of various genetic mistakes such as deleted sequences, premature stop codons, and other alleged inactivation mutations. These "mistakes" are simply inferences based upon the assumption that originally this gene was able to synthesize vitamin C, and so must once have been nearly identical to the GULO genes of rats. Gibbons, orangutans, chimpanzees, and macaques all seem to share the same presumed mutations. To explain this, it is assumed that in all primates the gene's shared features represent shared mistakes, which would seem to point to common ancestry. According to this hypothesis, the ape GULO sequence was formerly a functional gene that was disabled in a very early primate lineage, and was eventually passed down to humans and apes. We propose an alternative hypothesis. We propose that the human gene is not, and never was, the same as the GULO gene, and has always had a different function. That function has not yet been discovered (as is true with most "pseudogenes").

In 1988, a study conducted by Nishikimi and colleagues used the functional rat GULO gene and hybridized it with an unknown DNA sequence in humans.[44,45] They reported that the alignable sequence regions were only 75% similar, whereas most pseudogenes are typically around 90% similar. What is more problematic is that the alignable region consisted of only a tiny fraction of the entire rat GULO sequence. Out of the total 2,120 bases compared, only 158 bases in the reputed human GULO sequence were alignable with the rat GULO gene. Accounting for the vast non-alignable regions (i.e., most of the gene sequence) the actual genetic similarity amounted to a mere 13.4%. To explain this discrepancy, Nishikimi and colleagues speculated that the human GULO pseudogene was so different because it *"rapidly accumulated mutations under no selective pressure,"* even while the non-alignable regions were being deleted without leaving any evidence. This *ad hoc* hypothesis is not testable.[46] We argue that a more reasonable interpretation for why the rat and human genes are so different is simply because they are, and always have been, sequences with different functions.

Since that first study in 1988, genome sequencing technologies have greatly

44. Nishikimi M. et al., Occurrence in humans and guinea pigs of the gene related to their missing enzyme L-Gulono-γ-lactone oxidase, *Archives of Biochemistry and Biophysics* 267(2):842-846, 1988.

45. Nishikimi M. et al., Cloning and chromosomal mapping of the human nonfunctional gene for L-Gulo-no-γ-lactone oxidase, the enzyme for L-ascorbic acid biosynthesis missing in man, *J Biol Chem* 269(18):13685-13688, 1994.

46. Nishikimi M. *et al.*, Occurrence in humans and guinea pigs of the gene related to their missing enzyme L-Gulono-γ-lactone oxidase, *Archives of Biochemistry and Biophysics* 267(2):842-846, 1988.

improved. Scientists now have the ability to sequence large portions of DNA with a greater degree of accuracy and efficiency. With these advancements, more recent studies have compared the rat GULO sequence, base-for-base, to the reputed broken version in humans. Although these more recent studies still assume that humans harbor a broken GULO gene that is homologous to the functional GULO gene in rats, they acknowledge substantial genetic differences between the two, just as Nishikimi showed. The latest studies have revealed that rats have twelve protein-coding segments (exons) within their GULO gene, whereas humans have only six exons. The other six exons found in rats are completely absent from the human/ape GULO pseudogene. Geneticists have concluded that the six exons absent in humans and apes were lost due to deletion events in an early primate lineage. They were allegedly deleted *"without a trace"*[47]—leaving no remnant of the exons behind. An obvious alternative interpretation is that the exons did not "disappear"—they were never there to begin with.

This makes good sense considering that humans and apes don't generally need to synthesize vitamin C. We have always obtained it from our diet—a GULO gene would be convenient but not necessary in a natural environment where there is an abundance of fruits and vegetables. This would mean that the alleged "broken" vitamin C gene may not be broken at all. Instead, it could very well be an RNA gene with a different function, as is the case with a growing number of pseudogenes.

A study done in 2003 suggests a serious problem for the "broken" GULO common ancestry hypothesis. In the *Journal of Nutritional Science and Vitaminology,* Inai and colleagues noticed that numerous nucleotide bases (single genetic letter sites) were identical in the "broken" GULO pseudogene exons of humans and guinea pigs, but were different when compared to the corresponding exons in rats.[48] This did not fit with evolutionary expectations. Apparently, numerous "mutations" seems to be exactly the same in both humans and guinea pigs, even though rats and guinea pigs are rodents, and primates are very distant from rodents. This means that the numerous matching "mutations" found in both guinea pigs and humans cannot be attributed to common ancestry. Therefore it was assumed that the matching "altered bases" were coincidental, perhaps due to "mutational hotspots" —positions of the genome that are more prone to mutation. To the researchers, this seemed to be the only explanation. However, 47 out of the 129 positions were the same in humans and guinea pigs but different in rats. Statistically this would never happen by chance.

It is not rational or honest to invoke 47 identical "shared mistakes" in the GULO gene of guinea pigs and human. It is simply not honest to infer that matching

47. Yang H., Conserved or lost: molecular evolution of the key gene GULO in vertebrate vitamin C biosynthesis, *Biochem Genet* 51:413-425, p. 418, 2013.
48. Inai Y. *et al.,* The whole structure of the human nonfunctional L-gulono -gamma - lactone oxidase gene –the gene responsible for scurvy–and the evolution of repetitive sequences thereon, *J Nutr Sci Vitaminol* 49(5):315-319, 2003.

mutations in humans and primates proves common ancestry, while inferring matching mutations in humans and guinea pigs proves mutational hotspots. If mutational hotspots can be invoked for human/guinea pig similarities, why can't they be invoked for human/ape similarities? We suggest that neither shared mistakes nor mutational hot spots explain the human/chimp similarity. The most reasonable explanation for why humans, apes, and guinea pigs share so many "mistakes" (compared to rats), is that their "GULO" genes were never the same as the rat GULO gene. Their "shared mistakes" are really shared design.

C) Shared Dispersed Repeats ("Selfish Genes"): Until very recently, a powerful argument for human evolution has been based upon certain components of the human genome known as "dispersed repetitive elements." Dispersed repeats are sequences of DNA that exist in very large copy number, and which are scattered all across the genome (like a sentence repeated many times in a book, or like a line of code repeating many times in a computer program). The same basic sequence may be repeated up to a million times within the genome. About 50% of the human genome is composed of repetitive elements.

Dispersed repeats have been described as "junk DNA," and have also been called "selfish genes." These genetic elements have been considered proof that the genome arose in a haphazard and wasteful manner. This type of wasteful "junk DNA" has been seen as clear evidence that humans were the product of an error-prone evolutionary process. It has been further argued that because similar repetitive junk DNA is found within both humans and apes, this proves common descent. This line of reasoning was based on the faulty assumption that these mysterious repetitive elements had no function. But now, new discoveries are showing that these repeating elements have many crucial functions.

One of the most powerful examples of a DNA sequence that was presumed to be junk, but is now known to be essential, is the famous Alu sequence. Alu is a type of SINE (short interspersed element). The Alu sequence is only about 300 base pairs long, but is copied (with many variations) a million times in the human genome. The Alu sequence accounts for over 10% of the genome. Recent discoveries now show that these Alus are not junk, nor are they selfish (parasitic) genes. They encode many diverse functions that are vital to life. For example, this very short DNA repeat helps to control RNA processing and alternative splicing.[49] Alus also help regulate and control transcription and polyadenylation, serve as a source of miRNAs, act as miRNA target sites, can bind the essential cohesion protein, and bind a host of transcription factors.

Two of the most recently discovered functions of SINES (such as Alu) suggest that Alu elements operate on a very high level of genomic organization. First, it is

49. Lev-Maor G. *et al.*, Intronic Alus Influence Alternative Splicing, *PLOS Genetics* 2008 Sep 26; 4(9):e1000204. DOI: 10.1371/journal.pgen.1000204. http://journals.plos.org/plosgenetics/article?id=10.1371/journal.pgen.1000204

now known that many SINES (similar but not the same as Alu) can act as binding sites for the CTCF protein in mice. In mice, SINES and CTCF cooperate to help establish the dynamic 3-dimensional architecture of chromosomes (affecting loop formation, gene positioning and gene regulation, etc).[50] What is true in mice SINES is probably also true for human SINES (such as Alu). Secondly, it is now known that Alus are instrumental in what is called A-to-I editing.[51] A-to-I (Adenosine-to-Inosine) editing refers to editing of RNAs where the adenosines are modified into inosines. This editing is selective and is developmentally regulated, indicating that the Alu RNA sequences are acting like active RAM, and that information is being modulated through the Alu sequences. This editing is clearly functional and essential. This is evidenced by the fact that when various ADAR enzymes (needed for Alu A-to-I editing) are damaged in mice, the consequences ranges from brain damage to death. There are about 100 million Alu A-to-I editable sites in the genome of a single human cell, and so just the Alus in a single cell potentially provide a vast amount of active information.[52]

A paper in *Proceedings of the National Academy of Sciences* describes A-to-I editing of Alus:

> These findings bring to mind information storage models. As the number of potential editing sites in each Alu-containing transcript is high, usually several dozens, the potential for combinatorial encrypted information is enormous. Binary use of A or I in millions of sites in the neural cell transcriptome can be considered equivalent to the 0's and 1's used for information storage and processing by computers. It is tempting to speculate that the more abundant RNA editing found in the human brain may contribute to the more advanced human capabilities such as memory, learning, and cognition. This suggestion is consistent with the hypothesis that the advantage of complex organisms lies in the development of a digital programming system based on noncoding RNA signaling... The combinatorial posttranscriptional RNA editing of noncoding sequences may therefore contribute to higher brain functions and may play a role in the evolution of human specialization.[53]

These discoveries have resulted in radical reversals of our perception of the functionality of Alus. These reversals have happened within the very same labs that had formerly distanced themselves from claiming any function for Alu. For example, in 2004, a publication of Cold Spring Harbor laboratory said, *"Alu repeats have no known biological function."* But then in 2013 a publication from that very same lab said:

---

50. Schmidt D. *et al.*, Waves of retrotransposon expansion remodel genome organization and CTCF binding in multiple lineages, *Cell* 148(1-2):335-348, 2012.
51. Riedmann E.M. *et al.*, Specificity of ADAR-mediated RNA editing in newly identified targets, *RNA* 14:1110-1118, 2008.
52. Bazak L. *et al.*, A-to-I RNA editing occurs at over a hundred million genomic sites, located in a majority of human genes, *Genome Res*, Dec. 17, 2013. DOI: 10.1101/gr.164749.113.
53. Paz-Yaacov N. *et al.*, Adenosine-to-inosine RNA editing shapes transcriptome diversity in primates, *Proc Natl Acad Sci*, USA 107(27):12174-12179, 2010.

> Based on bioinformatic analyses and deep targeted sequencing, we estimate that there are over 100 million human Alu RNA editing sites, located in the majority of human genes. These findings set the stage for exploring how this primate-specific massive diversification of the transcriptome is utilized.[54]

Furthermore these editable Alus appear to also be important markers to define the start and end points of DNAs that are to be transcribed to double-stranded RNAs (dsRNAs). Thus, the Alu sequence is not just functional but is poly-functional. These Alu-delimited dsRNAs appear to have important regulatory roles, which continue to be actively studied.[55]

Lastly, even though the Alus of humans and other primates are very similar, the way humans use Alus is different than the way other primates use Alus. Humans use approximately twice as many A-to-I Alu edits as chimpanzees, which means that the way Alus are actually used by humans and chimps is very different.[56] Sequence similarity does not mean functional equivalence nor does it prove common ancestry.

Compare all these new findings to the traditional dismissal of Alus as junk—as represented by Francisco Ayala in 2010:

> There are also lots and lots of DNA sequences that are nonsensical. For example, there are about one million virtually identical Alu sequences that are each three-hundred letters (nucleotides) long and are spread throughout the human genome. ... Would a function ever be found for these one million nearly identical Alu sequences? It seems most unlikely ... Perhaps one could attribute the obnoxious presence of the Alu sequences to degenerative biological processes...[57]

Clearly, we are witnessing a series of incredible paradigm shifts. The scientists who are still talking about "shared mistakes" should think twice before they assume that dispersed repeats are junk DNA.

Chromosome 2 Fusion Model: Perhaps the most famous genetic argument for ape-human common ancestry (also used in the Kitzmiller v. Dover trial) is the claim that human chromosome 2 (chr2) arose by the fusion of two chromosomes in the hypothetical chimp-human common ancestor. The fusing ape chromosomes (previously called chr12 and chr13, now called chr2a and 2b) are claimed to have merged to create human chr2. This supposedly explains why chimps have 48 chromosomes and humans have 46. Technically this would not be a "shared mistake" but would be a unilateral mistake (with the original two chromosomes still being found in apes unchanged—while human chr2 would in a sense be a

54. Bazak L. *et al.*, A-to I RNA editing occurs at over a hundred million genomic sites, located in a majority of human genes, *Genome Res*, 2013. DOI: 10.1101/gr.164749.113.
55. Nishikura K., A-to-I editing of coding and non-coding RNAs by ADARs, *Nature Reviews Molecular Cell Biology* 17:83-86, 2016.
56. Paz-Yaacov N. *et al.*, Adenosine-to-inosine RNA editing shapes transriptome diversity in primates, *Proc Natl Acad Sci*, USA 107(27):12174-12179, 2010.
57. http://biologos.org/blogs/guest/on-reading-the-cells-signature/

"fossil" of an ancient mistake). The claimed fusion was originally based simply upon similarity (the two chimp chromosomes are very similar genetically to the two halves of human chr2). However, this was not strong evidence because similarity does not prove common descent. However, in 1991 it was claimed that we can actually see the exact place in human chr2 where the chromosome fusion occurred.[58] There is a very short sequence found within chr2 that is claimed to be the actual "fossilized" fusion site. This very short DNA sequence is said to perfectly match what would be expected if the hypothetical fusion actually happened— assuming the original chimp chromosome tips (telomeres) fused end-to-end. We will refer to this short DNA sequence within human chr2 as the reputed fusion sequence (RFS). The RFS has been used as a "proof" of human evolution in textbooks for over two decades. Remarkably, in the last several years this famous icon of human evolution has become hotly contested. The evidence for a chr2 fusion now appears to be collapsing.[59] Below, we describe the pros and cons of ten aspects of the fusion hypothesis:

A) Chromosome fusions do happen in nature, and the resulting fused chromosome can be transmitted to the next generation. However, such fusions are generally very deleterious (they reduce fertility and disrupt chromosome architecture), and so normally there is selection against such events (fusions are a manifestation of genetic entropy). While it is feasible there was a chr2 fusion, there is no reason to assume that the fusion happened millions of years ago, or that it happened in a pre-human population. The fusion could just as well have happened in the early human population. So even if there had been a fusion of two smaller chromosomes leading to our current human chr2, this would not be compelling evidence of ape-to-man evolution.

B) Most germline fusions (i.e., fusions that are passed on to the next generation) do not actually arise as end-to-end fusions, but instead arise due to mistakes in the crossing-over process. Chromosome fusions arise within cancer cells end-to-end, but these are not transmitted to the next generation. Cross-over fusions result in the deletion of the ends of each fusing chromosome. This means that the special telomere sequences at the ends of both chromosomes would be deleted, and any genes in the cross-over region would also be deleted. So there would not be any trace of a sequence such as the RFS, no associated sub-telomeric sequences, and there would be no trace of internal telomeric sequences. On the other hand, if there really was an end-to-end fusion, then both of the telomeres would be preserved (each one having 2000–3000 copies of the telomeric hexamer repeat). This would result in a very large and easily recognized inverted repeat, about 24,000–36,000 bases long. But this is not what is seen. What is actually seen is a very short sequence

58. Ijdo J.W. *et al.*, Origin of Human Chromosome 2: An Ancestral Telomere-Telomere Fusion, *Proc Natl Acad Sci,* USA 88 (20): 9051–9055, 1991.
59. Tomkins J.P., Debunking the debunkers: a response to criticism and obfuscation regarding refutation of the human chromosome 2 fusion, *Answers Res J* 10:45-54, 2017.

(798 bases long), containing just a few dozen imperfect repeats. It might be argued that since healthy telomeres help prevent end-to-end-fusions, maybe both of the two fusing chromosomes tips were severely degraded, with both telomeres eroded to near extinction. This is feasible, but is a very weak argument. It seems unlikely that both of the fusing chromosomes were degraded to exactly the same point, yielding a minimized and semi-symmetrical fusion site. The reduced size of chr2, compared to the two putative fusing chromosomes, also strongly suggests that if there was a fusion, it involved deletion of both chromosome ends as is observed in illegitimate crossing-over events.

C) The RFS is not only much smaller than would be expected, it is too divergent from the actual known telomeric repeat pattern (only 70% identity).[60] The mere fact that this short sequence has some limited homology to telomeric DNA carries little weight, because there are many very similar telomere-like sequences found throughout the human genome. While all such sequences are weakly homologous to short telomeric fragments, these intra-chromosomal telomere-like motifs do not show any evidence of being ancient fusion sites.

D) The sequences that flank the RFS should match up with sequences near the ends of the corresponding chimp chromosomes. Unfortunately we cannot easily test this, because the ends of the two corresponding chimp chromosomes have not yet been fully sequenced. However, the actual region that contains the RFS (which is assumed to derive from two ape chromosomes), now appears to be DNA that is uniquely human and is absent in all ape genomes. The UCSC genome browser shows that all the great ape genomes fail to align with either the RFS or the flanking 3000+ base pairs. This is a very serious problem for the fusion hypothesis.

E) Likewise, there should be nearly perfect homology between the much larger 200,000-base-pair region that flanks the "fusion site" of human chr2, and the corresponding regions of the two chimp chromosomes that are thought to have fused. But this is not what is seen. This entire region of human chr2 does not appear to have homology with any part of the two chimp chromosomes that are thought to have fused. Instead, this very sizeable region within human chr2 only aligns with various other chromosomes of the chimp genome such as chr9 and chr12, etc.

F) Chimps and the other apes have very distinctive and very large "satellite" sequences at the ends of their chromosomes (they are found just before the terminal telomeric tips). These are typically made up of a very prominent 32-base tandem repeating sequence. These large sub-telomeric repeat structures are in all ape genomes, but are absent in man. These high-copy satellite sub-telomeric sequences are the genetic basis of the heterochromatic knobs seen at the ends of ape chromosomes (which are large enough to be seen even with a light microscope).

60. Tomkins J.P., Debunking the debunkers: a response to criticism and obfuscation regarding refutation of the human chromosome 2 fusion, *Answers Res J* 10:45-54, 2017.

Therefore, these large ape-specific satellite sequences should be seen flanking the RFS on both sides. But they are not there. The ape-specific satellite DNA is completely absent in the region of the RFS. This is a very serious problem for the ape fusion hypothesis. However this observation is not necessarily inconsistent with a human fusion hypothesis (i.e., two human chromosomes fusing in the early human population).

G) While the expected sub-telomeric repeats are not present in the region of the RFS, there is a gene called DDX11L2 immediately adjacent to the RFS (as we will soon see, this gene is not just adjacent to the RFS, it actually *contains* the RFS). This gene is homologous to a gene family that is usually found in close proximity to human telomeres. At first, this might seem to support the fusion hypothesis (since the RFS is found close to a gene typically seen near telomeres). However, we need to look more closely. A similar family of genes is also found in the chimp genome. While these genes are also generally found toward the ends of chimp chromosomes, they are separated from the telomere by a sizeable amount of intervening DNA (the very same ape-specific satellite DNA described above). So if we assume that the DDX11L2 gene on chr2 came from an ape fusion, it should be separated from the telomere-like fusion site by this large ape-specific tandem repeat. Absence of this intervening DNA between the DXX11L2 gene and the RFS is not consistent with the idea that a fusion occurred in an ape population. However, this is not inconsistent with a fusion in a very early human population (because within the human genome this gene family is typically directly adjacent to the telomere).

H) The gene described above, DDX11L2, is called a "pseudogene". We have already explained that pseudogenes are not generally junk DNA, but are generally functional genes. This particular gene is similar to a telomere-associated gene family (DDX11L), which encodes an RNA helicase protein. Like many functional pseudogenes, DDX11L2 does not produce a protein (yet it still makes a variety of RNAs, so it is functional and not junk). Remarkably, this gene is not only immediately adjacent to the RFS—it actually overlaps with the fusion site. More accurately, the RFS is actually a functional part of the DDX11L2 gene! The person who discovered this, and who has investigated this entire issue more than any other scientist, is Dr. Jeff Tomkins (a long-time genomicist, and former Director of the DNA sequencing facility at Clemson University). Tomkins has recently published compelling evidence that the RFS is not a fusion site at all, but is a functional component of the DDX11L2 gene.[61] He has shown that the RFS lies within the first intron of this gene. Furthermore, he has shown that the RFS sequence has the following attributes: 1) it is an active promoter for the transcription of an alternative transcript; 2) it binds at least 12 transcription factors; 3) it initiates RNA transcription which begins within its own sequence; 4) it has a chromatin

---

61. Tomkins J.P., Debunking the debunkers: a response to criticism and obfuscation regarding refutation of the human chromosome 2 fusion, *Answers Res J* 10:45-54, 2017.

profile that further supports its active promoter status. Tomkins also provides evidence that the DXX11L2 gene produces RNA that helps regulate the DXX11L gene family (just as has been shown with other functional pseudogenes). Unless all of these many levels of evidence can be refuted, it appears that Tomkins has successfully falsified the hypothesis that the RFS is a fusion site.

I) The fused chromosome hypothesis not only requires demonstration of a legitimate fusion site, it also requires demonstration of a disabled second centromere (a "cryptic centromere") on chr2. In the very same paper, Tomkins also scrutinized the Reputed Crytic Centromere (RCC).[62] He shows that the 171-base-pair repeat that characterizes primate centromeres is indeed present within the RCC, but this repeat sequence is also present in many other parts of the human genome. Tomkins shows that the RCC is much too small, and the exact sequence is too human, to be the remains of an ancient chimp centromere. Most importantly, Tomkins has shown that the entire RCC sequence is internal to a functional gene (similar to what he found in the RFS). This would be impossible if the RCC sequence had ever been a real centromere. This strongly falsifies the hypothesis that there is an ancient, secondary, disabled centromere on human chr2.

J) It seems that there are profound problems with both the hypothetical fusion site, and also the hypothetical cryptic centromere. So the evidence for a chr2 fusion seems to be collapsing. Even if it could be shown that a fusion did occur in the general vicinity of the RFS, and there was strong support for a cryptic centromere, it would still not be evidence for ape-to-human evolution. Man might have originally had two chromosomes that fused early in human history, to yield what is now human chromosome 2 (converting a genome of 24 chromosome pairs into a genome of 23 chromosomes pairs). However, in light of Tomkins' new data, even a fusion in early human history now appears to be very unlikely. There is now no direct evidence for any type of fusion.

Conclusion—Genetic Barriers to Ape-to-Man Evolution are Insurmountable

Neither the fossil record nor genetics can be used to prove the ape-to-man story. Ironically, during the last two decades, many previous claims of genetic "evidences" of ape-to-man evolution have been over-turned. More and more, the genetic evidence is indicating that ape-to-human evolution is not credible. In fact, genetics now provides the very strongest arguments against human evolution.

---

62. Tomkins J.P., Debunking the debunkers: a response to criticism and obfuscation regarding refutation of the human chromosome 2 fusion, *Answers Res J* 10:45-54, 2017.

CHAPTER 14

A Simpler Model

No doubt about it, Australopithecines are like apes, and the Homo group are like humans.[1]

Leslie Aiello, Paleoanthropologist of the University College London

So Many Problems!

In the latter part of the 20th century, the paleo-community had constructed a simplistic, linear view of human evolution. It was thought that one hominin species evolved cleanly into the next, and the next, reminiscent of the iconic "ape-parade" visual. Lucy's kind (*Australopithecus afarensis*) was envisioned to evolve into Habilis, which evolved into Erectus, which finally evolved into *Homo sapiens*. Ernst Mayr championed this so-called "straight-line" view of human evolution in the 50s and 60s.[2]

During this earlier era, taxonomic diversity was assumed to be very limited, with each hominin species occupying its own discrete place in time. For instance, until just recently, Lucy's kind was believed to be the only hominin species living in Africa 3–4 million years ago. In recent decades, however, the paleo-community has universally abandoned Mayr's straight-line view of human evolution. Rather than a simple tree showing a traceable lineage of a few hominin species evolving

1. Leakey, R. and Lewin R., *Origins Reconsidered: In Search of What Makes Us Human*, Anchor Books (Double-day), New York, p. 196, 1992.
2. Delisle R.G., *Debating Humankind's Place in Nature, 1860-2000: The Nature of Paleoanthropology*, p. 289, Pearson Prentice Hall, Upper Saddle River, NJ, 2007.

one into the next, the paleo-community now describes the hominin fossil record as a "messy, tangled bush." In *Science*, Schwartz and Tattersall note, *"In contrast to Mayr's austere linearity, we may find that human evolution rivaled that of other mammals in its evolutionary experimentation and diversity."*[3] In the journal *Nature*, Aiello and Collard describe the time-period before Erectus saying, *"... evolutionary history now looks more like a tangled bush than a simple tree."*[4] Paleo-experts now claim they also see the same pattern of diversity higher up in the tree within the genus *Homo*. Neanderthals, Denisovans, Erectus,[5] Hobbit, Naledi, and anatomically modern humans all coexisted (see chapter 11). This does not reflect a discernable evolutionary progression. As Lee Berger and colleagues write in the journal *eLife* (2017), *"As others have noted (Stringer, 2016), the fossil hominin record of the Middle and Late Pleistocene shows no simple linear progression towards modern humans, and different morphological forms overlapped in time."*[6]

Virtually everything the evolutionary model predicted has been turned upside down. Meredith Small from Cornell University provides a glimpse of what the hominin fossil record actually shows:

> For anthropology students 30 years ago, learning human evolution was a breeze. It went from *Australopithecus* to *Homo habilis* to *Homo erectus* to various *Homo sapiens*. It was a straight shot that one could learn in a few minutes late at night while cramming for an exam. But in the late 1970s, we entered a golden age of human fossil discoveries that has repeatedly punched holes in the naïve idea that our evolution would be that clear, clean, and straight. Like most animals, humans have a checkered past, and our family album is now full of side branches and dead ends.... The straight line has blossomed into a spreading, rather uncontrolled bush and we don't like it. We want our history to be nice and neat, but the fossils keep messing us up.... we want the last 200,000 years of human evolution, the time when modern *Homo sapiens* appeared, to make some kind of sense, but it doesn't.[7]

Paleo-experts attribute the messiness of the bush to *"luxuriant diversity."*[8,9] Every new species that is discovered has added more branches and twigs to the hominin tree, making it even bushier. From the paleo-community's perspective, this newly found diversity has totally obscured the fossil trail leading to man. They freely

3. Schwartz J. and Tattersall I., Defining the Genus *Homo*, *Science* 349(6251):931-932, 2015.

4. Aiello L.C. and Collard M., Paleoanthropology: Our newest oldest ancestor? *Nature* 410, 526-527, 2001.

5. Johanson D., Johanson L., and Edgar B., *Ancestors: In Search of Human Origins*, Chapter 6, Random House, 1994. The coexistence of Erectus and *Homo sapiens* is dependent the currently debated age of certain Erectus sites in Java and contested classifications of Erectus (or Erectus-like) skulls from various sites in China, Java and Australian sites.

6. Berger L.R. *et al.*, *Homo naledi* and Pleistocene hominin evolution in subequatorial Africa, *eLife*, 2017, p. 6 of 19. DOI: 10.7554/eLife.24234

7. Small M.F., Human family tree now a tangled, messy bush, http://www.livescience.com/7376-human-family-tree-tangled-messy-bush.html

8. Schwartz J. and Tattersall I., Defining the Genus *Homo*, *Science* 349(6251):931-932, 2015.

9. Wood B. and Boyle E.K., Hominin Taxic Diversity: Fact or Fantasy? *Yearbook of Phys Anthropol* 159:S37-S78, 2016.

confess that no part of the hominin bush reveals an ape-to-man progression, with one hominin species evolving into the other. Is the fossil trail to man lost? Did it ever really exist?

There are now multiple hominin species claimed to have lived in East Africa during the time of Lucy. Yohhannes Haile-Selassie, australopithecine authority and current curator of the Natural History Museum in Cleveland, argues that we can no longer be confident Lucy was our ancestor—that it is difficult to make any certain claims about which (if any) of the *Australopithecus* bones in Hadar belong to our ancestor. Like so many others in the field, Haile-Selassie laments that the hominin fossil record is becoming increasingly confusing with every new discovery.[10] In the *Proceedings of the National Academy of Sciences* (2016), he asks in the title of his paper, *"Do more fossils mean less clarity?"* He answers his own question by confessing that every new hominin discovery is further *"complicating our understanding"* of human evolution. Paleo-expert Susan Anton of New York University has come to the same conclusion: *"All new discoveries make things more confusing."*[11] Donald Johanson agrees, *"The transition to Homo continues to be almost totally confusing."*[12] Paleo-expert John Hawks notes, *"What a mess early Homo is!"* Wood writes, *"Even with all the fossil evidence and analytical techniques from the past 50 years, a convincing hypothesis for the origin of Homo remains elusive."*[13]

As we have consistently shown in this book, the ancestral status of nearly every major hominin species is hotly contested. After 150 years of cataloguing thousands of hominin bones and fragments, the paleo-community now openly confesses that the human fossil record does not reveal any recognizable evolutionary progression from ape to man. Consider Bernard Wood's assessment of the hominin fossil record over the past few decades of extensive paleoanthropology research. In 1992, Wood made the following statement in *Nature*:

> It is remarkable that the taxonomy and phylogenetic relationships of the earliest known representatives of our own genus, *Homo* remain obscure. … reassessments of the fossils themselves have rendered untenable a simple unilineal model of human evolution, in which *Homo habilis* succeeded the australopithecines and then evolved via *H. erectus* into *H. sapiens*—but no clear alternative consensus has yet emerged.[14]

Twenty-five years later, Wood reaffirmed his earlier assessment. In his view hominin

10. Haile-Selassie Y. *et al.*, The Pliocene hominin diversity conundrum: do more fossils mean less clarity, *Proc Natl Acad Sci*, USA 113(23):6364-6371, 2016.

11. Balter M., Candidate human ancestor from South Africa sparks praise and debate, *Science* 328:154-155, 2010.

12. Balter M., Candidate human ancestor from South Africa sparks praise and debate, *Science* 328:154-155, 2010.

13. Wood B., Fifty years after *Homo habilis*, *Nature News* 508:31-33, 2014.

14. Wood B., Origins and evolution of the genus *Homo*, *Nature* 355(6363): 783-790, 1992. http://www.ncbi.nlm.nih.gov/pubmed/1538759

evolution has become even more uncertain than ever. In 2014, he provided an updated tree diagram in an article published in *Scientific American* (Figure 1).[15] It is shown as a complex bush with many twisted, broken, and disconnected branches. Wood acknowledges:

> Genetic and fossil evidence shows closely related hominin species shared the planet many times in the past few million years, making it more difficult to identify direct ancestors of modern humans than scientists anticipated even 20 years ago.[16]

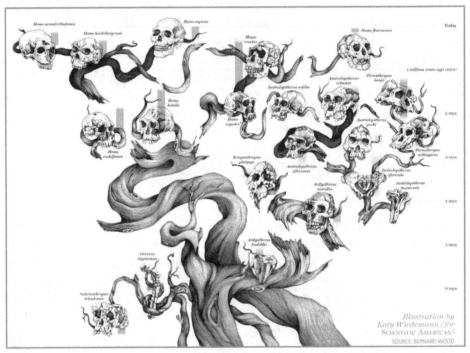

Figure 1. A recent tree diagram shows more complexity and uncertainty than tree diagrams 20 years ago. Few if any of the branches are shown connected to other hominin species. Wood's diagram shows two separate genera, *Australopithecus* and *Homo* with no clear ancestors. An ape-to-man progression is anything but decipherable.

Wood's tangled and disjointed bush supports the extensive coexistence of the *Australopithecus* and *Homo* genera within the fossil record (though not to the extent documented in this book). *Australopithecus* bones are commonly found with human (*Homo*) fossils and artifacts in the very same bone bed. These observations are routinely dismissed because ancestors and descendants should not typically live simultaneously in the same niche, and because the *Homo* bones and artifacts are showing up long before the genus *Homo* is said to have evolved (even at the

---

15. https://www.scientificamerican.com/article/the-origin-of-humans-is-surprisingly-complicated/
16. Wood B., Welcome to the Family, *Sci Am* 311(3):42-47, 2014. Wood writes, *"Our early ancestry looks more like a bundle of twigs–one might even think it looks like a tangled bush [see illustration on page 40]."*—referring to the illustration shown above (Figure 1).

time of Lucy, 3–4 million years ago, see chapter 11). This further obscures the possible evolutionary relationship of *Australopithecus* and *Homo*.

There can be no doubt that the evolutionary paleo-community is currently in a state of disarray. Things have become so muddled that Schwartz and Tattersall have even suggested scrapping various hominin classifications and starting from scratch. They state in their paper published in *Science* (2015):

> If we want to be objective, we shall almost certainly have to scrap the iconic list of names in which hominin fossil specimens have historically been trapped, and start from the beginning by hypothesizing morphs, building testable theories of relatedness, and rethinking genera and species.[17]

Leading evolutionary scientists acknowledge there are immense difficulties and inaccuracies in the reconstruction of hominin skeletons (see chapter 6 on Ardi); immense difficulties in correctly dating hominin sites (chapter 12); immense barriers to genetically morphing a hypothetical "chimp-like" ancestor into *Homo sapiens* via random mutations and natural selection (chapter 13); and still no convincing fossil evidence of the critical bridge species which might connect australopiths to *Homo* (see Section III, chapters on Habilis, Naledi, and Sediba).

Our Alternative Model

In light of the current confusion within this field, we humbly put forward an alternative scientific model. We confess we are coming at this from outside the field. But we have invested several years in the study of this subject. Minimally, we have earned the right to question the paradigm, to critically examine the consensus view, and to consider alternative models. We have dared to do all this research because we realize the great importance of this question: *"Where did we come from?"*

We feel we have the answer to the persistent question: *"Why can't the various hominin species be arranged into a coherent ape-to-man progression?"* We propose it is simply because man did not evolve from any australopithecine ape, or any other type of ape. This is the answer that most paleo-experts refuse to consider. We believe this explains why the field is so confused. Since the time of Darwin, paleoanthropologists have been obsessively trying to force the fossil record into an ape-to-man progression. All they have found is an incoherent, tangled, disjointed, messy bush. When the fossil evidence is taken at face value (when the bones are not forced into an ape-to-man framework) the "bush" suddenly becomes cleaner and untangled, consisting of a series of individual branching trees (Figure 3). Wood recently described it very similarly as a "bundle of twigs," which suggests that each species lived side-by-side, with no common ancestor (a bundle of twigs does not

17. Schwartz J. and Tattersall I., Defining the Genus *Homo*, *Science* 349(6251):931-932, 2015.

have a root).[18] This seems to be most consistent with the actual fossil evidence—as some paleo-experts are starting to admit. With that in mind, we encourage our readers to explore with us an alternative scientific model that we contend better explains the hominin fossil record.

Our model should come as no surprise to any careful reader of the previous chapters. We propose that the two basic hominin genera, *Australopithecus* (apes) and *Homo* (humans) do not have an ancestor-descendant relationship. They are simply independent forms of life. Remarkably, whenever well-preserved and nearly complete hominin skeletons are found, they can readily be identified as belonging to one or the other genus—they are either *Australopithecus* or *Homo*. There is only confusion when the data is incomplete. For example the various fragmentary Erectus skulls (most of which are distorted, crushed, and broken) had been difficult to classify. However, as soon as the first (and only) nearly complete Erectus skeleton was discovered ("Turkana Boy"; chapter 4) the paleo-community easily agreed on its distinctly human anatomy. We do not think it is a coincidence that the most fragmentary skeletons (e.g., Habilis) are the specimens that paleo-experts have promoted as the bridge species between the *Australopithecus* and *Homo* genera. However, when there are nearly complete skeletons there is no ambiguity—the bones can be readily identified as either *Australopithecus* or *Homo*.

Australopithecus Bones—Clearly Apes

The name "australopithecus" literally means "southern ape." As the name suggests, the australopiths have the overall body plan of an ordinary ape. Their anatomy indicates they were best suited for life in the trees (see Section II chapters on Lucy, Ardi, and Habilis). As such, it is not surprising that they share most of the features of living African apes. They are around 3–4 feet tall, with long arms and short legs; ape hands and feet with long curved fingers and toes; opposable "thumb-like" toes (abducted halluces); ape-sized and ape-shaped skulls; funnel-shaped ribcages with high-placed shoulders for suspensory behavior, etc. Yet they also exhibit their own unique morphology[19] (see chapter 6 on Ardi). The australopithecines are best described as an extinct ape genus. In the past, there appears to have been a greater diversity of apes than are alive today. The living great apes include Pan (chimpanzee), Gorilla (gorilla), and Pongo (orangutan). If they were not extinct, the australopithecines would be considered a fourth hominid genus. All four genera share many similarities and all four are unmistakably ape, yet each has their own unique set of features that merit their separate taxonomic designations. All of these ape types have historically coexisted with man, as did the australopiths before they went extinct (see Figure 5, chapter 11).

---

18. Wood B., Welcome to the Family, *Scientific American* 311(3):42-47, 2014. Wood writes, *"Our early ancestry looks more like a bundle of twigs–one might even think it looks like a tangled bush [see illustration on page 40]."*—referring to the illustration shown above (Figure 1).

19. Wood B. and Harrison T., The evolutionary context of the first hominins, *Nature* 470:347-352, 2011.

Two types of evidence were used to argue that the australopiths were more than apes. First, certain isolated bones were incorrectly assigned to australopiths, which were actually human bones. Second, certain artifacts (e.g., fossilized footprints, stone tools, butchered bones) had been incorrectly assigned to australopiths, which were actually of human origin (see chapter 7 on Afarensis, chapter 8 on Habilis, and chapter 11 on coexistence).

Homo Bones—Clearly Humans

The term "*Homo*" simply means human. Today humans come in many shapes and sizes. For example, there are people who have different shaped skulls and different shaped faces. There are people who are robust and heavy-boned and people who are gracile and light-boned. There are people who are very tall and people who are very short (Figure 2). There are people who have large cranial capacities (large brains) and people who have very small cranial capacities (tiny brains). Humans are wonderfully diverse. For instance, North American Indians who lived just 1,000 years ago had very unique skeletal features, as do the Pygmies of central Africa, and the indigenous Aleutians of Alaska. Yet despite all this skeletal diversity, we are still all one species. As famous paleo-expert, Donald Johanson, reiterates:

> A million years from now, if the proverbial anthropologist from Mars comes across the skeleton of a female pygmy in central Africa and then finds another skeleton—this one a male Eskimo in Alaska, will he know enough to assign both to the species *Homo sapiens*? Maybe not. Even within single populations our species shows marked differences in brain size, facial characteristics, jaw shape, and countless other traits.[20]

The same is true of people groups which have disappeared, such as Neanderthals, Erectus, Hobbit, and Naledi. Each type has certain unique features, yet they all display an overall modern human anatomy. They looked like us, walked on two feet like us, and clearly thought like us. Their technologies and cultures demonstrate that they were intelligent and fully human (see Section I chapters). According to conventional dating methods, Neanderthals, Denisovans, Erectus, Hobbit, and Naledi all coexisted (see chapter 11). Where genomic analyses

Figure 2: Sultan Kosen is the world's tallest man, standing 8 foot 3 inches tall. In 2014 Kosen met Chandra Dangi, the world's shortest man. Chandra Dangi stands a mere 21.5 inches in height. His short stature is due to a condition known as primordial dwarfism.

20. Johanson D.C. and Shreeve J., *Lucy's Child: The Discovery of a Human Ancestor*, Early Man Publishing, Inc., New York, p. 88, 1989.

have been possible (see chapter 3), they indicate that all these people groups interbred. We conclude that there is, and always has been, just one human species, *Homo sapiens*. Excluding the false taxon "Habilis" (see chapter 8), all major *Homo* classifications—Neanderthals, Denisovans, Erectus, Hobbit, Naledi and modern man—should be "lumped" together. We are all members of one beautifully diverse human family.

"Primitive" Features Does Not Mean "Less Evolved": The young dates that have just been assigned to the "primitive-looking" Naledi confirms it coexisted with anatomically modern *Homo sapiens* (see chapters 10 and 11). This has important ramifications for the popularized ape-to-man story. Students and the public are taught from an early age that primitive traits mean primitive origins. For instance, the discovery of the non-mineralized Neanderthal skullcap in Düsseldorf Germany in 1856 evoked a deep sense of the "great antiquity" of man to its onlookers. The primitive features such as heavy brow ridges and a low-sloping forehead had convinced casual observers and early anatomists alike that Neanderthals must have been an evolutionary precursor to man (as had been taught for many decades, see chapter 3). Thus it was assumed on the basis of appearance alone that Neanderthals must pre-date the origin of *Homo sapiens*. Again, this is assumed simply because we have been taught to believe that prominent brow ridges, elongated skulls, reduced chins, etc., suggests primitive origins (a less-evolved state). Yet now we are finding more and more examples of "primitive" Erectus-like bones and skulls that overlap in time with anatomically modern humans (see chapters 4, 5, 10, and 11). This is at odds with the ape-to-man narrative and has further confounded the paleo-community. Now with Naledi, paleo-experts like Bernard Wood warn that primitive-looking traits may be misleading.[21] Naledi was just assigned a young age (roughly 300,000 years old), yet it displays archaic features such as pronounced brow ridges, a tiny braincase, forward-projecting jaw, and other features ordinarily regarded as "sub-human." To find these features in specimens that date so young is exactly opposite to what the ape-to-man paradigm has always assumed. No wonder paleo-expert Chris Stringer was so surprised at Naledi's recent age assignment, saying, *"This is astonishingly young for a species that still displays primitive characteristics found in fossils about 2 million years ago."* A non-technical summary in the 2017 *eLife* report by Berger *et al.* now corrects this long-held evolutionary preconception:

> Berger *et al.* explain that the existence of a relatively primitive species like *H. naledi* living this recently in southern Africa is at odds with previous thinking about human evolution. Indeed, all other members of our family tree known from the same time had large brains and were generally much more evolved than our most ancient relatives. However, Berger *et al.* argue that we have only an incomplete picture of our evolutionary past, and suggest that old fossils might

---

21. https://www.newscientist.com/article/2130280-meet-neo-the-most-complete-skeleton-of-homo-naledi-ever-found/

have been assigned to the wrong species or time period.[22]

The discovery of Naledi clearly shows that primitive characteristics do not mean primitive evolutionary origins. It suggests an entirely different perspective. Perhaps archaic looking traits arose in modern *Homo sapiens* populations independent of any an ape-like ancestor. Is it a mere coincidence that all of the variant *Homo* types are described as living in extreme isolation? We propose a model that we feel better explains the so-called "primitive" looking features seen in *Homo* species like Erectus, Neanderthals, Hobbit, and Naledi. Our alternative model considers the effects of inbreeding to explain human diversity, particularly these strange-looking *Homo* variants.

So-called "Primitive" Humans are Inbred Sub-populations: Unfortunately, some of our human diversity arises from pathology. This is true in the present, and this was true in the past. There are aging people, there are people with disease, and there are people born with defects. This is sad but true. Geneticists now know that the human race is accumulating harmful mutations at an alarming rate, and must presently be degenerating genetically (see chapter 13).[23] This degenerative process accelerates whenever a small population is reproductively isolated for many generations. This results in inbreeding and accelerated mutation accumulation. Furthermore, when just a few closely related individuals start a new and isolated population, the result will be "founder effects," whereby their descendants will manifest the genetic peculiarities and defects of the founding individuals. We propose that founder effects, inbreeding, and genetic degeneration gave rise to the anomalous populations we now call Neanderthals, Erectus, Hobbit, and Naledi.

Interestingly, paleo-experts are now drawing attention to these populations which are now being described as living in isolation and inbred. Neanderthals lived in the harsh climate of glacial Europe where only a sparse population could survive by hunting. Naledi lived among the caves of the South African wilderness. Hobbit lived on the remote Indonesian island of Flores. Each of these settings would lead to founder-effects, isolation, and inbreeding. These things would lead to genetic pathologies and anomalous skulls. This would lead to many deleterious mutations arising and becoming fixed.

Five recent papers support our model of inbreeding and degeneration. The first paper reported an analysis of a complete genome sequence of a Neanderthal from the Altai Mountains of southern Siberia and was published in *Nature* (2014). The researchers cite evidence that Neanderthals were highly inbred: "*We present a high-quality genome sequence of a Neanderthal woman from Siberia. We show that her parents were related at the level of half-siblings and that mating among close relatives*

22. Berger L.R. *et al.*, *Homo naledi* and Pleistocene hominin evolution in subequatorial Africa, *eLife*, 2017, p.6 of 19. DOI: 10.7554/eLife.24234
23. Sanford J.C., *Genetic Entropy*, 4th Edition, FMS Publications, 2014. http://geneticentropy.org

was common among her recent ancestors."[24] In the second paper, researchers report in a study, also published in *Nature* (2014), providing evidence of decreased fertility among Neanderthal males.[25] They also reported that modern humans with genes of Neanderthal origin were more likely to have diseases such as lupus, Crohn's disease, and type-2 diabetes. In the third paper published in the *Proceedings of the National Academy of Sciences* (2016), Roebroeks and Soressi cite other findings that indicate Neanderthals had limited genetic variation.[26] They say that Neanderthal also had *"small effective population sizes and were inbred"* and they were *"thin on the ground"*[27] (living in small tribes that were widely dispersed), as expected for a cold-adapted nomadic people group. In the fourth paper published by the Genetics Society of America in the journal *Genetics* (2016), researchers observe that Neanderthals (and Denisovans) were inbred, with low genetic variation and a high *"mutational load."* High mutation load means many deleterious mutations had accumulated in their genomes. They write, *"Neanderthals had at least 40% lower fitness than humans on average."*[28] In the most recent fifth paper, published in *Proceedings of the National Academy of Sciences* (2018), paleo-expert Erik Trinkaus shows that early human populations were highly inbred, and had a vast number of bone distorting genetic pathologies including abnormal skulls and a suite of deformities relating to dwarfism.[29] He reports, *"It is apparent that the Pleistocene human fossil record is characterized by a plethora of developmental abnormalities..."* Trinkaus observed a total of 75 documented developmental abnormalities from 66 individuals spanning the Pleistocene. The odds of finding so many rare pathologies by chance is remarkable—a *"vanishingly small"* probability, Trinkaus says. This could only be possible if inbreeding was frequent and severe. These findings were summarized in a *Science* news article titled, *"Frequent inbreeding may have caused skeletal abnormalities in early humans."* The author writes:

> Many human fossils from the Pleistocene (roughly 2.5 million B.C.E. to 9700 B.C.E.) have unusual features. ... several bodies show abnormalities consistent with known genetic mutations, and multiple individuals from at least one site exhibited several different conditions, suggesting the people might be related. It's thought that most human populations at the time were small and isolated, Trinkaus says. In those conditions, inbreeding can lead to widespread harmful genetic mutations. Evidence of low genetic diversity among Pliestocene humans based on ancient DNA analysis also supports this hypothesis...[30]

24. Prüfer K. *et al.*, A complete genome sequence of a Neanderthal from the Altai Mountains, *Nature* 505(7481):43-49, 2014.

25. Sankararaman S. *et al.*, The genomic landscape of Neanderthal ancestry in present-day humans, *Nature* 507(7492):354-357, 2014.

26. Roebroeks W. and Soressi M., Neandertals Revised, *Proc Natl Acad Sci,* USA 113(23):6372-6379, 2016

27. Roebroeks W. and Soressi M., Neandertals Revised, *Proc Natl Acad Sci,* USA 113(23):6372-6379, 2016.

28. Harris K. and Nielsen R., The genetic cost of Neanderthal Introgression, *Genetics* 203: 881-891, 2016.

29. Trinkaus E., An abundance of developmental anomalies and abnormalities in Pleistocene people, *Proc Natl Acad Sci,* USA, 1-6, 2018. DOI:10.1073/pnas.1814989115. See also supplementary information: www.pnas.org/lookup/suppl/doi/10.1073/pnas.1814989115/-/DCSupplemental.

30. Price M., Frequent inbreeding may have caused skeletal abnormalities in early humans, *Science,* November 5, 2018. DOI:10.1126/science.aav9619

Hallie Buckley, bioarchaeologist from the University of Otago in Dunedin, New Zealand, comments on these findings saying, *"Of all the arguments put forward ... this seems the most likely explanation."*[31]

These new genetic findings strongly support our model of degeneration of small sub-populations. We came to this conclusion several years ago, even before these new papers were published. We further agree with those who observe that Erectus is essentially a variant of Neanderthal, except for a generally smaller body size, reduced brain volume, and a more severely sloping forehead.

It is now recognized that small, isolated populations with severely restricted diets are subject to selective reduction in body and brain size (due to the advantage of having a reduced caloric requirement).[32] We propose that the Erectus population was essentially the same as Neanderthal, but in a more advanced pathologic state, and with reductive adaptation involving reduced brain volume. We agree with Tim White and other paleo-experts that Naledi is simply a variant of Erectus, but in a more advanced state of degeneration (see chapter 4). We also agree with the paleo-experts who argue that Hobbit was a modern human pygmy with reduced brain and body size caused by inbreeding, island dwarfism, and reductive selection (see chapter 5).

Genetic degeneration appears to be the most plausible explanation. Inbreeding is increasingly being acknowledged by various paleo-experts. For example, Lee Berger attributed the "primitive" features seen in the bones of a <3,000-year-old small-bodied population of *H. sapiens* from Palau (a pacific island) to *"founder effects, genetic isolation and a high inbreeding coefficient..."*[33] Richard Potts of the Smithsonian National Museum of Natural History also attributes the development of "primitive" traits seen in Naledi and Hobbit to living in extreme isolation. He explains such traits can arise rapidly in those conditions:

> 'Island habitats' can occur on continents, too, in small environmental refuges that are sustained long term. Yes, on continents it's typically lizards, butterflies, fish, and small mammals that are susceptible to separation and isolated evolution, and the effects of that isolation can arise rapidly. To me, naledi and floresiensis are nature's experiments of isolated evolution in two of our evolutionary cousins.[34]

Paleo-experts sometimes call this "isolated evolution" but what they are essentially describing is a type of genetic degeneration caused by inbreeding, accelerated mutation accumulation, and reductive selection. This is not the kind of process that can genetically transform australopiths into man (see chapter 13). All of

31. Price M., Frequent inbreeding may have caused skeletal abnormalities in early humans, *Science*, November 5, 2018. DOI:10.1126/science.aav9619

32. Anton S.C., Natural History of *Homo erectus*, *Yearbook Phys Anthropol* 46:126-169, 2003. (p.155)

33. Berger L.R. *et al.*, Small-bodied humans from Palau, Micronesia, *PLOS ONE* 3(3):e1780, 2008.

34. Torchia C., Hominids lived alongside humans, South African scientists find, *The Times of Israel*, May 9, 2017. http://www.timesofisrael.com/hominids-lived-alongside-humans-south-african-scientists-find/ Accessed: 06/24/17

the reputed *Homo* species that are assumed to have been "almost human" or evolutionary precursors to man, appear to simply be aberrant modern human populations that lived in extreme isolation.

"Muddle in the Middle" Bones—All Muddle, No Middle

The paleo-community describes the crucial transition from australopith to man as the "muddle in the middle" or the "murky period,"[35] because there is so little real evidence of any transition.[36] Berger's recent discoveries (Sediba in 2008 and Naledi in 2013) were the latest attempts to fill the gap. These new bones seemed to provide candidate ancestors that might have bridged the vast gulf between ape and man. However, it now appears most of the paleo-community has rejected Berger's findings for two reasons: 1) they are not the appropriate age for a bridge species (both are too young); 2) they don't have the appropriate anatomy for a bridge species (Sediba is far too ape-like and Naledi is far too human-like). Paleo-experts now suggest that Sediba is a chimera consisting of *Australopithecus* and *Homo* bones and has gone the way of Habilis as a "wastebasket" species (see chapter 9 on Sediba). And so the vast gulf remains. We see a lot of muddle, but we see no middle. This supports our alternative model, which proposes that there is no bridge species between *Australopithecus* and *Homo* (see Section III chapters).

Our Alternative Framework for Understanding Human History

If we did not evolve from a common ape ancestor, how do we explain the origin of mankind and the extravagant diversity of primates? Evidence does not "speak for itself." All evidence must be interpreted. When it comes to the field of paleoanthropology, the fossil evidence has always been interpreted in light of the evolutionary view of human history. The ape-to-man story did not arise by scientific observations; it arose as a philosophically driven speculation, based on Darwin's writings. The ape-to-man story was narrated before any hominin fossil had been named. It is from within this ape-to-man framework that the paleo-community now admits they cannot make "evolutionary sense" of the hominin fossils. We suggest that the reason they have this problem is because they are interpreting the fossils in light of a flawed ideological presupposition that the Darwinian mechanism explains everything, even us. We wish to be open and transparent, and acknowledge that we too have our own presuppositions which affect our interpretation of the hominin fossils. We are not confessing a scientific sin—in fact, all honest scientists should openly disclose their preconceptions and philosophical commitments. Such "open disclosure" is essential to a scientist's professional integrity.

We are Bible-believing Christians, and we are convinced that man was created by God, in His image. We are not ashamed of this view, which is held by a large

---

35. Gibbons A., Skeletons Present an Exquisite Paleo-Puzzle, *Science* 333:1370-1372, 2011.
36. Fischman J., Malapa Fossils Part Ape, Part Human, *National Geographic*, August 2011.

part of humanity, including a significant number of living scientists, and includes most of the founding fathers of science. But we cannot prove our view of history scientifically—no more than evolutionists can prove the spontaneous origin of life. However, we can rigorously and scientifically demonstrate that the antithesis to a created humanity is not credible. This is the main thesis of this book.

In addition, we have previously shown that mutation/selection is not capable of genetically transforming an ape population into modern humans. This is for two major reasons: 1) the inordinately long waiting time required for even a tiny string of DNA "letters" (specific co-dependent mutations) to arise and become established in a model hominin-sized population[37] and 2) due to the relentless accumulation of harmful mutations that result in the systematic erosion of the human genome (see chapter 13).[38,39] Since it is not genetically feasible for man to evolve through a Darwinian trial-and-error process, we believe the most reasonable alternative model is the special creation of man (and apes) by God, as is recorded in the book of Genesis.

How can any scientist even consider a supernatural event? The answer is very simple. Most people accept a natural world and natural law, and simultaneously accept that above and beyond the natural is the supernatural. This applies to most of humanity, and applies to most scientists. Before Darwin, the large majority of the "founding fathers" of science believed in a biblical supernatural beginning.

We have found that the actual fossil evidence is remarkably supportive of the biblical view of human origins. Genesis chapter 1 records that man was specially created in the image of God. We read that on the same day Adam was formed, God created an incredible variety of creatures that were to multiply and fill the earth. This easily explains the extravagant diversity of primates. This straightforward reading of Genesis actually provides a coherent framework for interpreting the hominin fossil record. Our alternative model predicts that hominin fossils should fall into two groups—apes and humans. This would be because God created man separately from the apes (rather than apes evolving gradually into humans). And so we should not expect to find any credible transitional hominin types. There is no need for a bridge species between *Australopithecus* and *Homo*. Moreover, we should not be surprised to find a diversity of apes in the fossil record, many of which would have now gone extinct. We would also expect to find that the extinct australopithecine apes coexisted with man (prior to their extinction). There is an extensive overlap in time of *Australopithecus* and *Homo*. This is true even when we accept the conventional ages for these fossils (see Figure 5, chapter 11). Nevertheless, in chapter 12 we cite numerous studies that show the various hominin-dating methods are questionable. The possibility that hominin dates

37. Sanford J. *et al.*, The waiting time problem in a model hominin population, *Theor Biol and Med Modeling* 12:18, 2015. DOI: 10.1186/s12976-015-0016-z

38. Sanford J.C., *Genetic Entropy*, 4th Edition, FMS Publications, 2014.

39. For additional scientific studies showing genetic entropy see: http://www.geneticentropy.org/properties

are greatly inflated helps support our model, although the question of dates is a secondary issue.

Our Alternative Framework for Understanding Ape Diversity

The paleo-community currently attributes the luxuriant diversity of the hominin species to "evolutionary experimentation"—referring to many evolutionary "failed experiments." That means that a wide array of hominin species evolved, petered out, and eventually went extinct (shown as broken twigs and branches on the hominin bush). In our alternative framework, we expect much the same. Each ape type will multiply, diverge into sub-populations, and under-go limited local adaptation via selection. Some sub-populations will survive (extant species), and some will peter out. Local adaptation could have been accelerated due to pre-

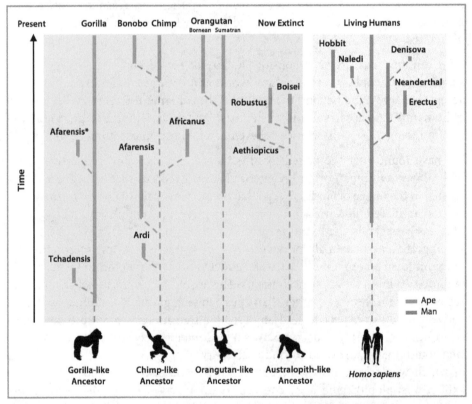

Figure 3. The paleo-community openly acknowledges that hominin fossil record (the actual data) does not reflect an ape-to-man progression. Instead, there appears to be a clear separation between the ape and human type. There is a lot of diversity within the ape type and a lot of diversity with in the human type (with many variants now extinct). There is also branching within each group. Yet we are not seeing a fossil trail connecting these two very distinct groups (ape and man) via a series of intermediate forms. A more accurate representation of the data is with multiple branching trees (reflecting adaptive radiation over time), rather than a single tree with single common ancestor of ape and man. Note: the Y-axis represents an inexact timescale. *Afarensis is shown twice. Paleo-experts descirbe certain Afarensis bones as indistinguishable from modern gorilla, whereas other bones are describd as remarkably like those of living chimpanzee. This is consistent with researchers who claim Afarensis is a jumble of multiple species (see chapter 7).

existing designed heterozygous alleles (gene variants).

To illustrate how primate diversity can arise apart from evolution from a common ancestor, envision a series of smaller trees as opposed to Darwin's single tree (or bush) (Figure 3). The base of each tree reflects the independent origin of each broad, genetically diverse ape type; we don't know how many there were originally. Each ape type would have "branched" out into its own diverse set of sub-populations (species). There could be numerous variations (branches) within those basic kinds—thus enabling their descendants to survive and adapt to a wide variety of environments. This is merely adaptation (microevolution), not the type of genetic change required for ape-to-man macroevolution. Macroevolution requires the spontaneous formation of a great deal of new functional genetic information. Adaptive speciation is simply the fragmentation of each created kind into diverse variant species through the sorting, reshuffling, and selection of pre-existing genetic information. Mutations can add to this genetic variation— but mutations almost always result in deleterious variations. Selection can cull the worst mutations, but the mutation/selection process can only create new information too little and too late (see chapter 13).

Our Alternative Framework for Understanding Human Diversity

Similar to apes and many other creatures, the first man and woman would have been created with built-in variation. There is no reason to assume that Adam and Eve were made as homozygous clones. Very reasonably, they would have contained in their genomes a great deal of desirable variation, and could have easily been created with tens of millions of single nucleotide variants. As the human population grew it would diverge into many small tribes. The smallest and most isolated tribes would quickly become inbred and would undergo accelerated genetic degeneration. Founder effects and assortative mating would quickly produce the superficial features associated with "race." This would not require the slow build-up of new mutations, it would occur simply and quickly, through genetic recombination (the reshuffling of pre-existing DNA variants) plus limited selection. In small populations, genetic drift would further help populations diverge, rapidly producing the various people groups (this is strikingly similar to the "instantaneous divergence" model proposed by evolutionary geneticists).[40] Selection would increase the frequency of traits adapted to specific climates.

Our Alternative Framework for Understanding the Human Dispersion

There are two competing evolutionary models for explaining how the human dispersion occurred.[41] The first is sometimes called the Multiregional Model,

40. DeGiorgio M. *et al.*, Explaining worldwide patterns of human genetic variation using a coalescent-based serial founder model of migration outward from Africa, *Proc Nat Acad Sci*, 2009. DOI: 10.1073/pnas.0903341106
41. Jin L. and Su B., Natives or immigrants: modern human origin in east Asia, *Nature Reviews Genetics* 1:127 2000.

which involves the evolution of Erectus in eastern Africa, followed by Erectus coming out of Africa into Europe and Asia (including various islands in Southeast Asia). After this, Erectus continued to evolve in parallel on all three continents (Africa, Europe, and Asia). This parallel evolution led to the intermediate forms such as Neanderthals and the Denisovans, eventually resulting in the simultaneous emergence of anatomically modern man on all three continents. The "parallel evolution" aspect of this story is not credible.

The second model is typically called the Out of Africa model, and is much more popular. This model also envisions Erectus coming out of Africa some 1–2 million years ago. Much later (roughly 200,000 years ago), anatomically modern man (*Homo sapiens*) evolved in Africa. This involved a near-extinction event—a severe decline in population size (a "genetic bottleneck"). Associated with this bottleneck, there arose what geneticists have called "mitochondrial Eve" and "Y chromosome Adam" (these are hypothetical ancestral genotypes that are based upon current genetic patterns around the world). Then a second "Out of Africa" event occurred. The tiny, endangered African population of early *Homo sapiens*, which included the genetic "Adam" and "Eve" lineages, suddenly recovered from the near extinction event and very rapidly spread throughout the world. The anatomically modern humans then exterminated (or perhaps assimilated) all the other human populations, such as Neanderthal, Erectus, Denisovans, and Hobbit. This story no longer seems credible, because the bottleneck is not feasible if early man was already established in Africa, Europe, Asia and Australia, and because such a bottleneck would be lethal or at least degenerative.

Our alternative framework for understanding the human divergence incorporates aspects of both evolutionary models. We embrace the genetic evidence supportive of the Out of Africa model and the fossil evidence supportive of the Multiregional Model. We call our model the "Out-of-Middle-East" Model (OME). Our model begins with a very small anatomically modern human population in the general region of the Middle East (which includes Northeast Africa). This human population undergoes rapid population growth and subsequent dispersion of tribes in all directions (into Africa, Europe, and Asia, and eventually into the Americas)[42] (Figure 4). Fragmentation of the original population leads to many isolated tribes—resulting in both genetic and linguistic founder-effects. Phenotypic differences between tribes become exaggerated due to assortative mating. The rapidly diverging tribes are driven apart due to competition for resources, as well as growing linguistic, cultural, and phenotypic differences. This would lead to rapid global dispersion and regional differences in certain skull features, as is consistent with what multiregionalists see in the fossil record.

---

42. To account for the fact that Africans are so genetically diverse, a disproportionate number of tribes need to migrate south and west, or else tribes have to fission more rapidly.

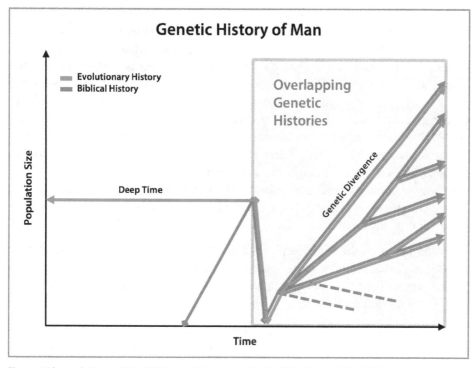

Figure 4. The evolutionary Out of Africa model compared to the biblical Adam/Flood/Babel model. The y-axis shows population size (on an inexact scale). The x-axis shows time (also on an inexact scale). In the Out-of-Africa scenario, humans lived as *H. erectus* in Africa for perhaps a million years with a population size of maybe a million individuals. Only a few tens of thousands of years ago, that population went through a prolonged and degenerative bottleneck, during (or just prior to) the evolution of *H. sapiens*. Sometime after that, modern man is said to have left Africa and spread across the world. In the biblical model, humanity begins with Adam and Eve, whose descendants rapidly multiply, and then, went through a one-generation bottleneck at the time of the Flood, then the population once again rapidly increased, followed by rapid divergence at the Tower of Babel event, creating today's people groups. Some isolated post-Babel people groups (i.e., Hobbit, Naledi, etc.) became genetically compromised due to inbreeding (blue dashed lines). Note that the two models of human history are remarkably similar, except for the deep time at the beginning of the evolutionary time scale, as would be required for ape-to-man evolution. With the advent of genome sequencing, the evolutionary model underwent a drastic revision to accommodate the mounting genetic data. Remarkably, the biblical model is already in agreement with the latest genetic data, no revisions necessary.

How do outlying populations such as Erectus, Neanderthal, and Hobbit fit into our model? Throughout this book we have pointed out that small isolated populations are subject to accelerated genetic deterioration,[43] and we have been quoting evolutionary paleo-experts who say the same thing in *Nature* (2014), *PNAS* (2016, 2018), *Genetics* (2015), and other mainstream journals. We, and they, have noted that Erectus, Neanderthal, and Hobbit all show evidence of pathologies and inbreeding. It seems very reasonable to conclude that very early in human history these anomalous populations split off from anatomically modern human populations, became isolated, and then experienced inbreeding, genetic

43. Krasovec R. *et al.*, Spontaneous mutation rate is a plastic trait associated with population density across domains of life, *PLOS ONE Biology* 2017. DOI: 10.1371/journal.pbio.2002731

drift, and eventual mutational meltdown. The decline of such populations could happen quite rapidly, resulting in bone beds that show various degrees of genetic degeneration. This would explain the variable degrees of pathology (dwarfing, distorted skulls, and reduced brain volumes) seen in Erectus, Hobbit, and Naledi. This is also consistent with multiregionalists who observe distinctive fossil traits retained in modern populations where their "archaic forbearers" once lived (for example, flatter face and prominent cheek bones of Erectus crania from China closely resemble modern oriental populations). The major difference in our model is that we propose the reverse—rather than Erectus regionally *evolving* into modern humans, modern humans *devolved* locally into Erectus, Hobbit, and Naledi. Those early inbred colonies were later replaced as larger (more viable) populations filled the world. The early isolated, and inbred colonies would leave behind the earliest bones, and would soon disappear.

Our alternative model neatly explains both the genetic evidence used to support the Out of Africa model and the fossil evidence used to support the Multiregional Model (evolutionary paleo-experts have always struggled to reconcile these two competing models).

Further explanation of this model (including Mitochondrial Eve, Y-Chromosome Adam, and designed genetic diversity), will be presented in a separate book.

Man Stands Alone—Unique in All of God's Creation

If the biblical text is a reliable account of origins, we should not be surprised to find that there is no other creature on the planet quite like us. Indeed, this is perhaps one of the most obvious facts of life. The evolutionary paleo-community openly acknowledges that man is unique. For example, respected paleo-expert Jonathan Marks in *History and Philosophy of the Life Sciences* journal writes:

> It is not that difficult to tell a human from an ape, after all. The human is the one walking, talking, sweating, praying, building, reading, trading, crying, dancing, writing, cooking, joking, working, decorating, shaving, driving a car, or playing football. Quite literally, from the top of our head (where the hair is continually growing, unlike gorillas) to the tips of our toes (the stoutest of which is non-opposable), one can tell the human part from the ape part quite readily if one knows what to look for. Our eye-whites, small canine teeth, evaporative heat loss, short arms and long legs, breasts, knees, and of course, our cognitive communication abilities and the productive anatomies of our tongue and throat are all dead giveaways.[44]

In certain respects, it is true that mankind is very similar to the various kinds of ape (gorilla, chimpanzee, and orangutan). For example, we have similar anatomy and biochemistry. Even in terms of our fallen behavior, we are too often quite "ape-ish." It is on this basis that evolutionists justify their claim that humans

---

44. Marks J., What is the viewpoint of hemoglobin, and does it matter? *Hist Philos Life Sci* 31(2):241-62, p. 246, 2009. https://www.ncbi.nlm.nih.gov/pubmed/20210111

are just another type of ape—essentially just a clever chimpanzee. However, we feel biological similarities between different kinds of life are better explained by a Common Designer than by common descent. Either way, organisms that look similar should also be genetically similar, and, prior to the sequencing of the respective genomes, neither side could have predicted how similar chimps and humans should be. Thus, any claim that a certain percent similarity proves common ancestry is logically invalid (see chapter 13).

While humans display some distinct similarities to apes, in the most important aspects we are utterly unique. Only humans can do science, sequence their own genome, reason, engineer cities, visit the moon, write books/programs/poetry/music, or show agape love. We clearly have dominion over the earth. Biblically, only man is a moral being with a soul, capable of communion with God. In all of these respects we are incredibly unique. As evolutionist Juan Arsuaga writes in *The Neanderthal's Necklace*:

> We are unique and alone now in the world. There is no other animal species that truly resembles our own. A physical and mental chasm separates us from all other living creatures. There is no bipedal mammal. No other mammal controls and uses fire, writes books, travels in space, paints portraits, or prays. This is not a question of degrees. It is all or nothing; there is no semi-bipedal animal, none that makes only small fires, writes only short sentences, builds only rudimentary spaceships, draws just a little bit, or prays just occasionally.[45]

Likewise, in the words of a famous evolutionist, Jacob Bronowski, *"Man is a singular creature. He has a set of gifts which make him unique among the animals: so that, unlike them, he is not a figure in the landscape—he is a shaper of the landscape."*[46] Evolutionary paleo-expert, Ian Tattersall, emeritus curator of the American Museum of Natural History writes:

> Even allowing for the poor record we have of our close extinct kin, *Homo sapiens* appears as distinctive and unprecedented...there is certainly no evidence to support the notion that we gradually became who we inherently are over an extended period, in either the physical or intellectual sense.[47]

Indeed, we were created in the image of God, and stand alone. The essential biblical difference between apes and man is the Spirit that was breathed into mankind on the day of our creation. While the Bible makes no scientific prediction about genetic similarities or differences, it makes profound claims about the spiritual difference between animals and man.

In this light, it is extremely important that we acknowledge that we are not just another primate species. Rather, in a taxonomic sense mankind should most accurately be placed in a separate kingdom (i.e., plant kingdom, animal kingdom, human

---

45. Arsuaga J.L., *The Neanderthal's Necklace*, NY: Four Walls Eight Windows Publishing, New York, p. 3, 2002.
46. Jacob Bronowski, *The Ascent of Man*, a television series produced by the BBC and Time-Life Films, 1973.
47. Tattersall I., *Masters of the Planet: The Search for Our Human Origins*, Palgrave MacMillan, New York, 266 pp., 2012.

kingdom). Evolutionists cannot even begin to explain how mutation/selection might have created consciousness, intelligence, moral accountability, or the human spirit. This is why so many continually downplay, even to the point of denial, these crucial human traits. It is clear that mankind is transcendent above all other living things, and that we are not part of an evolutionary continuum. We are spiritual beings. This is acknowledged by most human beings. This is certainly not contested among Christians, and is central to the biblical view of human origins. However, this is not compatible with a strictly evolutionary view. The genes that enable our unique capabilities, gifts, and talents (i.e., science, art, love, relation to God) could not arise by any series of random mutations filtered by natural selection, not in any amount of time. There is no credible evolutionary mechanism that could lead spontaneously to a mind, consciousness, intelligence, or spirit. Indeed, while these human traits are found within a biological context (i.e., within our animal-like body/brain), they clearly transcend mere biology. We are exquisitely programmed to be more than animals, and our bodies are well-designed vessels that house our immaterial being—mind, soul, spirit. This is the biblical perspective of mankind. We are fearfully and wonderfully made (Psalm 139:14). We are made in the image of God (Genesis 1:27). God breathed His life-giving Spirit into us (Genesis 2:7).

So What Went Wrong?

The hominin bones are not just contested—most people find the hominin bones disturbing. Dead things in dark holes. Skulls with bizarre, deformed faces. If God is so good, and Man is so special, then why does the fossil record look so much like a nightmare? Why does the fossil record speak so clearly of death, disease, mutation, degeneration, and even cannibalism? The final element of our alternative model must address the problem of physical and spiritual corruption. It is widely understood that we are all dying people in a dying world. Left to themselves, even the solar system and the universe will run down. We see evidence of physical and moral degeneration all around us. Our genetic research indicates systematic degeneration (see chapter 13). The Bible reveals systematic degeneration. We are convinced that the fossil record also indicates systematic degeneration.

One of the most fundamental questions that we can ask in life is, "Why is there so much suffering and evil?" No one seems to have a satisfactory answer. That is to say, no one has an answer apart from the Bible. Biblically, God made all things good, but men and angels rebelled against God, leading to the corruption of the whole world. The biblical Fall (Genesis 3)—is there any better answer? If everything in the world has been corrupted, including our bodies and our souls, what hope do we have? Biblically speaking, we have no hope at all—apart from Jesus and what He did for us. Our hope is not in this body, and not in this world. For the time being, our hope is the new life that comes from Christ. Our future hope is eternal life with Christ in *"a new heaven and a new earth"* (Revelation 21). This is the bright hope that all Christians share. It is a hope available to all who sincerely desire it.

Contrary to this biblical view, atheists and many theistic evolutionists insist that our hope must be earthly. For many, the only hope is on-going human evolution. They would say that in the past God has used random mutations, combined with the systematic death of the unfit, to transform an ape population into modern man. So in the future evolution will continue. They believe that in this way mankind will get better and better. Their hope is that we might naturally evolve into some type of utopian earthly paradise. Such people gladly embrace the very disturbing hominin bones as evidence supporting that belief system. They gladly embrace the australopiths as their kin. They gladly embrace Darwin and the Darwinian paradigm, and say this represents both true science and true spirituality. We have friends and loved ones who hold this popular view, but we must earnestly disagree. We humbly but firmly contend that this aspect of their science is not solid, and that personalized spirituality apart from God's Revelation (the Bible) is not a trustworthy hope.

This leads us to some final thoughts of a more personal nature.

CONCLUSIONS

Our Personal Perspective

Except for the last chapter of this book, we have focused on the scientific aspects of the hominin fossils. We have only briefly touched on a few philosophical issues. For example, we have emphasized the difference between taxonomic "splitters" versus "lumpers"—pointing out that the difference is largely philosophical (we are unashamedly lumpers).

We have pointed out that because paleoanthropology is a historical science (as opposed to operational science), interpretation of bones and artifacts is quite subjective, and is strongly influenced by philosophical presuppositions. Such presuppositions derive from prior intellectual commitments (based upon the ruling paradigm, the group think, and a scientist's personal worldview). We have seen that while the paleo-community is divided on many issues, there remains an unconditional commitment to the basic Darwinian paradigm, and there is unwavering fidelity to the basic ape-to-man narrative. The classifications of the bones keep changing, the dates keep changing, but the basic paradigm is never subject to critical re-examination.

We have gone to great lengths to show that this widely shared commitment to the paradigm is not based on the actual evidence. The paradigm consistently comes first—the evidence is consistently interpreted in light of the paradigm. This strong tendency for the paradigm to overshadow actual evidence is not unique to the paleo-community—it applies to us all. Our worldview colors how we see everything. In light of our own limited ability to know for certain what happened in the distant past, shouldn't there be room for all of us to be more humble? Shouldn't every paradigm be honestly questioned? Shouldn't there be room for respectful dialog?

Throughout this book we have made it very clear that we are skeptics of the ape-to-man story, which makes us academic dissidents. We do not dissent because we like to be difficult or argumentative—we dissent because we have a different point of view. Our worldview, our prior commitment, is that there is a creator God, and that mankind was made by God, and in the image of God. This view is shared by a very large part of humanity. This includes a large number of orthodox Christians, orthodox Muslims, and orthodox Jews. Many of these people are in the academic community, and many would openly dissent—if they dared.

Personally, we are both orthodox (i.e., traditional) Bible-believing Christians. The traditional Christian paradigm embraces nature, natural law and natural science. In addition to the natural world, Christians embrace the supernatural realm, the reality of the soul, the reality of good and evil, the reality of spiritual struggle, the reality of miracles, and the reality of life after death. The Christian paradigm centers on an infinitely good and loving God, and includes a literal Adam and Eve, a literal Fall, and the historical corruption of mankind. The Christian paradigm specifically affirms that we have all fallen short of God's Holy standard (we have all sinned), and this is what separates us from God. The sacrificial death of Jesus made a way for us to be washed clean of sin, and the resurrection of Jesus made a way for us to be redeemed and reconciled with Him and all who receive Him, for all eternity. For those who choose to accept it, this is incredibly good news! Hundreds of millions of people have joyfully embraced this Good News.

Yet there are many people who are offended by such things. We do not wish to offend anyone—but we wish to share the Good News with everyone. We did not invest years of effort on this book just so we could "win the argument." We did it because we love people, and countless people are turning away from the Good News because they have been persuaded that ape-to-man evolution makes traditional Christian faith impossible. More specifically, hundreds of millions have been persuaded that ape-to-man evolution disproves: a) a loving creator-God; b) the supernatural creation of man; c) a supernatural Fall; d) the reality of sin; e) the need for a savior; and f) the hope of heaven. We urge all people to trust in God more and trust in man less. God wants us to believe Him—with or without physical evidence. Yet in His mercy, God is giving us various evidences that can help us trust Him more. We hope that this book will encourage many people to trust God more.

In closing, we ask our readers to seriously consider seven personal questions:

1) If you could choose, would you prefer to be an extremely clever ape, or a beloved child of God?

2) If you could choose, would you prefer to someday be reduced to rotting bones, or to someday become an eternal citizen of heaven?

3) If you could choose, would you prefer the praise of men or the praise of God?

4) If heaven has a cost, what cost do you think might be too great? Would you go so far as consider taking the risk of being called a fool?

5) Can you imagine saying "no" to human evolution? How much evidence would you need?

6) Can you imagine saying "yes" to Jesus? How much evidence would you need?

7) If you wanted to believe Jesus, but you struggled with unbelief, what evidence might God give you to help you trust in Him? If God, in His mercy, gave you evidence like that—might you then become a true believer and give your life to Jesus?

Resources for "Digging Deeper"

1) *Contested Bones* (book and website); contestedbones.org

2) *Genetic Entropy* (book, video, and website); geneticentropy.org

3) *Biological Information–New Perspectives* (technical volume); BINP.org

4) Origins-related science articles (website); LogosRA.org

5) The Waiting Time Problem (paper); doi.org/10.1186/s12976-015-0016-z

6) *Searching for Adam* (book); answersingenesis.org

7) *One Human Family,* (book); creation.com

Image Sources & Acknowledgments

Front Cover

Credit: John Reader/Science Photo Library; http://www.gettyimages.com/license/680791579; Photoshop edits courtesy Jessica Carpenter

Chapter 1

Chapter Opener Image: Adapted from Dreamstime; credit line: © Goce Risteski | Dreamstime.com; https://www.dreamstime.com/royalty-free-stock-photography-human-evolution-image1658437#res2591555

Chapter 2

Figure 1: Reece, Jane B., Urry, Lisa A., Cain, Michael L., Wasserman, Steven A., Minorsky, Peter V., Jackson, Robert B., Campbell Biology (10th Edition) (Page 743) Benjamin Cummings. Kindle Edition. **Figure 2:** Wood B., Welcome to the Family, Sci Am 311(3):42-47, 2014. https://www.scientificamerican.com/article/the-origin-of-humans-is-surprisingly-complicated/ **Figure 3:** Klein R.G., Darwin and the recent African origin of modern humans, *Proc Natl Acad Sci*, USA 106(38): 16007–16009, 2009. http://www.pnas.org/content/106/38/16007.figures-only

Chapter 3

Figure 1: https://www.donsmaps.com/neanderthaloriginal.html **Figure 2:** https://en.wikipedia.org/wiki/Denisovan **Figure 3:** https://www.researchgate.net/figure/278715782_fig1_FIGURE-41-Reconstruction-of-the-La-Chapelle-aux-Saints-Neanderthal-by-the-Czech-artist **Figure 4:** https://www.quora.com/Were-the-Neanderthals-smarter-than-the-members-of-Homo-sapiens; http://www.brighthub.com/science/genetics/articles/35497.aspx **Figure 5:** American Museum of Natural History: https://i.pinimg.com/originals/07/e9/fa/07e9faa683debb94576af974700b0209.jpg **Figure 6:** http://allrus.me/tallest-and-heaviest-russian-boxer-nikolai-valuev/ **Figure 7:** http://www.alamy.com/stock-photo-homo-sapiens-cranium-qafzeh-6-66713187.html; https://en.wikipedia.org/wiki/Skhul_and_Qafzeh_hominids#/media/File:Skhul.JPG **Figure 8:** https://gradhiva.revues.org/2907; https://en.wikipedia.org/wiki/Divje_Babe_Flute; https://en.wikipedia.org/wiki/Vogelherd_Cave#/media/File:MUT-9846.jpg

Chapter 4

Figure 1: https://en.wikipedia.org/wiki/Java_Man#/media/File:Pithecanthropus_erectus-PeterMaas_Naturalis.jpg **Figure 2:** http://www.sciencephoto.com/search?subtype=keywords&matchtype=exact&searchstring=trinil+2&media_type=images **Figure 3:** http://science.sciencemag.org/content/344/6182/360.1/tab-figures-data **Figure 4:** http://www.alamy.com/stock-photo-kenya-nairobi-national-museums-15-myo-lake-turkana-boy-12-years-old-11926381.html **Figure 5:** Alan G. Thorne, Milford H. Wolpoff, Regional continuity in Australasian Pleistocene hominid evolution, American Journal of Physical Anthropology, 55:337-349, 1981. http://onlinelibrary.wiley.com/doi/10.1002/ajpa.1330550308/abstract; A. G. Thorne, P. G. Macumber, Discoveries of Late Pleistocene Man at Kow Swamp Australia, Nature, 238:316-319, 1972. http://www.nature.com/nature/journal/v238/n5363/abs/238316a0.html **Figure 6:** Adapted from Google Earth **Figure 7:** Adapted from Dreamstime; credit line: © Indos82 | Dreamstime.com; https://www.dreamstime.com/royalty-free-stock-photo-silhouette-man-image4830675

Chapter 5

Figure 1: https://en.wikipedia.org/wiki/Liang_Bua#/media/File:Homo_floresiensis_cave.jpg **Figure 2:** https://3c1703fe8d.site.internapcdn.net/newman/gfx/news/hires/2014/hobbitmoreli.jpg **Figure 3:** credit line: © Djuna Ivereigh; http://djuna.photoshelter.com/image/I0000X2.cVr41BoA **Figure 4:** Adapted by FMS Foundation, from Dreamstime; credit line: © Victor Zastol`skiy | Dreamstime.com; https://www.dreamstime.com/stock-images-elephant-calf-image9583284; Adapted by FMS Foundation from Dreamstime; credit line: © Alanjeffery | Dreamstime.com; https://www.dreamstime.com/stock-photography-elephant-white-image16161102 **Figure 5:** http://www.sciencedirect.com/science/article/pii/S0305440313002343

Chapter 6

Figure 1: Tim D. White et al., Ardipithecus ramidus and the Paleobiology of Early Hominids, Science 326:5949, p.64-86, 2009. http://science.sciencemag.org/content/326/5949/64/tab-figures-data **Figure 2:** White T.D. et al., Australopithecus ramidus, a new species of early hominid from Aramis, Ethiopia, Nature 371:306-312, 1994; http://www.nature.com/nature/journal/v371/n6495/abs/371306a0.html?foxtrotcallback=true **Figure 3:** Gibbons A., A new kind of ancestor: Ardipithecus unveiled, Science 326:36-39, 2009; http://science.sciencemag.org/content/326/5949/36 **Figure 4:** credit: J.H. Matternes; http://www.agenciasinc.es/var/ezwebin_site/storage/images/multimedia/imagenes/el-antepasado-mas-antiguo-de-los-hombres-ya-no-es-lucy-es-ardi/634589-1-esl-MX/El-antepasado-mas-antiguo-de-los-hombres-ya-no-es-Lucy-es-Ardi.jpg; Photograph by Dr. Frans de Waal, courtesy Frans de Waal and Frans Lanting, Bonobo: The Forgotten Ape, University of California Press, 1997. **Figure 5:** Gen Suwa, et al. The Ardipithecus ramidus Skull and Its Implications for Hominid Origins, Science 326:68; 2009 http://science.sciencemag.org/content/326/5949/68/tab-figures-data **Figure 6:** Gen Suwa et al., The Ardipithecus ramidus Skull and Its Implications for Hominid Origins, Science 326:68, 2009; http://science.sciencemag.org/content/326/5949/68/tab-figures-data **Figure 7:** Davenport et al., A New Genus of African Monkey, Rungwecebus: Morphology, Ecology, and Molecular Phylogenetics, Science 312:1378-1381, 2006; http://science.sciencemag.org/content/312/5778/1378 **Figure 8:** Tim D. White et al., Ardipithecus ramidus and the Paleobiology of Early Hominids, Science 326:5949, p.64-86, 2009; http://science.sciencemag.org/content/326/5949/64/tab-figures-data **Figure 9:** Suwa G. et al., Paleobiological implications of the Ardipithecus ramidus dentition, Science 326:69-99, 2009; http://science.sciencemag.org/content/326/5949/69/tab-figures-data **Figure 10:** Lovejoy, C. O. et al., Combining Prehension and Propulsion: The Foot of Ardipithecus ramidus, Science, 326(5949):72, 2009; http://science.sciencemag.org/content/326/5949/72/tab-figures-data

Chapter 7

Figure 1: Johanson, D., The Paleoanthropology of Hadar, Ethiopia, Human Palaeontology and Prehistory, 2:140-154, 2017; https://doi.org/10.1016/j.crpv.2016.10.005 **Figure 2:** Johanson, D., The Paleoanthropology of Hadar, Ethiopia, Human Palaeontology and Prehistory, 2:140-154, 2017; https://doi.org/10.1016/j.crpv.2016.10.005 **Figure 3:** https://askananthropologist.asu.edu/sites/default/files/styles/aab-gallery-large/public/gallery-images/hadar_camp.jpg **Figure 4:** Johanson, D., The Paleoanthropology of Hadar, Ethiopia, Human Palaeontology and Prehistory, 2:140-154, 2017; https://doi.org/10.1016/j.crpv.2016.10.005 **Figure 5:** Johanson, D., The Paleoanthropology of Hadar, Ethiopia, Human Palaeontology and Prehistory, 2:140-154, 2017; https://doi.org/10.1016/j.crpv.2016.10.005 **Figure 6:** https://www.ncbi.nlm.nih.gov/pubmed/815823 **Figure 7:** Credit line: Donald C. Johanson; https://www.livescience.com/12805-human-ancestor-foot-bone-bipedalism.html **Figure 8:** John Reader/Science Photo Library: https://www.sciencephoto.com/media/170811/view; https://elifesciences.org/content/5/e19568 **Figure 9:** Johanson, D., The Paleoanthropology of Hadar, Ethiopia, Human Palaeontology and Prehistory, 2:140-154, 2017; https://doi.org/10.1016/j.crpv.2016.10.005; Adapted from: https://i1.wp.com/www.bigfootencounters.com/images/anthropoid_feet.jpg **Figure**

10: https://medium.com/@johnhawks/the-plot-to-kill-homo-habilis-94a33bee2adf

Chapter 8

Figure 1: https://en.wikipedia.org/wiki/Olduvai_Gorge#/media/File:Olduvai_Gorge_or_ Oldupai_Gorge.jpg **Figure 2:** https://en.wikipedia.org/wiki/OH_5 **Figure 3:** Credit: John Reader/Science Photo Library; http://www.gettyimages.com/license/680791579 **Figure 4:** Carol V. Ward et al., Associated ilium and femur from Koobi Fora, Kenya, and post cranial diversity in early Homo, Journal of Human Evolution, 81:48-67, 2015; https://www.researchgate.net/publication/273326379_Associated_ilium_and_femur_from_Koobi_Fora_Kenya_and_postcranial_diversity_in_early_Homo **Figure 5:** Wood B., Human evolution: Fifty years after Homo habilis, Nature 508(7494):31-33, 2014; http://www.nature.com/polopoly_fs/1.14957!/menu/main/topColumns/topLeftColumn/pdf/508031a.pdf

Chapter 9

Figure 1: A New Species of Homo-Like Australopith from South Africa, Lee R. Berger, Darryl J. de Ruiter, Steven E. Churchill, Peter Schmid, Kristian J. Carlson1,6, Paul H. G. M. Dirks, Job M. Kibii, Science, vol. 328, Issue 5975, pp. 195-204, 2010; http://science.sciencemag.org/content/328/5975/195/tab-figures-data **Figure 2:** https://commons.wikimedia.org/wiki/File:Mathew_Berger_with_Malapa_Hominin_1.JPG **Figure 3:** https://commons.wikimedia.org/wiki/File:Malapa_fossil_site,_August_2011_site_of_discovery_of_Australopithecus_sediba_-_view_North.jpg **Figure 4:** Created by FMS Foundation **Figure 5:** Barras C., Human 'missing link' fossils may be jumble of species. New Scientist, 2964: April 09, 2014; https://www.newscientist.com/article/mg22229643-200-human-missing-link-fossils-may-be-jumble-of-species/ **Figure 6:** Tracy L. Kivell et al., Australopithecus sediba Hand Demonstrates Mosaic Evolution of Locomotor and Manipulative Abilities, Science, Vol. 333, Issue 6048, pp. 1411-1417, 2011; http://science.sciencemag.org/content/333/6048/1411/tab-figures-data; Adapated by FMS Foundation from: http://www.godandscience.org/images/chimp_human_sediba_hands.jpg **Figure 7:** Paul H. G. M. Dirks et al., Geological Setting and Age of Australopithecus sediba from Southern Africa, Science, vol. 328, Issue 5975, pp. 205-208, 2010; http://science.sciencemag.org/content/328/5975/205/tab-figures-data

Chapter 10

Figure 1: https://bloximages.chicago2.vip.townnews.com/host.madison.com/content/tncms/assets/v3/editorial/9/dd/9dd3e297-8776-56c9-9951-f3cb7f9b5166/55f0b6c71305e.image.jpg **Figure 2:** https://en.wikipedia.org/wiki/Homo_naledi#/media/File:Homo_naledi_skeletal_specimens.jpg **Figure 3:** Hawks J. et al., New fossil remains of Homo naledi from the Lesedi Chamber, South Africa, eLife, 6:e24232, 2017; https://elifesciences.org/articles/24232/figures; Image credit: Natural History Museum, London / Alamy Stock Photo https://www.alamy.com/stock-photo-homo-sapiens-human-mandible-66748412.html; Johanson, D., The Paleoanthropology of Hadar, Ethiopia, Human Palaeontology and Prehistory, 2:140-154, 2017; https://doi.org/10.1016/j.crpv.2016.10.005; Johanson, D., The Paleoanthropology of Hadar, Ethiopia, Human Palaeontology and Prehistory, 2:140-154, 2017; https://doi.org/10.1016/j.crpv.2016.10.005 **Figure 4:** Stringer C., Human Evolution: The many mysteries of Homo naledi, eLife, 2015; https://elifesciences.org/articles/10627 **Figure 5:** Berger L.R. et al., Homo naledi, a new species of the genus Homo from the Dinaledi Chamber, South Africa, eLife 4:e09560, 2015; https://elifesciences.org/articles/09560; http://www.alamy.com/stock-photo-foot-medical-xray-broken-bone-patient-treatment-148053311.html; Image credit: Jakub Zajic / Alamy Stock Photo **Figure 6:** Berger L.R. et al., Homo naledi, a new species of the genus Homo from the Dinaledi Chamber, South Africa, eLife 4:e09560, 2015; https://elifesciences.org/articles/09560; Image credit: Zoonar GmbH / Alamy Stock Photo; http://www.alamy.com/stock-photo-hand-x-ray-71771471.html **Figure 7:** Berger L.R. et al., Homo naledi, a new species of the genus Homo from the Dinaledi Chamber, South Africa, eLife 4:e09560, 2015; https://

elifesciences.org/articles/09560 **Figure 8.** Rosenberg K.R. et al., Evolution of the Human Pelvis, The Anatomical Record, 300:789-797, 2017; https://www.ncbi.nlm.nih.gov/pubmed/28406563 **Figure 9:** Kruger A. et al., Multimodal spatial mapping and visualisation of Dinaledi Chamber and Rising Star Cave, South African Journal of Science, 2016; https://www.researchgate.net/figure/303595255_fig9_Figure-9-Point-cloud-data-generated-from-an-amalgamation-of-three-dimensional-data **Figure 10:** Kruger A. et al., Multimodal spatial mapping and visualisation of Dinaledi Chamber and Rising Star Cave, South African Journal of Science, 2016; https://www.researchgate.net/figure/303595255_fig4_Figure-4-Photograph-of-the-small-confined-nature-of-the-'Chute'-within-the-Rising-Star **Figure 11:** Wild S., Small-brained early human lived more recently than expected, Nature News, May 9, 2017; https://www.nature.com/news/small-brained-early-human-lived-more-recently-than-expected-1.21961

Chapter 11

Figure 1: Created by FMS Foundation with Dreamstime illustration of stone tool (adapted); https://www.dreamstime.com/stock-illustration-ancient-stone-tools-set-isolated-white-background-primitive-culture-stone-age-tool-flat-style-vector-illustration-image94662066; Credit line: © Nikolay Plotnikov | Dreamstime **Figure 2:** https://en.wikipedia.org/wiki/Hans_Reck#/media/File:Hans_Reck.jpg **Figure 3:** http://www.gettyimages.com.au/detail/news-photo/tansania-oldoway-schlucht-ausgrabungsstätte-von-werkzeugen-news-photo/542915805; **Figure 4:** Leakey R., Australopithecus, Homo erectus, and the single species hypothesis, Nature 261:572-574, 1976; https://www.nature.com/articles/261572a0 **Figure 5:** Created by FMS Foundation

Chapter 13

Figure 1: Adapted by FMS Foundation, from Sanford J. et al., The waiting time problem in a model hominin population, Theor Biol and Med Modeling 12:18, 2015; https://www.ncbi.nlm.nih.gov/pmc/articles/PMC4573302/

Chapter 14

Chapter Opener Image: Adapted by FMS Foundation, from Dreamstime; credit line: © Goce Risteski | Dreamstime.com; https://www.dreamstime.com/royalty-free-stock-photography-human-evolution-image1658437#res2591555 **Figure 1:** Wood B., Welcome to the Family, Sci Am 311(3):42-47, 2014; https://www.scientificamerican.com/article/the-origin-of-humans-is-surprisingly-complicated/ **Figure 2:** http://www.breakingnews.ie/discover/the-worlds-tallest-man-and-shortest-man-met-each-other-yesterday-651012.html **Figure 3:** Created by FMS Foundation; gorilla silhouette from: http://www.supercoloring.com/silhouettes/gorilla; chimp silhouette from: https://www.shutterstock.com/image-vector/collection-apes-silhouettes-92230849; orangutan silhouette from: https://www.123rf.com/photo_46524587_stock-vector-ape-and-monkey-silhouette-set-isolated-on-a-white-background.html; Credit line: © Yulia Ryabokon; australopith silhouette from: https://animagehub.com/funny-monkey-vector-images/monkey-vector-4/; Adam and Eve silouette from: http://www.kellygogas.com/uploads/1/8/9/6/18963095/1003746_orig.jpg **Figure 4:** Created by FMS Foundation, adaption of original courtesy of R. Carter.

Back Cover

Adapted from Dreamstime; credit line: © Goce Risteski | Dreamstime.com; https://www.dreamstime.com/royalty-free-stock-photography-human-evolution-image1658437#res2591555

Index

A

CPSIA information can be obtained
at www.ICGtesting.com
Printed in the USA
BVHW061631250619
551925BV00002B/3/P

9 780981 631677